Biology: The Science of Life

Stephen Nowicki, Ph.D.

THE
GREAT
COURSES®

PUBLISHED BY:

THE GREAT COURSES
Corporate Headquarters
4840 Westfields Boulevard, Suite 500
Chantilly, Virginia 20151-2299
Phone: 1-800-832-2412
Fax: 703-378-3819
www.thegreatcourses.com

Stephen Nowicki, Ph.D.

Professor of Biology
Duke University

Professor Stephen Nowicki is Bass Fellow and Professor of Biology at Duke University, where he also holds appointments in the Department of Psychological and Brain Sciences and in the Neurobiology Department at Duke University Medical Center. He completed both his undergraduate work and a masters degree at Tufts University and received his Ph.D. from Cornell University. Prior to taking his position at Duke, Professor Nowicki was a postdoctoral fellow and assistant professor at the Rockefeller University.

Professor Nowicki has published more than 65 scholarly articles in academic journals, and he is co-author of the book *The Evolution of Animal Communication: Reliability and Deceit in Signaling Systems*, published by Princeton University Press. He has served as President of the Animal Behavior Society and as Chair of the Division of Animal Behavior of the Society for Integrative and Comparative Biology. Professor Nowicki introduced a thorough revision of the approach to teaching introductory biology at Duke University, a curricular reform effort that has received widespread recognition.

Professor Nowicki has been awarded fellowships from the Mary Flagler Cary Charitable Trust, the Alfred P. Sloan Foundation, and the John Simon Guggenheim Foundation. He also is the recipient of the Robert B. Cox Distinguished Teaching Award from Duke University. ∎

Table of Contents

Table of Contents

Table of Contents

Table of Contents

Table of Contents

Table of Contents

Table of Contents

SUPPLEMENTAL MATERIAL

Biology: The Science of Life

Scope:

Biology—the "science of life"—matured as a discipline in the previous century and will surely be the branch of science that most affects our daily lives in the next. Our expanding knowledge of how living systems work at all levels of scale, from the function of biological molecules to the integration of global ecosystems, is providing us with tools we can use to control and manipulate those systems to our benefit—allowing us to grow more food, design better medical treatments, build better products, and even to change the fundamental nature of the world in which we live. As the social, economic, and political significance of biology continues to grow, however, people are confronted with an ever-increasing set of practical questions. What does it mean to say that the human genome has been "sequenced" and why should we sequence the genomes of other species? How is an organism "genetically modified" or "cloned," and what are the benefits—or potential costs—of doing so? What are "stem cells," and how can they contribute to human health and welfare? Why is HIV/AIDS so difficult to treat? What will happen if vast tracks of tropical rainforest are cut down? Why does it matter that the temperature of the Earth is rising? Our ability to answer these kinds of questions and, thus, to be informed consumers, citizens, and decision-makers depends on our understanding of how living things work, an understanding that is difficult for non-specialists to gain given the tremendous explosion of knowledge in this field over the last few decades.

Understanding biology also satisfies our natural curiosity about the living world around us. Why do children look like their parents? What causes plants to bend toward light? Where are memories stored? Why do some birds have very long tails? How did life on Earth begin? Answering these kinds of questions, whether they are passing fancies or profound inquiries into our very being, also depends on understanding the principles of biology, but here again, it is daunting for the average educated person to sort through a swelling mountain of relevant data and theory without guidance.

This course provides the background and guidance needed for the curious listener to explore in depth the fundamental principles of how living things work; in so doing, it offers the tools needed to understand not only the science of life, but also the impact and importance of the many ways that advances in the biological sciences touch our lives. It presents this material at the level of a typical first biology course taken by university science students, but without assuming prior background in biology or science in general. It also presents material in a conceptual format, emphasizing the importance of broad, unifying principles—facts and details are offered in abundance, but in the context of developing a framework listeners can use to work with information and to understand issues in biology they may encounter in the future. Finally, the course takes a historical approach wherever possible, explaining how key experiments and observations led to our current state of knowledge and introducing many of the people responsible for creating the modern science of biology.

The 72 lectures of this course are divided into three main sections, with each section organized around a major unifying theme in biology. Lectures 1 through 24 explore the theme of "Information and Evolution" in living systems. This exploration begins by asking how life might have arisen spontaneously on the newly formed planet Earth and by describing the hierarchical organization of living systems as we know them today. This discussion leads to the question of how living things reproduce, the most enigmatic aspect of which involves explaining how information about the structure of complex biological molecules called *proteins* can be stored and transmitted. The solution to this problem is found in the structure and function of an equally complex molecule, DNA. The lectures go on to explain what DNA is, how we know it is the genetic material, how DNA stores information about proteins, and how this information is copied and passed on from parents to offspring. One important conclusion of this discussion is that the DNA of an offspring is almost never exactly the same as that of its parents, a fact that means species inevitably change over time, that is, that life evolves. This conclusion leads to an analysis of how Darwin came to his theory of natural selection, followed by an in-depth examination of evolutionary mechanisms and a discussion of how those mechanisms are thought to be responsible for generating the enormous diversity of species we see on the planet today.

Lectures 25 through 48 turn to the second organizing theme of the course, "Development and Homeostasis." This dual theme focuses on the consequences of being an organism made of more than one cell. Many organisms, such as bacteria, are single-celled, but other kinds of organisms—including ourselves—are made up of a large number of cells, with different cell types specialized to perform different functions. This series of lectures begins by considering how different cells having the same genome can turn on or off subsets of the genes they possess, a necessary prerequisite for producing different types of cells from a single fertilized egg, and by examining how cells communicate, necessary for the different cells in an organism to integrate their activities. Against this background, the lectures then explore, in more detail, patterns and mechanisms of animal development, the remarkable process through which one cell formed by the union of a sperm and egg yields a complex, multicellular organism, potentially having trillions of cells of hundreds of different types, all arrayed in precise spatial positions relative to each other. After discussing how a multicellular organism is "built," the lectures then turn to the question of what is needed for a multicellular organism to maintain itself and coordinate its parts, a question that frames the concept of *homeostasis*. This discussion answers a number of questions, including how organisms maintain a constant physiological state, such as a particular body temperature; how chemical signals called *hormones* and specialized cells called *neurons* transmit physiological information across great distances in a body; and how the body is defended against attack by disease-causing agents. The section culminates with the idea that an animal's behavior—even in the simplest case of detecting and responding adaptively to the environment—may be viewed as a kind of highly derived homeostatic mechanism enhancing an organism's ability to survive and reproduce.

The third major theme of the course focuses on "Energy and Resources," the subject of Lectures 49 through 72. This section begins at the level of cells and molecules, showing how living things obtain, store, and deploy the "power" they need to survive and illustrating how this energy ultimately all comes from sunlight. Next, the lectures turn to consider the implications of how energy and other resources necessary for life are distributed and used at progressively higher levels of biological organization, from the level of whole organisms, to populations of organisms, to communities of different species, and finally, to the level of ecosystems, including the entire biosphere. Because the amount of energy and other resources available to organisms may be limited, there often is not enough to go around, a fact that plays a major role in determining the distribution and abundance of different species on the planet. This point sets the stage for introducing fundamental principles of the discipline of ecology and for showing how these principles fit in the broader context of how living systems function and how they change over time.

The course concludes by considering the fact that, just as biologists are on the verge of a truly revolutionary understanding of the "science of life," we are at the same time facing an unprecedented crisis in the loss of biodiversity—potentially a loss of much of the natural world—because of the unprecedented success of a single species, our own. The final lecture discusses the origin of this crisis and considers what is being done, and what still can be done, by biologists and citizens alike to preserve the wonders of the living world around us. ■

The Scope of "Life"
Lecture 1

A great and growing volume of facts about life as it goes on about us and within us becomes available for practical application ... [But] this new material is still imperfectly accessible to ordinary busy people.

This quote is a good description of biology's situation at the beginning of the 21st century. However, it was written almost 75 years ago by H. G. Wells, in his book *The Science of Life*. As with his *Outline of History*, Wells intended *The Science of Life* to be read by "ordinary busy people" from all walks of life. Wells felt it was imperative that laypersons be educated about important basic biology and new developments, but he realized that the volume of scientific information was too great for most people to sift through. And now the amount of biological information has increased significantly since Wells wrote *The Science of Life*, making it even more difficult for the layperson to gain knowledge.

Examining the origins of living things helps define *life* and is, therefore, the area that is studied by biology. Definitions of *life* are elusive because many properties of living things (for example, movement, orderliness, or energy use) also occur occasionally in "non-living" things. Wind moves, crystals grow, and fire uses energy, but we do not consider these to be alive.

Though life developed relatively late in Earth's history, the origins of Earth and the universe are important to fully understanding it. The universe is between 10 and 20 billion years old and began at a moment called the *Big Bang*. Our Sun is about 5 billion years old. The Earth, which was formed from an accumulation of cosmic dust, is about 4.6 billion years old. The early Earth, shortly after its formation about 4.6 billion years ago, was an inhospitable place that could not have supported "life" by any definition we might use today. However, 3.5 billion years ago (approximately 1 billion years after its formation), the Earth was teeming with life in the form of organisms that resemble modern-day bacteria. This development is extremely fast, especially considering that the molten Earth needed half a billion years to cool enough to form a solid rock surface. Some biologists now think that there is evidence for life even earlier, at about 4 billion years ago.

In any case, life appeared on Earth as soon as it was possible. Most scientists now think that life arose spontaneously from non-living matter. Many religions believe that life was bestowed on non-living Earth by a deity. Some scientists suggest the *panspermia* hypothesis, which says that the original life on Earth arrived here from another planet. Both of these alternatives, however, ignore the question of how living matter could emerge from non-living matter.

The most fundamental, most essential property of life is a dependence on organic chemistry, a chemistry based on organic compounds (chemical compounds built around carbon). There are four general classes of organic compounds:

- Amino acids are the building blocks of proteins.

- Nucleic acids include DNA and RNA.

- Carbohydrates include sugar, starch, and cellulose (wood fiber).

- Lipids include fats and hormones.

Organic compounds have complex properties as compared to inorganic compounds. The first step toward the origin of life must involve the formation of organic compounds from inorganic ones. However, organic compounds are generally produced only by living things. As far as we know, the early Earth was entirely inorganic.

A now-classic experiment by Stanley Miller in 1953 demonstrated that it is possible to synthesize many organic compounds under conditions simulating those thought to have prevailed on the early Earth. For many years, scientists speculated about the possibility of spontaneously generating organic compounds. Earth's current atmosphere is largely made up of nitrogen and oxygen. Because oxygen tends to break down organic molecules, spontaneous generation of organic compounds is impossible today.

In the 1920s, Alexander Oparin and J. B. S. Haldane suggested that Earth's early atmosphere had little oxygen—that it was composed primarily of hydrogen, methane, and ammonia. This composition would be conducive to spontaneous production of organic molecules. So Miller tried to reproduce early Earth conditions with an apparatus that used heated water in one flask (the "ocean") and another flask (the "atmosphere") that contained hydrogen, methane, ammonia, and water vapor. Miller also exposed the gases in the "atmosphere" to electrical energy to mimic lightning, volcanism, and ultraviolet radiation. Within a few days, Miller's apparatus had synthesized a wide range of organic compounds, including such complex ones as amino and nucleic acids. Research following Miller's original experiment has shown that all major classes of organic compounds can be synthesized under early Earth conditions.

Most scientists now think that life arose spontaneously from non-living matter.

However, molecules synthesized this way are still rather simple compared to the compounds that make up living things. In addition to the ability to synthesize more complex compounds, three additional things are required to create life: (1) We need to be able to make more of any compound at any time, without relying on random chemistry, which may not produce the same compound every time; (2) we need a method of combining and organizing compounds into larger functional units; and (3) we need to find a way to accumulate and store energy, because living things do not rely on lightning or volcanism to power themselves.

Another characteristic of living systems is that they are organized in a hierarchical fashion, from molecules to cells to organisms to communities of species to ecosystems. At the same time, three unifying principles that cut across all levels of organization form a useful way to look at systems as a whole. The first principle is Information and Evolution, which explores how the structure and organization of living things is encoded in the DNA molecule, how this information is transmitted and modified, and the implications of these processes for understanding life at all scales of organization. The second principle is Development and Homeostasis which considers two related issues for understanding the workings of complex organisms: how single cells (i.e., fertilized eggs) proliferate and transform into complex, multicellular organisms and how the various parts of complex organisms remain coordinated and maintain their integrity in the face of various challenges. The third principle is Energy and Resources, which explains how living systems obtain the energy and other materials needed to maintain their highly ordered state and the implications of these processes for understanding the organization of biology at all levels of scale. This principle is especially interesting because it dictates the structure of all levels of organization. ■

Suggested Reading

Campbell & Reece, *Biology* (6th ed.), chapter 26.

Freeman, *Biological Science*, chapters 2 and 3.

Liebes et al., *A Walk through Time: From Stardust to Us: The Evolution of Life on Earth.*

Wells et al., *The Science of Life*, introduction.

Questions to Consider

1. How does the idea that life arose spontaneously on the early Earth affect your view of humanity and what it means to be human?

2. Given our current understanding of the origin of life on Earth, do you think life exists elsewhere in the universe?

More on the Origin of Life
Lecture 2

Remember, our interest in the origin of life is that it's going to tell us something about how to define life; but where this material will take us, today and in the next lecture, is to begin to introduce the concept of information in living systems, framing the central theme for this first part of the course.

The creation of simple organic molecules (*biomolecules*) is only the first small step in the origin of life from non-living matter. Biomolecules typically are long strings (*polymers*) of simpler organic building blocks (*monomers*). In modern cells, the reactions needed to build such strings (*polymerization*) are catalyzed and controlled by other biomolecules. In the late 1950s, Sydney Fox created short chains of amino acids (polypeptides or proteins) spontaneously in the lab but under only a narrow range of conditions. Fox and other scientists suggested that hot clay could be used as a non-biological *catalyst* (a substance that speeds or enables chemical reactions) to produce polypeptides *abiotically* (without other biological material). James Ferris has since shown that hot clay can produce not only polypeptides but also chains of nucleic acids. Hot clay on the shores of early Earth could have produced polymers that then washed back Into the ocean, creating an increasingly rich "primordial soup" from which life emerged. Spontaneously produced polymers are produced randomly, though, and are generally non-functional.

The cell represents a fundamental "package" of life; it is the smallest level of organization for a completely self-contained living system.

The next critical step in the origin of life from non-life must have been the evolution of primitive cells. The cell represents a fundamental "package" of life; it is the smallest level of organization for a completely self-contained living system. One reason cells are important is that they define, through their outer surface, a barrier between what is living and what is non-living. Laboratory experiments have created cell-like structures (*protobionts*) that contain enzymes and perform some basic chemistry typical of living systems. Some biomolecules (e.g., lipids) spontaneously form protobionts. Coacervates are remarkable protobionts that self-assemble from a solution of polypeptides, nucleic acids, and polysaccharides (polymerized sugars) under certain conditions. When enzymes are added to a coacervate solution, they are taken inside the coacervate and begin to function normally. In spite of remarkable experiments showing the ability of biomolecules and simple cells to be created abiotically, many questions remain unanswered about how life might have arisen spontaneously on the early Earth.

The most difficult problem for the origin of life is understanding how early cells (or organisms in general) can reproduce while maintaining continuity of biological information. Reproduction leads to both questions and answers about the origin of life and the role of information in life. Simple reproduction is not the problem; primitive cell-like structures created in the laboratory will divide spontaneously when they become large enough. When a cell has a modification that makes it more likely to survive than other cells, the beneficial molecules are divided into two cells in simple reproduction. This "dilutes" the modification as more cells are produced. The more difficult problem is to replicate and transmit the information needed to specify the functional properties of a cell and build new, accurate copies.

In modern cells, we know that the "blueprint" containing the required information is DNA (deoxyribonucleic acid), a kind of nucleic acid. DNA transfers its information into RNA, which then transfers its information into proteins. Because proteins do most of the work of modern cells, most of DNA's information is dedicated to making proteins.

There is a serious catch, however, for understanding how a blueprint might have functioned in early cells. DNA cannot replicate itself; it is replicated in modern cells only through the catalytic action of a large number of proteins. However, proteins can be produced in modern cells only if there is a DNA molecule specifying their structure. And neither DNA nor proteins can exist in modern cells without the other; which came first in primitive cells?

Current thinking suggests that RNA in early cells could store and transmit information, perform other catalytic functions in cells, and replicate itself.

Experiments show that short chains of RNA can replicate themselves. In 1983, Thomas Cech discovered that certain types of RNA (ribozymes) perform catalytic functions in modern cells. Before this, catalytic functions were believed to be the sole domain of proteins. These results suggest that protobionts may have reached a stage in which RNA carried out most cell functions. This stage would have been followed by the modern process, in which DNA and proteins perform most functions and RNA is a helper molecule. The transition to the modern stage makes sense, because DNA and proteins are specialized and much better at their tasks than RNA. Biological information specifies the construction and replication of biologically useful molecules and structures; one property of living things is that they can organize, transmit, and replicate this information. ∎

Suggested Reading

Campbell & Reece, *Biology* (6th ed.), chapter 26.

Freeman, *Biological Science*, chapters 2 and 3.

Liebes et al., *A Walk through Time: From Stardust to Us: The Evolution of Life on Earth.*

Questions to Consider

1. Of the several things that had to occur on the early Earth for non-living matter to give rise to a living system, what do you think most defines the transition from non-living to living?

2. Recent work in the laboratory has produced simple proteins that essentially can replicate themselves. How might this finding change our views on the origin of a primitive genetic system?

The Organism and the Cell
Lecture 3

A fundamental characteristic of life, as we've already discussed, is that it is very orderly. The orderliness of life is obvious if you look at any living thing, whether it's a bacterium, a tree, a bird or yourselves. When you do look at a living thing, you immediately get an intuitive sense that life must involve a high degree of order.

What becomes equally as apparent as you start to look at living systems more closely is that this orderliness of life occurs in a hierarchy of structural levels. What do I mean by this? By hierarchy, I simply mean that living systems exhibit order across a range of different scales or sizes of things, starting at the smallest size of molecules that we have already talked about a little bit, and going all the way up to the scale of the entire planet. Living systems are fundamentally orderly and form a hierarchical progression from small, simple units to large, complex ones.

Startin with the smalles biological units, *molecules* are where biology most closely interfaces with physics and chemistry. *Cells* are specially organized collections of molecules. Organized collections of cells make up *tissues* and *organs*, which together make up *organisms*. Organisms of the same type are *populations*, and collections of populations of different types in the same geographical location are *communities*. *Ecosystems* are collections of communities linked together by geophysical processes; The *biosphere* is the largest possible ecosystem on a planet and incorporates all life on that planet is the *biosphere*.

Although each level of this hierarchy is built on the levels before it, each level of organization has properties that could not be predicted by examining the smaller levels. These are called *emergent properties*. For example, the way neurons in the human brain function is well understood, but this understanding does not predict or explain higher brain functions, such as memory or emotion. Emergent properties arise from the organization of components at a particular level, rather than from the components' individual capabilities. One consequence of emergent properties is that, to understand any living system deeply, it is usually necessary to examine the system on all hierarchical levels.

Two levels of organization, however, play particularly important roles in understanding how life works. The first is the organism. Organisms (which can be single-celled or multicellular) are particularly important, because they are usually the level of organization that reproduces and are, therefore, subject to evolution through natural selection. Heritable traits are traits passed from a parent organism to its offspring through the transfer of information in reproduction. It is unlikely that each copy of the information will be identical, however, because errors may creep in during the copying process. Even modern DNA, with its error-prevention mechanisms, is prone to errors. When errors occur, offspring will not be identical to each other, producing variation. Because errors are random, variations are difficult to predict. A consequence of variation is that some individuals may be better at obtaining and using resources than others, for example. As the number of organisms in the same place grows, they will compete for resources. Offspring with characteristics that make them better at competing for resources will reproduce more often and, eventually, outnumber individuals with less advantageous characteristics. Variation and competition leads to *evolution through natural selection*; characteristics that make organisms better at competing for resources are called *adaptations*. Modern living systems can be largely understood as a collection of adaptations resulting from evolutionary processes. Because organisms reproduce, natural selection acts on individual organisms, rather than the components of an organism or groups of individual organisms.

Even modern DNA, with its error-prevention mechanisms, is prone to errors. When errors occur, offspring will not be identical to each other, producing variation. Because errors are random, variations are difficult to predict.

The cell is the second critically important level of organization for understanding how life works, for two reasons. Cells are the smallest units of biological organization that can be considered complete living systems. Many features of the molecular processes underlying life are best understood in the context of how and where they occur in a cell. Multicellular organisms are composed of many types of cells, each with different functions; however, each specific cell function needs to be understood on the cellular level.

Cells are also important because of their packaging—that is, their ability to separate "insides" from "outsides" and different kinds of molecules from each other. The chemistry of life is complex; it is this chemistry that enables the complexity of modern life. The packaging and separation provided by cells allows many distinct chemical processes to coexist in the same organism.

Cells can be categorized into two broad classes: *prokaryotes* and *eukaryotes*. *Prokaryotes* are structurally simple with little or no internal compartmentation. They are enclosed by a single cell membrane (or plasma membrane) made of lipids. All prokaryotic cells are single-celled organisms, though they sometimes occur together in large masses. Bacteria are characteristic of modern prokaryotes.

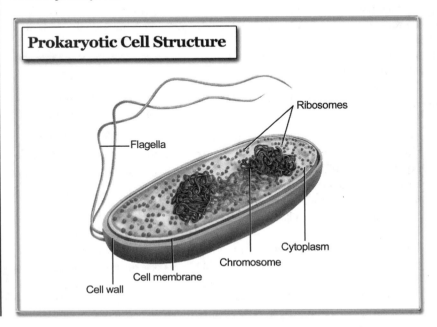

Prokaryotic Cell Structure

Ribosomes

Flagella

Cytoplasm

Chromosome

Cell membrane

Cell wall

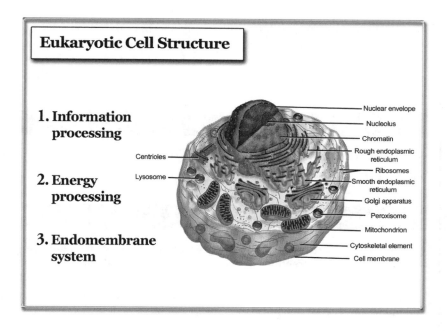

Eukaryotic Cell Structure

1. Information processing

2. Energy processing

3. Endomembrane system

Centrioles
Lysosome

Nuclear envelope
Nucleolus
Chromatin
Rough endoplasmic reticulum
Ribosomes
Smooth endoplasmic reticulum
Golgi apparatus
Peroxisome
Mitochondrion
Cytoskeletal element
Cell membrane

Eukaryotes are more complex cells with many internal compartments. All multicellular organisms are eukaryotes, though some eukaryotes are single-celled. The internal compartments of a eukaryotic cell are called *organelles*, each of which has its own lipid membrane. Organelle function can be divided into three main categories: information processing, energy processing, and packaging of chemical products.

The nucleus is the organelle most associated with information processing. It is surrounded by two membranes (the nuclear envelope). This envelope has pores for input and output. The nucleus contains long, single strands of DNA called *chromosomes*, which become visible during cell division.

Mitochondria (which break down sugars) and *chloroplasts* (which capture energy from the sun through photosynthesis and store it in sugars) are associated with energy processing. Only plant cells and certain single-celled organisms have chloroplasts. Mitochondria and chloroplasts have their own internal structures and DNA.

The set of packaging organelles is collectively known as the *endomembrane system*. Its most prominent organelle is the *endoplasmic reticulum*. This system as a whole is a collection of biological containers that can move, separate, package, and transport chemicals, similar to a chemical manufacturing plant. ■

Suggested Reading

Campbell & Reece, *Biology* (6th ed.), chapters 1 and 7.

Purves et al., *Life* (7th ed.), chapters 1 and 4.

Questions to Consider

1. Honeybees are *eusocial* insects, in which the queen is the only individual in a hive that can reproduce, but she cannot do so without the help of many sterile workers. If all organisms were like honeybees, how would this change our view of the central importance of the "organism" as an important level of organization in the hierarchy of biology?

2. "Thought" is an emergent property of neurons working together. Can you think of other examples of emergent properties of living systems?

Proteins—How Things Get Done in the Cell
Lecture 4

So let's begin talking about proteins by looking at what they do. In Greek, the word *proteos* means, "first place." This is a fitting origin for the name *protein*. It would be a little bit of an exaggeration to say that proteins do absolutely everything in cells.

There are some things that proteins don't do, but it wouldn't be much of an exaggeration; and it is no exaggeration at all to say that proteins play at least some role in almost everything that cells and organisms do. Biological information (DNA) serves as a "blueprint" in cells to build proteins. Proteins are the workhorses of the cell; they play at least some role in almost every cellular process.

- Proteins form structural elements, acting as supports and girders to support cells. They form the *cytoskeleton* (cell skeleton).

- Proteins perform mechanical work by acting as small motors, changing cell shape, or transporting materials within cells.

- Proteins act as vehicles for other substances; for example, hemoglobin transports oxygen in the blood.

- Proteins act as signal receptors for molecular signals between cells, and they can act as the signals themselves.

- Proteins regulate cell functions by switching cellular processes on and off.

- Proteins also act as catalysts for chemical reactions; when they are engaged in this process, they are called *enzymes*. Enzymes make the chemical processes of life work in the environment of the cell.

- Proteins can perform so many different functions because there are many different kinds of proteins. In an *E. coli* cell, there may be 10,000 different proteins; in a typical human cell, 50,000.

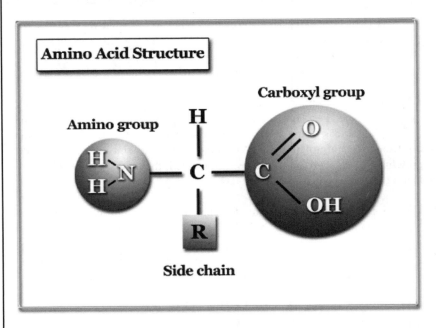

Amino Acid Structure

Amino group

Carboxyl group

H

H—N
H

C

C

O

OH

R

Side chain

The function of a particular protein is determined largely by its shape. Proteins are strings of amino acids folded into three-dimensional shapes. The shape of a protein is often intuitively linked to its function; a structural protein will often be shaped like a girder, for example. Enzymes are shaped to fit other chemical compounds involved in a chemical reaction. The chemical properties of amino acids provide a starting point for understanding protein shape and, therefore, function.

Each amino acid is a carbon atom surrounded by a carboxyl group, an amino group, and a hydrogen atom. Because carbon can form four chemical bonds, one bond is available.

The fourth bond is attached to the *side chain* or *R group*, which can be a number of different chemical structures. The 20 different amino acids found in living systems are differentiated by their side chains.

The physical and chemical characteristics of the side chain determine the unique characteristics of each amino acid and, therefore, contribute to the properties of a protein.

Amino acids form strong peptide bonds between their carboxyl groups, forming polymer chains (polypeptides).

Polypeptides have a "backbone," formed by the repeating pattern of one nitrogen atom and two carbon atoms in each amino acid. One end of the polypeptide will have a free nitrogen (the *N-terminus*), while the other end will have a free carbon (the *C-terminus*). Each terminus is chemically different from the other, giving each polypeptide an inherent polarity. The length of a protein may be quite variable, from as few as 50 amino acids to as many as 5,000.

Proteins perform mechanical work by acting as small motors, changing cell shape, or transporting materials within cells.

Polypeptides do not remain stretched out but, instead, bunch up into compact, globular, three-dimensional shapes. This complex shape determines protein function. The three-dimensional shape of a protein is determined by the linear sequence of its amino acids. The particular folding of a specific polypeptide is caused by the way in which the amino acid side chains interact with each other and with their (usually watery) environment. This interaction has both physical and chemical components. Proteins have several structural levels, each more complex than the last.

A protein's primary structure is simply the sequence of amino acids in the polypeptide chain. Early work in protein biochemistry focused on the primary structure.

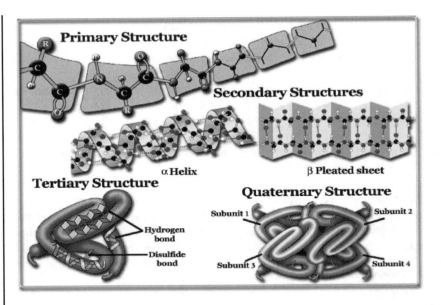

Primary Structure

Secondary Structures

α Helix

β Pleated sheet

Tertiary Structure

Hydrogen bond

Disulfide bond

Quaternary Structure

Subunit 1

Subunit 2

Subunit 3

Subunit 4

The secondary structure is the first level of folding that emerges as the carbon and nitrogen in the polypeptide backbone form very weak "hydrogen bonds" with each other.

The tertiary structure begins to determine protein function. Because it is the result of interactions between the variable side chains of amino acids, the folding on this level can be complex. There are three kinds of interactions:

Some side chains are *hydrophobic* ("water hating"), while others are *hydrophilic* ("water loving"). Hydrophobic side chains twist to avoid water in the cell, ending up in the protein's center, while hydrophilic side chains twist toward water and emerge on the protein's surface. Water-based folding is a major determinant of protein shape. Hydrogen bonds and other weak chemical bonds can form between side chains, further influencing the tertiary structure. Certain kinds of amino acids can form strong covalent bonds with each other, changing and strengthening the tertiary structure.

The quaternary structure occurs in proteins that comprise several polypeptides and results from the association of several different polypeptides with each other. The relationship between shape and function in proteins, coupled with the fact that a protein's shape is determined largely by its primary structure, means that the amino acid sequence is the information that must be encoded, replicated, and transmitted to build proteins. ■

Suggested Reading

Campbell & Reece, *Biology* (6th ed.), chapter 5.

Purves et al., *Life* (7th ed.), chapter 3.

Questions to Consider

1. The function of a protein is determined by its three-dimensional shape, but the only aspect of a protein's structure coded for by DNA is its linear sequence of amino acids. Why is this amount of information sufficient?

2. There are many kinds of amino acids, but only 20 are found in naturally occurring proteins. Can you think of one or more reasons why proteins do not include more—or fewer—kinds of amino acids?

Which Molecule Holds the Code?

Lecture 5

What is the blueprint that we are going to use to build proteins physically made of? That is, what kind of molecule is it?

Before anyone could understand how the blueprint or code worked, it was necessary to understand what it was made of. The simple answer—that "genes" on "chromosomes" somehow transmit information—is common knowledge today and was actually known at the beginning of the 20th century. Cell biologists had discovered that the movements of chromosomes corresponded to some patterns of inheritance, suggesting that these structures held the genetic code. This discovery, combined with the work of Gregor Mendel, became known as the *chromosomal theory of inheritance.*

An experiment in 1928 by Fredrick Griffith, an English physician trying to find a vaccine for *Streptococcus pneumoniae* (a bacteria that causes pneumonia), provided the first insights into the chemical nature of genetic information. Griffith worked with two strains of the bacteria, one virulent (the S strain) and one benign (the R strain). Virulence is an inherited trait; thus, this trait, or the lack of it, must be genetically encoded. Griffith found that heat-killed S-strain bacteria did not cause immunity in mice. He next injected a mix of dead S-strain and live R-strain bacteria into a mouse. Unexpectedly, this mouse died, and Griffith found living S-strain bacteria in it. Griffith concluded correctly that the living bacteria had incorporated something from the dead bacteria that transformed them into live S-strain bacteria. Griffith later showed that this could even be done in a beaker. The substance responsible for this transformation must be genetic material, although Griffith's work could only isolate this "transforming principle" (as he called it), not identify it.

Many scientists at this point assumed that genetic material must be a protein, for several reasons. Because proteins are the workhorses of the cell, it seemed likely that they would also handle information transfer and storage as well. Eukaryotic chromosomes contain 5–10 times more protein by weight than DNA. The diversity and specificity of proteins also suggested that they were better candidates for genes than nucleic acids, especially since they include up to 20 amino acids, but nucleic acids have only 4 functional units. However, proteins tend to break apart (denature) under heat, which made it unlikely that the "transforming principle" could survive in, for example, heat-killed S-strain bacteria if it were a protein.

Work in the 1940s by Oswald Avery and his colleagues used biochemical techniques to identify the "transforming principle." The molecule responsible for the transformation was subjected to selective degradation of the four major classes of biomolecules. For example, the S-strain "transforming principle" made live R-strain bacteria virulent even after carbohydrates, lipids, and proteins were degraded; only when nucleic acids were degraded did transformation no longer occur. Although this work provided strong evidence that DNA was genetic material, most scientists still considered proteins a likely candidate for this role because so little was known about the structure and function of DNA. Some critics also argued that Avery's techniques made it impossible to prove whether *all* of a particular class of biomolecules was removed.

An experiment by Alfred Hershey and Martha Chase published in 1952 provided definitive evidence that DNA was the genetic material. Viruses are non-cellular entities made of DNA with an outer coat of protein. Viruses cannot reproduce on their

Viruses cannot reproduce on their own; instead, they typically attach themselves to cells and inject material that causes the cells to produce viruses until they explode.

own; instead, they typically attach themselves to cells and inject material that causes the cells to produce viruses until they explode. Hershey and Chase worked with a *bacteriophage* ("bacteria-eating virus") and used radioactive isotopes to label and independently track the movement of proteins and DNA. Hershey and Chase demonstrated conclusively that the material injected into the bacteria cell by the virus was DNA, not protein; they reasoned that the substance injected into the cell must be genetic material if it could take over control of the cell.

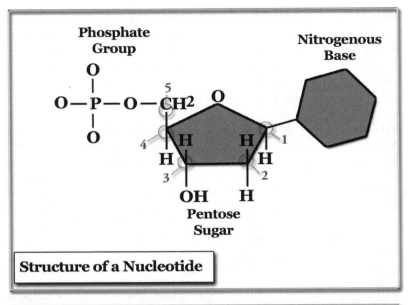

Phosphate Group

Nitrogenous Base

Pentose Sugar

Structure of a Nucleotide

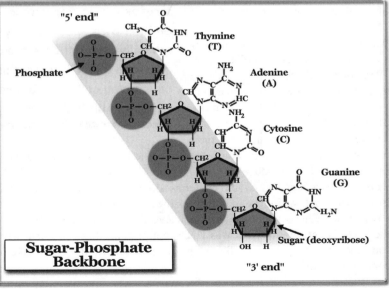

"5' end"

Thymine (T)

Phosphate

Adenine (A)

Cytosine (C)

Guanine (G)

Sugar (deoxyribose)

Sugar-Phosphate Backbone

"3' end"

Like proteins, DNA is a polymer of monomeric building blocks (nucleotides). There are only four nucleotides—thymine, guanine, adenine, and cytosine—each of which has a five-carbon sugar group (*pentose*), a phosphate group, and one of four different nitrogenous bases. Nitrogenous bases fall into one of two groups.

Pyrimidines have a single 6-element ring of carbon and nitrogen. Cytosine and thymine are pyrimidines.

Purines have a 6-element ring with a 5-element ring of carbon and nitrogen attached to it. Adenine and guanine are purines.

Nucleotides are referred to by a single letter, indicating the nitrogenous base: A is adenine, G is guanine, C is cytosine, and T is thymine. The backbone of a DNA molecule is an alternating pattern of sugar and phosphate groups with attached nitrogenous bases. Because of the way nucleotides bond, DNA is polarized—one end has an available 5 carbon (the 5' end), and the other end has an available 3 carbon (the 3' end). ■

Suggested Reading

Campbell & Reece, *Biology* (6th ed.), chapter 16.

Purves et al., *Life* (7th ed.), chapter 11.

Watson, *The Double Helix: A Personal Account of the Discovery of the Structure of DNA*.

Watson and Berry, *DNA: The Secret of Life*.

Questions to Consider

1. DNA is often referred to as a kind of "blueprint," but what are some differences between DNA and a blueprint that might be used, for example, to build a house?

Would Hershey and Chase's experiment have been as convincing in demonstrating that DNA is the genetic material if Griffith and Avery and his colleagues had not done their earlier work?

The Double Helix
Lecture 6

To understand replication and how it might work, scientists were convinced that they needed to know the three-dimensional structure of the DNA molecule. It was this impetus that led to the discovery of the now-famous DNA double helix by Watson and Crick.

Because both proteins and DNA are polymers with variable groups, it seemed intuitive that there was a mapping between the two. However, DNA's linear structure did not reveal any clues about how DNA could be replicated. Successful work on the relationship between protein structure and function led scientists to believe that understanding the three-dimensional structure of DNA might reveal its replication mechanism.

In x-ray crystallography, diffraction patterns produced by x-rays passing through a crystallized substance provide clues about the physical structure of the substance. Rosalind Franklin and Maurice Wilkins, working at Kings College in London, were able produce well-resolved x-ray crystallographs of very pure crystallized DNA. They were not, however, able to fully deduce the three-dimensional structure of DNA from the clues provided by their own crystallographs.

Another source of insight came from the work of Erwin Chargaff, who performed biochemical analyses of the relative amounts of different nitrogenous bases in samples of DNA from many species. Chargaff discovered that, in any sample of DNA, the amount of adenine (A) always equals the amount of thymine (T), and the amount of cytosine (C) always equals the amount of guanine (G). These equivalencies of the amounts of A and T and the amounts of C and G, known as Chargaff's Rule, were considered curious, and the significance of this finding was not immediately apparent.

James Watson and Francis Crick, working at Cambridge University, deduced the three-dimensional structure of DNA from insights they obtained from Franklin and Wilkins's x-ray crystallograph of DNA and from Chargaff's

Rule. Watson realized the significance of Franklin and Wilkins's data when he saw their findings on a lecture trip to London; he noted some key dimensions from the crystallograph, and he and Crick began formulating several physical models that might conform to these data. The x-ray data made it clear that DNA normally occurs as a double-stranded helix and that each turn of the helix contained 10 nucleotides. Watson and Crick made physical models of DNA to test whether different helix formations conformed to their observations. They realized that the nitrogenous bases must go on the inside of the helix, which makes sense given that the bases are hydrophobic and would tend to face inward. They also realized that the two strands of a DNA molecule are antiparallel (that is, they run in opposite directions).

"Complementary base pairing" provided the last piece of the puzzle. Because purines and pyrimidines are different sizes, random base pairs across the helix would give DNA a variable width, which is unstable. Chargaff's Rule helped Watson and Crick realize that purines must always pair with pyrimidines and, further, that A must always pair with T, and G must always pair with C. In 1953, they published a short paper describing their model for the three-dimensional structure of DNA.

Watson and Crick suggested that the DNA double helix must "unzip," and new complementary strands must form from the originals.

More significant than the structure of DNA itself was the fact that, as expected, this structure suggested a mechanism whereby DNA could be accurately replicated. Watson and Crick's paper ends with "It has not escaped our attention that the specific pairing we have postulated immediately suggests a possible copying mechanism for the genetic material." The complementary base pairing of A with T and G with C suggested that the double helix could unwind into two single strands of DNA, each of which could serve as an unambiguous template for the complementary strand.

Watson, Crick, and Wilkins—but not Rosalind Franklin—won the Nobel Prize for Physiology and Medicine in 1962 for the discovery of DNA's double helix. Some have suggested that Franklin was denied credit for what

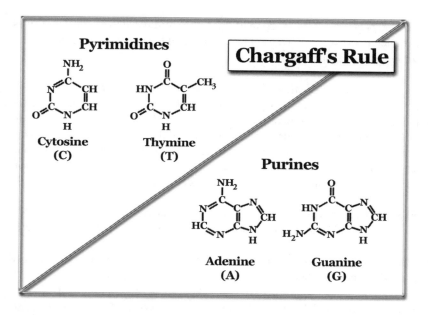

Pyrimidines

Cytosine (C)

Thymine (T)

Chargaff's Rule

Purines

Adenine (A)

Guanine (G)

may be the single most important contribution to the discovery of the double helix. Franklin had a difficult relationship with Maurice Wilkins and her colleagues at Wilkins's lab; she was asked to leave and cease work on DNA altogether. She eventually did so and began to work on viruses. Accounts of the discovery of DNA from the 1960s and 1970s minimize Franklin's contribution and emphasize Watson and Crick's work. The main reason Franklin did not win a Nobel Prize, however, is that she died in 1958, and Nobel Prizes are not awarded posthumously. Fortunately, her contributions are now more fully recognized and taught.

Watson and Crick suggested that the DNA double helix must "unzip," and new complementary strands must form from the originals. Two alternatives to this model were proposed.

The *conservative model* suggested that the double helix remained intact and was used whole as a template for copies.

The *dispersive model* suggested that the original DNA molecule was completely broken down during replication and the new copy was created by some unknown mechanism.

Based on what was known in the 1950s, both of these alternatives were completely likely, though they seem improbable now. They still retain value, though, as ways to compare predictions made by Watson and Crick's model. Watson and Crick's model became known as the *semiconservative model*, because the DNA is disassembled during replication, but the original strands are incorporated whole in the new copies. The competing models each predicted a different mixture of genetic material after a copying process.

The semiconservative model leads to a prediction that each new DNA molecule would be made of one original strand and one freshly created strand.

The conservative model predicts that new copies would contain freshly created strands but that the originals would also remain intact.

The dispersive model predicts that the original DNA would be destroyed and its components randomly scattered across the strands of the new copies.

Although distinguishing original DNA from new copies is conceptually straightforward, it took several years for anyone to figure out how to accomplish this experimentally. ∎

Suggested Reading

Campbell & Reece, *Biology* (6th ed.), chapter 16.

Maddox, *Rosalind Franklin: The Dark Lady of DNA*.

Purves et al., *Life* (7th ed.), chapter 11.

Watson, *The Double Helix: A Personal Account of the Discovery of the Structure of DNA*.

Watson and Berry, *DNA: The Secret of Life*.

1. In your opinion, is the kind of competition that surrounded the discovery of the DNA double helix good for the process of science?

2. Watson and Crick proposed a model for the three-dimensional structure of DNA. Did they "prove" the existence of the double helix and, if so, how?

The Nuts and Bolts of Replicating DNA
Lecture 7

> The prediction of Watson and Crick's semi-conservative hypothesis is that each of the two daughter double helices, after one round of replication, should be made up of one old strand, entirely intact, and one new strand, also intact.

Experiments by Matthew Meselson and Franklin Stahl in the late 1950s supported the semiconservative model of DNA replication, as proposed originally by Watson and Crick. Testing this model is conceptually simple; one need only identify the distribution of newly synthesized DNA compared to the distribution of original DNA after replication. The real difficulty with testing the model lay in developing a new method for labeling or otherwise identifying original and new DNA.

Nitrogen is an important chemical constituent of DNA. Meselson and Stahl raised bacteria in growth media enriched either with normal nitrogen (^{14}N) or with a stable, slightly heavier isotope of nitrogen (^{15}N). After many generations of replication, Meselson and Stahl could assume that new DNA synthesized in the normal medium incorporated only normal nitrogen and that new DNA from the ^{15}N medium incorporated only heavy nitrogen. The problem remained, however, of measuring extremely minute differences in the weight of DNA molecules that differed only by the added mass of a single neutron in the heavy isotope of nitrogen. Meselson and Stahl devised a new measurement technique to identify the relative amounts of original and new DNA after replication.

Meselson and Stahl's new technique was called *density gradient centrifugation*. If the density of a liquid and an object in it are about equal, the object will neither sink nor float but stay at its original depth. If there is a range (*gradient*) of densities in a liquid, denser (heavier) objects will move toward the bottom and less dense (lighter) objects will move toward the top. Meselson and Stahl found that a solution of cesium chloride (CsCl) has approximately the same density as DNA. When they centrifuged tubes of CsCl at very high speeds for long periods, the CsCl formed a density gradient. DNAs of different densities in such a tube will form bands at their precise densities. This technique is sufficiently sensitive to detect the difference between ^{14}N DNA and ^{15}N DNA. Meselson and Stahl took ^{15}N bacteria, transferred it to ^{14}N growth medium, and waited for it to replicate once. They then extracted the new DNA and measured its density.

The distribution of DNA densities following one round of replication ruled out the conservative model, which predicts no mixing of lighter and heavier DNA, but could not distinguish between the dispersive and semiconservative models. After one generation, all the DNA formed one intermediate density band. The distribution of densities following a second round of replication, however, was consistent only with the semiconservative model, which predicts a lighter and a heavier band.

Research by Arthur Kornberg in the 1950s demonstrated that DNA could be synthesized artificially. Watson and Crick suggested that complementary base pairing might not even require an enzyme but would, instead, self-assemble new DNA. Kornberg, however, discovered that one protein, DNA

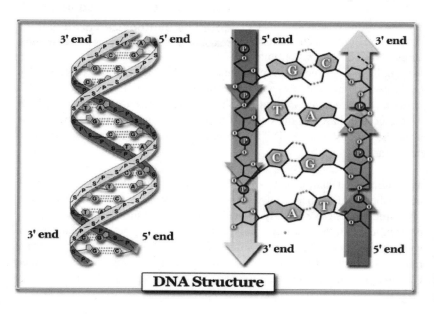

DNA Structure

polymerase, was in fact the enzyme responsible for DNA polymerization. Decades of subsequent research have identified dozens of other enzymes and molecules that play supporting roles in this complex process.

DNA replication proceeds in the following way. The two strands of the double helix are separated by the enzyme helicase, starting with a small bubble and proceeding outward in both directions. Single-strand binding proteins hold the single strands of DNA open so that they cannot close back into a double helix. DNA replication starts only at specific sequences of nucleotides, called *origins of replication*. These origins are different in prokaryotes (single-celled organisms) and eukaryotes (many-celled organisms). Prokaryotes have a single, circular strand of DNA, forming a single *chromosome* with one origin of replication. Eukaryotes have multiple, independent strands of DNA (i.e., multiple *chromosomes*). Each chromosome may have hundreds or thousands of origins of replication. Each replication bubble has two Y-shaped regions called *replication forks*, where the double strand is being separated by helicase.

Research by Arthur Kornberg in the 1950s demonstrated that DNA could be synthesized artificially.

As the strands separate, DNA polymerase uses each exposed single strand as a template for synthesizing a new complementary strand. The monomers connected by DNA polymerase are not nucleotides but related compounds called *deoxynucleoside triphosphates* (dNTPs). Complementary base pairing lines up the correct bases in the correct order for each strand. DNA polymerase uses the energy in the dNTP phosphate groups to bond new bases to new strands.

The antiparallel nature of DNA's two strands means that only one can be transcribed continuously. DNA polymerase can synthesize new DNA only in one direction (it can add only to the 3' end). As a result, synthesis proceeds continuously on the leading strand (5' to 3' direction) but can occur only in short segments on the lagging strand (3' to 5'), because DNA polymerase must work backward there. The segments on the lagging strand are called *Okazaki fragments* and are eventually stitched together by the enzyme

DNA ligase. Understanding DNA replication has been the key to both understanding and manipulating biological systems. ■

Suggested Reading

Campbell & Reece, *Biology* (6th ed.), chapter 16.

Freeman, *Biological Science*, chapter 12.

Holmes, *Meselson, Stahl, and the Replication of DNA: A History of "The Most Beautiful Experiment in Biology."*

Questions to Consider

1. Meselson and Stahl, Kornberg, and other early molecular biologists could never actually "see" a molecule of DNA, yet they worked out the mechanisms of DNA replication. Do you find this approach to doing science convincing? If not, why not?

2. DNA replication involves a piece-by-piece mechanism for copying the "lagging strand." Can you think of another way nature might have solved this problem?

The Central Dogma
Lecture 8

We still don't know how the code works. That is, we still don't know how the structure of a DNA molecule contains information about the structure of a protein. And that is where we want to begin to turn our attention to now.

We know that a code needs to specify only the sequence of amino acids in a protein, which ultimately determines protein shape and function. Before we look at how this code might work, we need to take a broader look at how genetic information flows in living systems.

Francis Crick proposed what he called the *Central Dogma of molecular biology*, which is a conceptual model of genetic information flow. It has two main points. The first point is the suggestion that genetic information does not pass directly from DNA to proteins but passes through an intermediate molecule: ribonucleic acid, or RNA. The second point is that information passes in only one direction, from DNA to RNA to proteins. Crick said, "Once information has passed into proteins, it cannot get out again."

The nature of DNA gives rise to the one-way flow of genetic information described by the Central Dogma. The information in DNA is stored as a sequential pattern of nucleotide bases. The process of replication transmits this information to newly synthesized DNA, preserving the sequential pattern. The information in DNA can be transmitted to a molecule of RNA through a process called *transcription*. The biochemical language of RNA is essentially the same as that of DNA, and RNA synthesis is similar in many respects to synthesis of new DNA. Information is not very useful in RNA; RNA's main purpose is to pass genetic information to the process that builds proteins.

RNA structure is similar to DNA structure, with three important differences. The pentose sugar in RNA is called *ribose* and has a hydroxyl group in the second carbon position. The pentose in DNA lacks this hydroxyl group and is therefore *deoxyribo*nucleic acid. In RNA, the base uracil (U) replaces

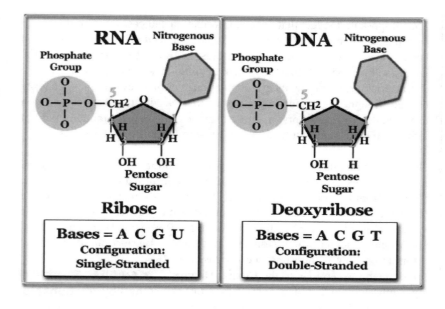

the thymine (T) base found in DNA. Uracil forms a complementary base pair with adenine (A) in RNA. RNA usually occurs only in single-strand polymers, instead of DNA's double helix. There are several different types of RNA. RNA that acts as an intermediate, or messenger, for information is called *messenger RNA* (mRNA). The information in mRNA is used to specify the structure of proteins through a process called *translation*. This term describes the process through which information is changed from its functionally useless form in DNA and RNA into the functionally useful form of proteins.

The Central Dogma provides a convenient framework for organizing our thinking about the molecular basis of genetic information. We have used the term *gene* loosely, but the Central Dogma makes clear that a gene must be, at least to a first approximation, a segment of DNA that carries the code for making a particular protein. Protein synthesis has many potential control points, which generally occur where information passes from one molecular form to another.

Most important, the fact that genetic information can pass only from DNA to protein and not in reverse means that changes induced in proteins cannot feed back to the DNA coding for those proteins; DNA can be changed *only* if the DNA itself is modified directly. Because evolution is a change in the average characteristics of individuals in a population over time, evolutionary changes can be brought about only by changes to DNA itself. Changes to DNA can include copying errors or direct damage, but they are random and not influenced by the environment. Any change to DNA is called a *mutation*.

Notwithstanding its name, there are notable exceptions to the Central Dogma, representing cases in which the flow of genetic information does not follow the path from DNA to RNA to protein. Many viruses, including for example the tobacco mosaic virus, use RNA as their primary genetic material. These viruses transcribe new RNA directly from other RNA strands, instead of from DNA, and generate proteins directly from RNA. Because the direction of information flow is the same, these viruses are not dramatic exceptions to the Central Dogma. By synthesizing a complementary strand that is used as a mold for other RNA strands, however, they demonstrate an interesting solution to the lack of an inherent template that double-stranded DNA normally provides.

One key relationship of the Central Dogma has no exceptions as yet: Changes to proteins do not feed back to modify the information stored in RNA or DNA.

Some RNA viruses use an enzyme called *reverse transcriptase* to synthesize DNA from an RNA template and actually reverse the normal flow of information. These retroviruses include HIV and certain tumor-producing viruses. When a retrovirus infects a host cell, the virus's RNA is reverse transcribed into DNA that becomes incorporated into the host's own DNA. The modified host DNA then serves as a template for synthesizing more viral RNA, which is translated into proteins.

Retroviruses such as HIV are difficult to treat; because they insert their material into the host's DNA, the only cell functions that can be blocked or targeted are those specific to the virus. More general treatments will stop or impede the function of every cell in the body. Azidothymidine (AZT) resembles and is mistaken for thymine by reverse transcriptase (DNA polymerase does not often make the same mistake). When taken up by reverse transcriptase, AZT stops the polymerization of viral DNA. Reverse transcriptase is also prone to making errors in transcribed DNA; these errors allow retroviruses to evolve rapidly inside a patient. Evolution of the virus can then defeat the effectiveness of such treatments as AZT.

One key relationship of the Central Dogma has no exceptions as yet: Changes to proteins do not feed back to modify the information stored in RNA or DNA. In one case, however, proteins seem to be able to modify other proteins. Prions (proteinaceous infective particles) are responsible for such diseases as mad cow disease, kuru, and other spongiform encephalopathies ("sponge brain diseases"). Prions are proteins that can apparently alter the shape of other proteins and, in so doing, destroy their function. In this sense, prions alter the information in other proteins, although the mechanism by which they do so is unclear. ■

Suggested Reading

Freeman, *Biological Science*, chapter 13.

Judson, *The Eighth Day of Creation: Makers of the Revolution in Biology.*

Purves et al., *Life* (7th ed.), chapter 12.

Questions to Consider

1. If RNA acts only as an intermediate "messenger" in the Central Dogma, linking the information in DNA to the production of proteins, why should RNA be part of the system at all?

2. Why are retroviruses such as HIV so difficult to treat?

The Genetic Code
Lecture 9

Crick suggested that there must be an adapter molecule; a molecule with two functionally different ends. On the one end, he suggested, there must be a mechanism for attaching a specific kind of amino acid. At the other end, there must be a mechanism for interacting with a specific sequence of nucleotide bases. Indeed, Crick was correct.

The lecture describes how differences in the structure of DNA and protein molecules impose a limitation on how the former can encode information about the latter, and it shows how this limitation suggests an inherent structure for the code. The lecture then discusses the clever combination of experimental work and puzzle-solving that was used to crack the code and describes the code's defining properties.

A cryptoquote puzzle is an example of a simple substitution code. All the original letters have been substituted, but the substitutions are always the same—for example, *W* is always substituted for *A* and so on. Solving the puzzle involves figuring out the appropriate substitutions. *Transfer RNA* (tRNA) are small, specialized segments of RNA that perform this function. The DNA code cannot be a simple substitution code because DNA has only 4 variable elements, while proteins have 20. This means that sequences of more than one nucleotide must code for single amino acids.

How many nucleotide base "letters" are required to provide an adequate code for amino acid "words"? A two-letter code would yield 16 possible words (4 x 4 = 16), which is not enough to unambiguously code for 20 different amino acids; a four-letter code would yield 256 possible combinations (4 x 4 x 4 x 4 = 256), which is far more than needed. A three-letter code yields 64 combinations (4 x 4 x 4 = 64) and would appear to be the most likely candidate for the number of nucleotides required to code unambiguously for amino acids.

Francis Crick and his colleagues proved that a three-letter code is correct. First, they used acridines to delete or add single base pairs from DNA molecules. Each addition or deletion offset the code by one unit, essentially turning it into meaningless gibberish. Crick and his partners found that the deletion or addition of three base pairs brought the code back into register, similar to deleting a word in a sentence made of three-letter words.

The genetic code is a triplet code, with unique combinations of three nucleotide bases referred to as *codons*. Many experiments have verified this conclusion, but how did molecular biologists eventually discover which codons specified which amino acids? The solution to this problem came from the development in the 1960s of the ability to synthesize artificial DNA sequences in the laboratory, then to use these synthetic sequences as templates for protein synthesis. Scientists started by polymerizing a single base, such as uracil, then forming proteins from those sequences. The only possible conclusion is that the protein formed (phenylalanine) is coded for by UUU.

The genetic code is universal. With only a few minor exceptions, particular codons specify the same amino acids in all organisms.

Decoding mixed codons involved adding different proportions of nucleotides to a synthesis reaction. By calculating the proportions of the resulting codon combinations and comparing these results to the proportions of amino acids produced, scientists eventually filled in the amino acid definitions for all 64 possible combinations of three nucleotide bases. Techniques developed later permit more precise codon synthesis, but work with these methods only confirmed the original codon definitions.

A brief look at the codon "dictionary" illustrates several important features. First, 61 of the 64 possible codons code for a particular amino acid. Because there are only 20 kinds of amino acids used in proteins, some amino acids are coded for by more than one codon. This redundancy mostly involves variation in the last nucleotide in a codon. The triplet code is unambiguous, however; each codon codes for only a single amino acid. Three codons do not code for any amino acid but, instead, serve solely as "stop" signals.

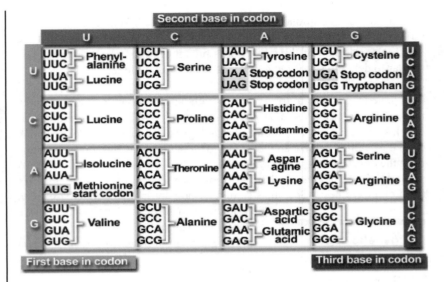

Second base in codon

	U	C	A	G	
U	UUU UUC Phenyl-alanine UUA UUG Lucine	UCU UCC UCA UCG Serine	UAU UAC Tyrosine UAA Stop codon UAG Stop codon	UGU UGC Cysteine UGA Stop codon UGG Tryptophan	U C A G
C	CUU CUC CUA CUG Lucine	CCU CCC CCA CCG Proline	CAU CAC Histidine CAA CAG Glutamine	CGU CGC CGA CGG Arginine	U C A G
A	AUU AUC AUA Isolucine AUG Methionine start codon	ACU ACC ACA ACG Threonine	AAU AAC Aspar-agine AAA AAG Lysine	AGU AGC Serine AGA AGG Arginine	U C A G
G	GUU GUC GUA GUG Valine	GCU GCC GCA GCG Alanine	GAU GAC Aspartic acid GAA GAG Glutamic acid	GGU GGC GGA GGG Glycine	U C A G

First base in codon   **Third base in codon**

One codon (AUG) serves a dual function; it codes for methionine and serves as a "start" signal, indicating where an RNA transcript should begin. All mRNA begins with AUG, which provides an unambiguous marker of the first nucleotide base in a sequence of codons. Without this codon, offsets in transcription by 1 or 2 bases would yield an entirely different set of codons and, thus, an incorrect protein structure. All polypeptides, therefore, begin with methionine, but it is often stripped off by an enzyme after the protein is produced.

The genetic code is universal. With only a few minor exceptions, particular codons specify the same amino acids in all organisms. The universality of the genetic code is essential for the modern revolution in biotechnology. Because all organisms share the same code, we can perform genetic engineering by transferring DNA from one organism to another. Common examples of genetic engineering include insulin-producing bacteria, plants with built-in pesticides, and gene therapy. The universality of the genetic code also suggests that the code and its fundamental mechanisms arose very early in the history of life on Earth. This, in turn, suggests that all life derived from a single, common, primitive ancestor. Exceptions to the genetic code are rare, minor, and usually involve (1) assigning one of the stop codons to an amino acid or (2) an ancient divergence, such as the development of mitochondria or chloroplasts. ■

Suggested Reading

Campbell & Reece, *Biology* (6th ed.), chapter 17.

Judson, *The Eighth Day of Creation: Makers of the Revolution in Biology*.

Purves et al., *Life* (7th ed.), chapter 12.

Questions to Consider

1. How might the way DNA encodes information about proteins be different if there were more kinds of nucleotides than four?

2. Why is it essential that the genetic code be "unambiguous" but not a problem that it is "redundant"?

From DNA to RNA
Lecture 10

So, let's begin today with *transcription*. Remember, transcription is a kind of DNA-directed RNA synthesis. Thus, it is how information in DNA somehow passes to RNA. We call this process transcription because the biochemical language of RNA, as a nucleic acid, is the same as the biochemical language of DNA, a sequence of nucleotides.

This is the first of two lectures that complete the description of the journey of genetic information from DNA to functional proteins. It begins by describing the key features of how DNA is transcribed into RNA. It then goes on to show how initial transcriptions of RNA are cut up and pasted back together to produce a functional message. *Introns* are stretches of DNA that lack obvious coding function. Introns are excised from the initial transcript, and the remaining *exons* are stitched together to produce a contiguous message, leaving much of the original transcript on the cutting-room floor. Armed with this background, we conclude the lecture by revisiting the molecular definition of a gene.

The molecular mechanisms of transcription (the synthesis of RNA) are conceptually quite similar to those involved in replication (the synthesis of new DNA), largely because RNA and DNA are very similar molecules. RNA is used as an intermediate, or messenger, passing information from DNA to the protein-synthesis process. The key enzyme involved in transcription is RNA polymerase, which acts much like DNA polymerase. As in replication, the DNA double helix must first unwind, after which RNA polymerase uses complementary base pairing to synthesize a polymer that maintains information as a unique sequence of nucleotide bases.

There are some important differences between replication and transcription. RNA polymerase requires fewer enzymes to work than DNA polymerase; for example, RNA polymerase typically opens the double helix itself without the help of helicase. Only one of the two DNA strands is copied during transcription, because only one sequence of nucleotides is needed to code for amino acids. The transcribed strand is called the *template*, or *coding strand*; the opposite strand is called the *complementary strand*. The template strand, however, is not always on the same side of the double helix, and the distribution of meaningful information on a particular side of the helix is random. A complementary strand is unlikely to be a template strand for another gene, because the constraints of complementary base pairing make such compactness difficult.

In transcription, only selected pieces of DNA are transcribed, not the entire molecule. Specific nucleotide sequences, called *promoters*, mark the beginning of transcription for each gene, and other sequences, called *termination sites*, signal the end of each gene. (Start and stop codons are instructions to the protein synthesizers, not RNA polymerase.) Together, a promoter, termination site, and the DNA in between are called a *transcription unit*.

During replication, only one copy of the DNA molecule is made. During transcription, a single gene may be copied hundreds or thousands of times, depending on the needs of the protein-synthesis process. RNA polymerase

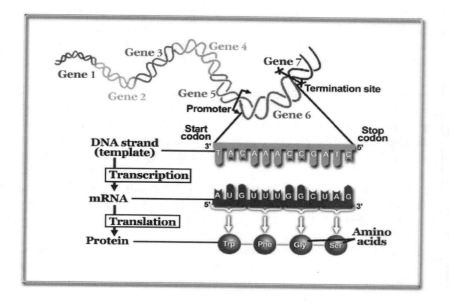

does not on its own recognize promoters; instead, particular stretches of DNA to be transcribed are specified by other proteins that recognize them. The presence or absence of these transcription factors serves as a kind of switch to control when stretches of DNA are to be transcribed into RNA.

DNA contains quite a bit of apparently useless material whose purpose is not known. In eukaryotes, the initial RNA transcript includes large segments of RNA that are not part of the code needed to produce a protein. These stretches must be eliminated somehow in order to make a fully functional transcript for the protein. The average size of a transcription unit is about 8,000 nucleotides long. Once the noncoding nucleotides are removed, the average size of a transcript is about 1,200 nucleotides. This means that as much as 85% of the transcribed mRNA is cut out and not translated! The pieces of RNA that are cut out and thrown away are called *introns*, while the remaining pieces that are spliced together are called *exons*.

The excision of introns and splicing of exons to form a final RNA transcript is done by a set of enzymes and catalytic RNAs known as *snRNPs* (small nuclear ribonucleoproteins), which act together as a *spliceosome*. snRNPs identify the ends of introns, break the RNA at these locations while maintaining a connection with the adjacent RNA pieces, then bring these pieces together physically and rejoin the broken strand. The end product is a mature mRNA strand that includes only exons.

In addition to having introns spliced out, the ends of eukaryotic RNA strands are also chemically modified before the strands are exported from the nucleus. At the 5' end of the polarized RNA molecule, a modified form of guanine is added (the *guanine cap*); at the 3' end, a string of several hundred adenines (the *polyA tail*) is added. The guanine cap and polyA tail appear to have two functions. First, they stitch up the ends of the RNA molecule, protecting it from degradation by enzymes that normally break down RNA. Second, they appear to increase the efficiency with which the final RNA transcript is translated into protein after it has left the nucleus.

Several hypotheses have been advanced to explain the presence of introns. One possibility is that the splicing process controls the rate and/or timing of processing mRNA strands. Introns may also be genetic hitchhikers that serve no purpose and have been introduced into DNA in some way, possibly through retroviruses. In some organisms, the same transcription unit can produce different proteins depending on which parts are excised—one gene's introns may be another gene's exons. Many different genes share the same exons, which may be interchangeable structural functions (functional domains), similar to interchangeable machine parts. Introns may be a way of separating common functional domains for easy reuse.

Many different genes share the same exons, which may be interchangeable structural functions (functional domains), similar to interchangeable machine parts.

Our discussion to this point makes it clear that, even on the molecular level, we can define a gene in several ways. Clearly and most simply, a gene is a physical length of DNA that codes for a protein, but even this simple definition is complicated by the fact that some regions of DNA associated with genes play a regulatory role, while other regions are spliced out and thrown away. ■

Suggested Reading

Campbell & Reece, *Biology* (6th ed.), chapter 17.

Purves et al., *Life* (7th ed.), chapter 12.

Questions to Consider

1. Now that the human genome has been completely sequenced, there still remains a significant challenge to determine the function of much of that sequence. Why should this be especially a challenge for eukaryotic organisms as compared to prokaryotes?

2. If only one strand of DNA is normally transcribed for any particular gene, why is it nonetheless essential for DNA to be a double-stranded molecule to serve its function?

From RNA to Protein
Lecture 11

In today's lecture, what we want to do is to complete our description of this journey of information, taking a closer look at the process that we call translation, where the mRNA transcript is used as a template for building the protein itself. But before we do that, I want to spend just a moment locating where in the cell these processes are occurring.

There are three major players in the process of translation: the message, the translator, and the protein builder. The message is mRNA. The translator is a different form of RNA, transfer RNA (tRNA), that converts the biochemical language of nucleic acids into the biochemical language of amino acids. The protein builder is the ribosome, a complex structure composed of a number of different catalytic proteins, as well as a third type of RNA, ribosomal RNA (rRNA). This lecture describes how these three players interact and contribute to the final conversion of a sequence of nucleotides into a useful protein.

Transcription and translation happen in distinctly different areas of the eukaryotic cell. The defining difference between prokaryotes and eukaryotes is whether or not they have a nucleus—eukaryotes do; prokaryotes do not. Eukaryotic DNA resides in the nucleus, while prokaryotic DNA is not separated from the rest of the cell. In eukaryotes, then, replication and transcription must and do occur in the nucleus. Translation in eukaryotes, on the other hand, occurs in the cytoplasm—the parts of the cell outside the nucleus or other organelles. This means that, for eukaryotes, mRNA must leave the nucleus and enter the cytoplasm.

The defining difference between prokaryotes and eukaryotes is whether or not they have a nucleus—eukaryotes do; prokaryotes do not.

The molecular mechanisms of translation (the synthesis of proteins) are quite different from those we have encountered earlier in DNA replication and RNA transcription. These differences arise from the fact that triplets of nucleotides correspond to single amino acids and that a specific correspondence between a sequence of nucleotides and a sequence of amino acids requires a molecule that can "speak" the biochemical language of these two different kinds of biomolecules.

Translation involves three major players. The message is mRNA, which after processing is a sequence of codons that specify a sequence of amino acids that make up a particular protein. The translator is a different kind of RNA called transfer RNA (tRNA). A single strand of RNA about 80 nucleotides long is tRNA. Unlike mRNA, tRNA has a complex three-dimensional structure that arises from complementary base pairing.

On one end, tRNA has a three-base sequence (the *anticodon*) that binds to a specific codon on mRNA. The anticodon is variable, but there are only about 45 types of tRNA, because some types of tRNA recognize multiple codons that differ only in their last bases. The other end of a tRNA is invariable, but it bonds with the correct amino acid through the help of aminoacyl-tRNA synthetase. There is a different synthetase for different anticodon/amino acid

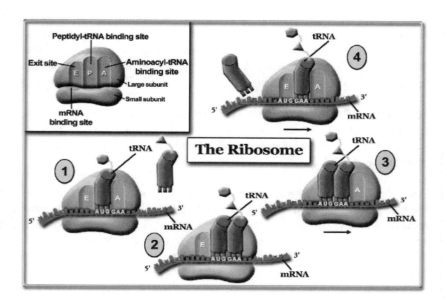

pairs; aminoacyl-tRNA synthetase binds a tRNA and the appropriate amino acid and catalyzes a chemical bond between them, producing a charged, or activated, tRNA. The protein builder is the ribosome, a complex structure composed of both a variety of proteins and a third kind of RNA (ribosomal RNA, or rRNA). It is essentially a "protein polymerase," bringing tRNAs together with mRNA in the proper fashion and catalyzing the chemical bonding of amino acids in sequence to the protein being manufactured. Translation has three stages, initiation, elongation, and termination.

Initiation: The ribosome is divided into two main subunits (a larger and a smaller) that are normally separated. Initiation begins when the small subunit binds a strand of mRNA and a tRNA that has the anticodon for the start codon AUG. The two subunits come together and the formation of an amino acid string begins.

Elongation: Binding sites on the ribosome serve to bring together tRNAs in sequence with their corresponding codons on the mRNA strand. The P site is where the initiator tRNA first attaches. When the initiator tRNA attaches, the next tRNA in sequence will enter the A site, and the ribosome will form a strong bond between its amino acid and the methionine coded for by the initiator tRNA. The initiator tRNA will move to the E site and drop off the ribosome. The ribosome and mRNA then shift 1 codon relative to each other in order to attach the next amino acid. The elongation stage lasts as long as necessary until the polypeptide is finished.

Termination: No tRNA will bind to the stop codons; thus, once the ribosome reaches one of these, the open A site will bind to a release-factor protein, which breaks the bond between the tRNA and the P site and releases the polypeptide chain.

Once a polypeptide has been synthesized, it is processed in several ways. Methionine is often removed from the beginning of newly synthesized proteins. Some ribosomes are free-floating in the cytoplasm, but ribosomes attached to the endomembrane system release synthesized proteins inside their membranes. The endomembrane system then performs any or all of the following processing functions:

- Chaperone proteins help new proteins form the correct shapes.

- Sugars may be added to form glycoproteins.

- Proteins are also "labeled" with molecular tags that tell the endomembrane system where to send them. ■

Suggested Reading

Campbell & Reece, *Biology* (6th ed.), chapter 17.

Purves et al., *Life* (7th ed.), chapter 12.

Questions to Consider

1. Why is tRNA appropriately referred to as a "translator," and why is aminoacyl-tRNA synthetase appropriately referred to as a "matchmaker"?

2. A mutation occurring in a codon in mRNA may change a single amino acid in a single protein, whereas a mutation in the anticodon of a tRNA will have a profound effect on the amino acid sequence of all proteins that are being synthesized. Why should this be so?

When Mistakes Happen
Lecture 12

In today's lecture, we are going to look at the causes and consequences of errors that are introduced to the DNA code. We will see that the cell puts a lot of effort into avoiding and correcting such errors. We will also see that such errors are unavoidable.

Not only is the copying process prone to error, but DNA is a fragile molecule that can be damaged by a number of external forces. Errors in the DNA code sometimes go unrepaired, however, and such errors can lead to unfortunate outcomes, including cancer. In other, less deleterious cases, errors provide the fodder for evolution by natural selection.

In spite of the extraordinary coordination, precision, and elegance of the molecular machinery used in the task of DNA replication, errors can and do occur. For example, DNA polymerase might fail to insert an appropriate complementary base, or DNA might be damaged. We call these errors *mutations*. In most cases, base pair mismatches are detected and repaired immediately. The number of errors remaining after the replication process is complete is very low, on the order of 1 mismatch for every 1 billion nucleotides. The number of errors made during the replication process, on the other hand, might be 1 mismatch for every 10,000 base pairs. This number may not seem large, but it represents an enormous number of errors when summed over the entire genome of an organism.

The difference is due to mismatch repair mechanisms associated with the replication process that detect errors shortly after they occur and replace an incorrectly matched base with a correct one. DNA polymerase has its own error-checking process and usually replaces an incorrect base with the correct one. This lowers the error rate to about 1 in 10 million—which is still quite high, given that a human genome has about 3.2 billion base pairs. Mismatch repair enzymes constantly inspect newly synthesized DNA for incorrect base pairings. When they discover a mistake, they cut out the incorrect base or section and let DNA polymerase replace the section.

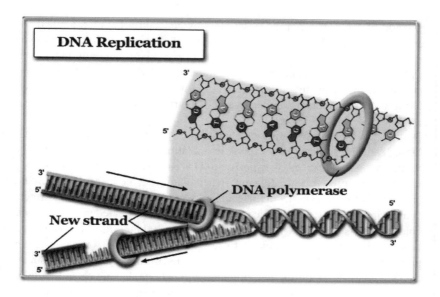

DNA Replication

3'
5'

DNA polymerase

5'

New strand

3'
5'

3'
5'

3'

As a result of complementary base pairing, finding errors should be simple, but determining the correct replacement must be difficult, because there is no way to know which base in a pair is the correct one. Molecular biologists discovered that DNA is gradually methylated as it ages, and mismatch repair enzymes use differences in methylation to determine which base is correct and which is not. Although the final error rate of 1 mismatch in 1 billion base pairs is quite small, these mistakes add up in potentially harmful ways.

Mutations can also be introduced to DNA outside the replication process. DNA is a relatively fragile molecule, and a number of physical and chemical agents can break, modify, or otherwise damage the strand. Ultraviolet (UV) light, X-rays, or other kinds of radiation are absorbed by nucleotides and may cause chemical bonds to break. This bond breakage can damage bases or base pairs or break apart entire DNA molecules. Reactive chemicals (such as aflatoxin, free radicals, and chemicals found in tobacco smoke) can also break chemical bonds in DNA. By one estimate, the DNA in a single human cell may be damaged in one or more of these ways a thousand times per day.

Outside of the replication process, DNA is constantly being examined for errors; when errors are detected, dozens of different types of excision repair enzymes attempt to repair the damage. Excision repair generally involves a suite of enzymes that cut out a stretch of the damaged strand of DNA around the site of the error, then resynthesize a new segment of DNA in its place using the complementary, undamaged DNA strand as a template.

Despite these error-correcting mechanisms, some damage goes unrepaired. Many cancers are caused by genetic mutations to oncogenes (or tumor suppressor genes) caused by exposure to DNA-damaging agents. Oncogenes regulate cell growth and division; when damaged, cells begin to divide uncontrollably. A genetic disease called xeroderma pigmentosum affects about 1 in every 250,000 people in the United States. Affected individuals are unusually sensitive to UV light from the sun. Normal individuals can develop cancer from prolonged exposure to UV light, but people with xeroderma pigmentosum can develop the same problems from only brief exposures. Genetic analysis of xeroderma pigmentosum patients has revealed that they all lack one or more excision repair enzymes and cannot repair UV damage.

Types of mutations include point mutations, insertion or deletion mutations, and chromosomal mutations. *Point mutations* involve only the substitution of one base for another. *Insertion* or *deletion mutations* involve the insertion or deletion of a base pair in a DNA molecule. *Chromosomal mutations* involve the deletion, inversion, duplication, or rearrangement of large sections of DNA and occur when the double helix is broken apart.

Mutations can be deleterious but are not necessarily so. Some point mutations are silent, meaning that they do not affect the amino acid sequence; in other cases, a mutation may affect amino acid sequence but not in a way that affects a protein's structure (and, therefore, function). These kinds of mutations are essentially neutral. Mutations that do change protein shape and function can render the protein dysfunctional. Such changes in protein structure and function can be lethal. Occasionally, a mutation may change the structure and function of a protein in a slightly advantageous way.

Unrepaired mutations in DNA, if they do not have a measurably deleterious effect, provide a source of genetic variation in a population. Genetic variation, in turn, provides the essential substrate on which natural selection and other evolutionary processes act. The only types of mutations that matter for evolution are ones that can be passed on to offspring. For single-celled organisms, every mutation may be passed on. Multicellular organisms typically have a small number of reproductive cells (germ-line cells), and mutations in the other (somatic) cells will not be transmitted to offspring. ∎

Suggested Reading

Campbell & Reece, *Biology* (6th ed.), chapter 17.

Freeman, *Biological Science*, chapter 12.

Weinberg, *One Renegade Cell: How Cancer Begins.*

Questions to Consider

1. Some DNA repair enzymes may actually introduce a change in an otherwise "correct" sequence of bases. Why might such a mechanism have evolved?

2. What are several reasons older people are more likely to develop cancer than younger people?

Dividing DNA Between Dividing Cells
Lecture 13

Let's begin by looking at how DNA is distributed in normally dividing cells through the process of mitosis. Single-celled organisms, of course, reproduce simply by dividing in two. When they do, each daughter cell has to get a complete copy of the original parent's DNA. In multicellular organisms, such as us, cells divide for all sorts of reasons other than reproduction.

In this lecture, our discussion of biological information transitions from the molecular level to the level of cells and organisms. The lecture begins by focusing on the question of how DNA, packaged as chromosomes, is distributed in dividing cells through the process of mitosis, a process that maintains the continuity of information among daughter cells. Many organisms also exhibit a kind of cell division called *meiosis*, a process that creates specialized daughter cells that combine with each other during sexual reproduction. The lecture concludes by discussing how meiosis and sex create genetic variation, providing the essential substrate for evolution by natural selection.

The first question to consider is how DNA is packaged and distributed in cells when they divide. The answer to this question will help us understand the ways in which offspring inherit genetic traits from their parents. This involves two issues. First, we need to understand how cells maintain continuity of the information transferred between generations, which requires a mechanism by which dividing cells can distribute the two copies of their replicated genome between them. Second, we need to understand how variation is introduced when cells combine during sexual reproduction.

A single-celled organism may reproduce asexually simply by dividing in two; this is called *mitosis*. Cells in multicellular organisms undergo mitosis for a variety of reasons other than reproduction. When cells divide, each daughter cell must receive a complete copy of the parent cell's genome. In prokaryotic cells, the entire genome is contained in one circular piece of DNA. When the cell divides, it is relatively simple to ensure that one copy goes into each

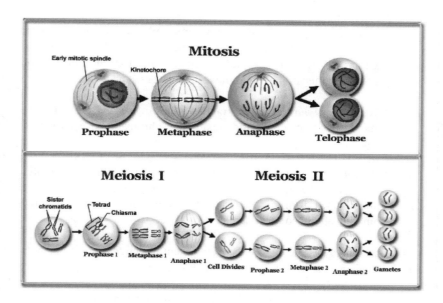

Mitosis

Early mitotic spindle · Kinetochore

Prophase · Metaphase · Anaphase · Telophase

Meiosis I · **Meiosis II**

Sister chromatids · Tetrad · Chiasma

Prophase 1 · Metaphase 1 · Anaphase 1 · Cell Divides · Prophase 2 · Metaphase 2 · Anaphase 2 · Gametes

daughter cell. Eukaryotic cells contain much more DNA than prokaryotic cells, and their DNA is in the form of many different linear pieces, each called a *chromosome.*

The life of a cell (the *cell cycle*) has two major phases. The *mitotic phase* is when the cell reproduces, splitting into two daughter cells. *Interphase* is the remainder of the cell cycle; it occupies up to 90% of each cell cycle. Interphase itself has three phases: G1, S, and G2. During the S phase, DNA replication takes place. Once DNA replicates during the S phase, the duplicated DNA must be evenly divided between the two daughter cells through mitosis.

Mitosis is an intricate ballet of chromosome movements, with four stages marking the progression of these movements.

- *Prophase* occurs when the chromosomes start to coil and condense and the nucleus begins to break down. At this stage, each chromosome consists of two copies. The two copies are called *sister chromatids* and are attached near the center by the *centromere.*

- During *metaphase*, the chromosomes physically line up along the midline of the cell. The movements of the chromosomes are controlled by protein spindles, which connect to centrioles on the cell wall; this arrangement moves the chromosomes.

- During *anaphase*, the centromere breaks apart and the centrioles move the sister chromatids apart, one chromatid to each side of the cell.

- *Telophase* is when the cell divides by pinching along the midline until two separate daughter cells are formed. New nuclear membranes form in the daughter cells, and the chromosomes unwind and become invisible.

Mitosis preserves genetic continuity from parent to daughter cells in single-celled organisms and in cells within multicellular organisms.

Many organisms reproduce sexually. Sexual reproduction combines genetic material from each parent into the offspring. Cells and organisms with two sets of chromosomes are called *diploid*, and we refer to the two copies of a chromosome as a *homologous pair* (or *homologs*). For example, human cells each have 46 chromosomes, but these come in 23 pairs, with one copy of each pair obtained from the mother and one copy from the father. Sexually reproducing organisms produce a special kind of cells called *gametes* that have only a single copy of each kind of chromosome. (Cells with a single copy are called *haploid*.) Otherwise, the number of homologous chromosomes would continually double each time sexual reproduction occurs.

Meiosis is a special form of cell division that separates homologous pairs of chromosomes, creating haploid daughter cells from a diploid parent cell. Meiosis shares many features with mitosis, in terms of the way that chromosomes move in a highly orchestrated fashion and separate neatly into daughter cells.

Meiosis differs significantly from mitosis in that there are two rounds of cell division, resulting in four daughter cells. In the first meiotic division, homologous pairs of chromosomes line up at the midline of the cell and are separated into the first two daughter cells, which are haploid. The second meiotic division proceeds like normal mitosis, with each of the haploid cells from the previous division dividing again. The sister chromatids of each chromosome are divided evenly between the daughter cells.

Meiosis has more stages than mitosis. In the prophase of meiosis I (prophase I), the chromosomes condense and the nuclear membranes break down. Unlike in mitosis, however, homologous pairs become closely associated. The chromatids of the homologous chromosomes may form connections with each other, called *chiasmata*, and can exchange comparable sections of DNA (crossing over). During metaphase I, homologous pairs of chromosomes line up along the cell midline. When the cell divides, homologous pairs will be split, instead of sister chromatids, producing haploid cells. Prophase II is very similar to mitotic prophase, except that the cell is haploid. During metaphase II, the chromosomes line up along the midline of the cell. In anaphase II, the chromatids divide into daughter cells. At the end of these divisions, there are four gamete daughter cells, each haploid. During sexual reproduction, gametes fuse to form a diploid zygote.

Mutation is one process by which variation is introduced. Sexual reproduction (specifically independent assortment of chromosomes during meiosis) creates significant additional variation.

The most important consequence of meiosis and sexual reproduction is that these processes introduce genetic variation to the resulting offspring. Asexual reproduction creates essentially exact copies of the parent, which may make the line of offspring less likely to survive as living conditions change over the long run. Parents that produce genetically variable offspring will be more successful over the long run, because their offspring will be more likely to meet the challenges of a changing environment.

Mutation is one process by which variation is introduced. Sexual reproduction (specifically independent assortment of chromosomes during meiosis) creates significant additional variation. When homologous pairs of chromosomes line up during the first meiotic division, they do so randomly with respect to the parent from which they were originally derived. This means that the parent chromosomes are effectively shuffled, generating new combinations of genetic traits that can be passed on to offspring. The number of combinations increases exponentially with the number of chromosomes—humans have 23 homologous pairs, which leads to more than 8 million unique combinations. An additional source of variation comes from the fact that homologous chromosome pairs may exchange material when they line up during the first meiotic division and before they are separated. This crossing over allows shuffling even within the same chromosome, adding even more genetic diversity. ■

Suggested Reading

Campbell & Reece, *Biology* (6th ed.), chapters 12 & 13.

Purves et al., *Life* (7th ed.), chapter 9.

Questions to Consider

1. Some kinds of organisms are made of haploid cells. What, if anything, would be different about the way cells of these organisms undergo mitosis compared to cells of diploid organisms?

2. Haploid organisms can reproduce sexually, but what must happen first for this to occur?

Mendel and His Pea Plants
Lecture 14

It turns out that the discovery of the fundamental mechanisms by which traits are transmitted from parents to offspring actually preceded the discovery of chromosomes by many years, and was made by a very unlikely person, an Augustinian monk named Gregor Mendel, who unlocked the secrets of modern genetics by growing pea plants in the abbey garden.

This lecture describes the first of Mendel's experiments and shows how Mendel's *Law of Segregation* anticipated our modern understanding of genes, chromosomes, and the formation of gametes during meiosis, even though Mendel himself had no knowledge of these phenomena. At Mendel's time, plant and animal breeders recognized that offspring resembled parents and used this fact to select for desirable varieties of organisms. The prevailing view, however, was that the factors responsible for inheritance simply blended together when parents mated, yielding an

Mendel's Punnet Square

Gametes from F 1 Parent

Genotype: 1 PP : 2 Pp : 1 pp

Phenotype:

intermediate form. If the blending hypothesis were true, then any distinct variations among organisms should quickly vanish as the traits of sexually reproducing organisms all converged toward some mean value. Mendel realized, however, that variation is maintained in natural populations, leading him to search for an alternative way to explain patterns of inheritance.

Mendel's experiments examined trait inheritance in garden pea plants, which proved to be advantageous experimental organisms for several reasons. Mendel could manipulate fertilization between parental plants by cutting off their stamens (the source of pollen), then using a small brush to fertilize a plant with pollen from any other plant he chose. Pea plants also have several characteristics that occur in discrete alternative forms. For example, flower color might be purple or white or seed shape might be wrinkled or smooth, with no obvious intermediate forms. These dichotomous traits provided Mendel with a way to test the blending hypothesis explicitly. Mendel developed "true-breeding" lines for several traits; this meant that he had breeding lines of plants that would invariably produce only one version of a character (such as all purple- or all white-flowered offspring). Mendel could assume that these true-breeding lines were uniform with respect to the factors responsible for the inheritance of the character.

Mendel's now-classic experiment involved cross-pollinating true-breeding purple-flowered plants with true-breeding white-flowered plants. The results of this monohybrid cross were completely at odds with the prediction of the blending hypothesis.

Mendel's now-classic experiment involved cross-pollinating true-breeding purple-flowered plants with true-breeding white-flowered plants. The results of this monohybrid cross were completely at odds with the prediction of the blending hypothesis. In the first (F1) generation, all offspring had purple flowers, with no evidence of inheritance of the white-flowered trait. By contrast, the blending hypothesis predicted that all offspring should have whitish-purple flowers intermediate in color from the parents.

When Mendel crossed F1 individuals to produce a second (F2) generation, he observed an even more surprising result: The offspring of this cross had either purple or white flowers, which always occurred in a 3:1 ratio. The white-flower trait that apparently had been lost in F1 individuals reemerged in some F2 individuals. Mendel found the same 3:1 ratio for all other dichotomous traits (seed color, seed shape, plant height, and so on). To account for his observations, Mendel developed a hypothesis that described the action of genes and the division of chromosomes long before either was physically discovered. Mendel's hypothesis can be divided into four related ideas.

- Mendel proposed a *particulate* ("particle-based") theory of inheritance, in which different versions of "heritable factors" were responsible for inherited traits, such as flower color. We now call "heritable factors" *genes*, and different versions of the same gene are called *alleles*.

- Mendel also concluded that each individual must have two alleles for every gene, one from each parent.

- Mendel's third suggestion was that one allele may be *dominant* over other alleles. That is, if an individual possesses two alleles for the same trait, only the dominant one will have an effect. The allele that has no effect is called *recessive*. For example, Mendel's F1 flowers each inherited one dominant purple-flower allele and one recessive white-flower allele; because only the dominant allele is expressed, all F1 offspring are purple.

- Mendel's fourth idea was that when a parent produces gametes, each gamete includes only *one* of the parent's alleles for each gene. This has several implications.

  ○ A parent with two of the same allele will necessarily produce gametes with that allele.

  ○ If a parent has two different alleles, 50% of their gametes will have one allele, and 50% will have the other.

Dominant and recessive alleles and the resulting patterns of offspring led Mendel to propose the *Law of Segregation*. Modern terminology describes the patterns that Mendel observed.

- A *homozygous* individual has two of the same alleles for a given gene.

- A *heterozygous* individual has two different alleles for a given gene.

- When discussing pea flowers, we will use P for the purple-color allele and p for the white-color allele. Using upper- and lowercase versions of the same letter to denote different alleles is common in genetics.

Because the parent pea flowers in Mendel's cross were homozygous and because Mendel only crossed white flowers with purple flowers, all members of the F1 generation were heterozygous. However, all F1 individuals had purple flowers. Mendel correctly argued that this was because the P allele is dominant. The *phenotype* of an organism refers to its appearance, which results from the traits it expresses. The *genotype* of an organism refers to its genetic makeup. A given phenotype may be produced by more than one genotype.

- Because the P allele is dominant, two genotypes (PP and Pp) produce the purple-flower phenotype.

- Because the p allele is recessive, only one genotype (pp) will produce the white-flower phenotype.

- This explains why the white-flower phenotype "disappeared" in F1; all F1 individuals had the Pp genotype. However, the allele did not vanish, and pp individuals appeared in F2.

Examining the gametes of the F1 generation explains the 3:1 ratio Mendel found.

- All F1 individuals were heterozygous and, thus, would produce equal numbers of P and p alleles in their gametes.

- The possible combinations of F1 gametes can be plotted on a Punnett square, which lists each possible allele on a row and again on a column. The boxes inside the square contain the possible genotypes.

  - A Punnett square reveals that combining F1 gametes will produce two homozygous genotypes (PP and pp) and two copies of the heterozygous genotype (Pp).

  - This 1:2:1 ratio (PP : Pp : pp) is expressed as a 3:1 ratio of phenotypes, because the P allele is dominant and occurs in three genotypes.

Mendel realized that the "loss" of a recessive trait and its eventual reappearance could be explained if alleles existed and if alleles separated into different gametes. This is known as Mendel's Law of Segregation. The Law of Segregation not only refuted the blending hypothesis but also provided a much more comprehensive framework for examining the genetics of inheritance. ■

Suggested Reading

Campbell & Reece, *Biology* (6th ed.), chapter 14.

Freeman, *Biological Science*, chapter 10.

Henig, *The Monk in the Garden: The Lost and Found Genius of Gregor Mendel, the Father of Genetics*.

Purves et al., *Life* (7th ed.), chapter 10.

Questions to Consider

1. Why might Mendel have suspected that the blending hypothesis of inheritance was wrong before he did his work? How did his work demonstrate that it was wrong?

2. What aspects of the process of meiosis could Mendel have predicted from his Law of Segregation if he had known of the existence of chromosomes?

How Sex Leads to Variation
Lecture 15

In today's lecture, we are going to build on our knowledge of Mendelian genetics specifically to look at how sexual reproduction actually generates genetic variation in offspring. The question we'll begin with is this: What happens if we cross parents differing in two phenotypic characters, not just one?

This lecture continues the discussion of Mendel's contributions to genetics, turning to subsequent experiments in which Mendel looked at the transmission of more than one trait, leading to his *Law of Independent Assortment*. The lecture summarizes independent assortment, linkage, and crossing over, all of which result from the way chromosomes and the genes located on them move during gamete formation and sexual reproduction. The lecture concludes by recapping the sources that contribute to genetic variation in the replication of DNA and the transmission of traits from one generation to the next, variation that is essential for evolution to occur.

Mendel continued his experiments by crossing pea plants that had two phenotypic differences instead of one. From these dihybrid crosses, Mendel inferred additional properties of trait transmission from parents to offspring, properties consistent with knowledge gained later about the movement of genes on chromosomes. As with flower color, seed color in pea plants depends on a single gene with two alleles: the dominant yellow allele (Y) and the recessive green allele (y). For example, when crossing a female pea plant with purple flowers and yellow seeds with a male pea plant with white flowers and green seeds, we know that the female genotype is PPYY and the male genotype is ppyy. F1 individuals will all have purple flowers and yellow seeds, because they are all heterozygous for both traits. As in the monohybrid cross, the recessive traits "disappear" in F1.

When F1 individuals make gametes, do the alleles from the original parents stay together or are they separately mixed? If parental alleles are linked, an F1 individual could produce only PY and py gametes; F2 would then contain only the two parental phenotypes. Furthermore, these phenotypes would have the same 3:1 ratio as in the monohybrid cross. This would mean that sets of parental alleles essentially acted as single alleles. If parental alleles are not linked, F1 individuals would produce four types of gametes in equal proportion: PY, py, Py, and pY. A Punnett square using these gametes results in 16 possible combinations and 9 distinctive F2 genotypes. These 9 genotypes would produce 4 possible phenotypes, which would occur in a 9:3:3:1 ratio. Two of these phenotypes would not have existed in the parental generation; these are called *recombinant phenotypes*. Mendel observed 4 phenotypes in a 9:3:3:1 ratio in his F2 generation, which he correctly concluded to mean that alleles are inherited independently of each other. From this conclusion, Mendel formulated what is now known as the *Law of Independent Assortment*, which simply says that alleles of different genes segregate independently of each other during gamete formation.

Independent assortment of genes during meiosis is an important source of genetic variation. During the first meiotic division, homologous pairs of chromosomes line up in the cell and are separated into two daughter cells. The assortment of maternal and paternal homologs for one chromosome has no effect on the assortment of any other chromosome. If the genes for two different traits are on different chromosomes, they will assort independently of each other, as Mendel saw, and independent assortment produces recombinant phenotypes. The number of unique combinations of alleles on different chromosomes can be very high. Humans have 23 homologous pairs of chromosomes; thus, the possible number of assortments is 2^{23} or about 8.4 million.

If two genes occur on the same chromosome, an obvious conclusion is that they will be transmitted together as a unit during meiosis. Such genes are called linked genes.Campbell & Reece, *Biology* (6th ed.), chapter 14.

Independent assortment is different from mutation as a source of variation. Mutations essentially generate new alleles—usually dysfunctional but not always. Independent assortment does not create new alleles but, rather, new

Lecture 15: How Sex Leads to Variation

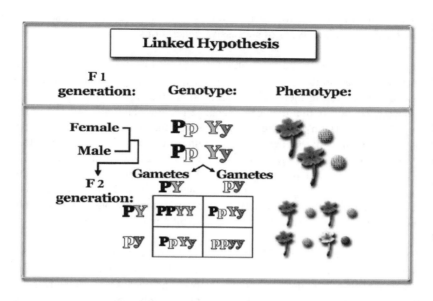

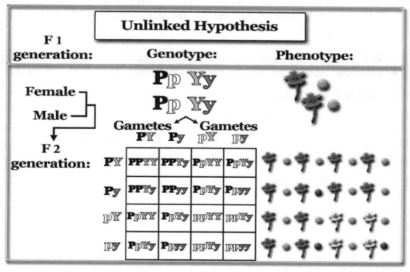

assortments of alleles. However, both mutation and independent assortment can change the phenotypes of successive generations.

If two genes occur on the same chromosome, an obvious conclusion is that they will be transmitted together as a unit during meiosis. Such genes are called *linked genes*. During meiosis, however, homologous pairs of chromosomes associate so closely that they can exchange genetic material, which is called *crossing over*. If linked genes cross over to other chromosomes, they can assort independently. Geneticists expanding on Mendel's work found that in dihybrid crosses, F2 generations with linked genes would occasionally produce recombinant phenotypes, though a far fewer number than if the genes were unlinked. Linked genes, however, should not produce any recombinant phenotypes. The farther apart two genes are on a chromosome, the more likely crossing over and recombinant phenotypes will be.

Though he essentially established the science of genetics, Mendel's work was ignored for about 40 years, because nothing was then known of the physical basis of Mendel's "heritable factors" and because he used advanced probability mathematics to calculate his ratios. Only when biologists began to see the patterns Mendel described did anyone realize that his work might be significant. ■

Suggested Reading

Campbell & Reece, *Biology* (6th ed.), chapter 14.

Freeman, *Biological Science*, chapter 10.

Henig, *The Monk in the Garden: The Lost and Found Genius of Gregor Mendel, the Father of Genetics*.

Purves et al., *Life* (7th ed.), chapter 10.

1. Would Mendel have been able to infer his Law of Independent Assortment if he had been able to work only with traits coded for by genes on the same chromosome? Why or why not?

2. What is the relationship between sex and evolution? Is sex necessary for evolution?

Genes and Chromosomes
Lecture 16

In the early part of the 20ᵗʰ century, a new generation of biologists interested in inheritance began to see some of the same patterns that Mendel had described long before. This led to the rediscovery of Mendel's work. With this rediscovery, the field of genetics simply exploded. Every biologist in the early 20ᵗʰ century was, in one way or another, interested in the problem of inheritance.

This lecture extends the discussion of how the movement of DNA explains patterns of trait expression observed by Mendel in the middle of the 19ᵗʰ century and moves to a more modern understanding of the cellular and molecular basis of genetics that began at the turn of the 20ᵗʰ century. It covers Thomas Hunt Morgan's discovery of the fact that some traits are more likely to be transmitted to offspring of one sex than the other. This discovery provided a key piece of evidence that chromosomes are the cellular structures responsible for trait transmission, and it played a key role in the reemergence of Mendel's work, which had been virtually ignored for decades.

Mendel's laws are consistent with what we now know about the movements of chromosomes during gamete formation, but Mendel himself knew nothing of this and his work was largely forgotten for a generation or more. Biologists in the second half of the 19ᵗʰ century began to observe dark bodies in the nuclei of cells before they divided. Walter Sutton and Theodor Boveri independently observed that the movement of these bodies reduced the number of bodies by half during gamete formation and realized that this might explain the patterns of trait inheritance Mendel had described. Sutton and Boveri published their ideas in 1903, introducing the *chromosomal theory of inheritance*, in which each gene has its own location, or *locus*, on a chromosome. Genes can then independently assort, producing the patterns Mendel observed.

Thomas Hunt Morgan, working at the turn of the 20ᵗʰ century, was interested in mechanisms of inheritance and set out to find a suitable living system on which to work. Morgan was especially interested in how mutations arose and wished to study this phenomenon in guinea pigs but could not obtain funding for this work. Morgan began to work with fruit flies (*Drosophila melanogaster*), which have since become the dominant model system for understanding genetics at all levels. Fruit flies have many advantages.

- They are cheap and easy to obtain.

- They are easy to raise in the laboratory

- They have a very short generation time, allowing experimental crosses to be done in a short period of time.

Fruit flies had a problem, however; they have no obvious phenotypic variations. To remedy this, Morgan attempted to create his own variants by exposing flies to agents known to induce mutations.

Morgan's terminology has become the standard for many geneticists. Morgan and his colleagues referred to fruit flies found in nature as having *wild-type* phenotypes. Any flies with unusual phenotypic characteristics were referred to as *mutant* phenotypes, based on the assumption that the characteristic resulted from a mutation in an allele. Morgan and later fruit fly geneticists labeled alleles in a slightly different way than we have seen. For example, a reduction in wing size is called the *vestigial wing mutation*, and the mutant allele is labeled vg. The wild-type allele for that gene would then be vg$^+$.

For any mutation we examine, we can assume that a wild-type fly is homozygous for the wild-type allele. Mutants, therefore, are at least heterozygous for the mutant trait. Normally, the wild-type allele is dominant; thus, mutants often are homozygous for the recessive mutant allele. Most mutations make alleles dysfunctional. For example, in pea plants, the dominant purple-flower allele might code for a purple pigment protein, whereas the recessive white allele codes not for a white pigment but for no pigment at all.

After many failed attempts to induce mutations, an undergraduate working with Morgan was washing the milk bottles used to raise flies and noticed a single male fly in one bottle that was unlike all the rest—instead of red eyes, it had white eyes. This fly eventually enabled Morgan and his colleagues to prove that genes reside on chromosomes. When Morgan crossed this mutant white-eyed male with a wild-type red-eyed female, all the F1 offspring had red eyes, just as we would predict if the red-eye allele is dominant. When Morgan crossed F1 individuals, he found the expected 3:1 ratio of red eyes to white eyes in the F2 generation. However, all the female flies had red eyes, while half the males had red eyes and half had white eyes. That is, the allele for white eyes seemed to transmit only to male offspring. A *sex-linked trait* is one whose expression depends on the sex of the organism.

Morgan showed that females could have white eyes, but they needed two copies of the white-eye allele, while males needed only one copy.

Morgan showed that females could have white eyes, but they needed two copies of the white-eye allele, while males needed only one copy. Morgan proposed that the white-eye gene must occur on the sex chromosomes, a unique pair of chromosomes that comprises a large X chromosome and a smaller Y chromosome that carries few functional alleles. If the eye-color gene is located on the X chromosome, females (which are XX in flies, as in humans) carry two alleles, while males (XY) carry just one. Males are referred to as *hemizygous* in this respect, because many genes on the X chromosome can occur only once in them.

Sex-linked traits explain F1 generation genotypes and phenotypes. All F1 females have red eyes but are heterozygous because they receive one X chromosome from the mother and one from the father. Because the white-eyed father has only one X chromosome, it can transmit only the white-eye allele to all of its offspring. All F1 males carry the wild-type allele, because they must receive a Y chromosome from the father and an X chromosome from the mother.

As expected, sex-linked traits also predict F2 generation genotypes and phenotypes. Because F1 females are heterozygous, half their gametes will have the wild-type red allele and half will have the mutant white allele. Because F2 males are hemizygous and get their single allele from the

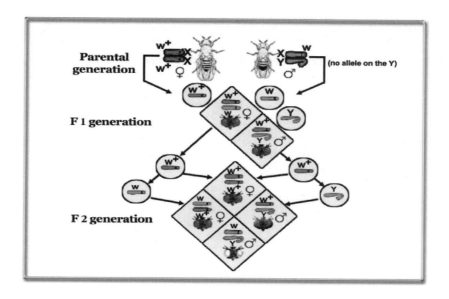

mother, half of them will have red eyes and half will have white eyes. The X chromosome that F2 females receive from their fathers will always have the wild-type allele. Because this allele is dominant, F2 females will have red eyes, regardless of which allele is in the gamete from the mother. Morgan was then able to unambiguously connect the distribution of sex-linked phenotypic traits to allele distribution, proving that genes actually resided on sex chromosomes (and, therefore, on all other chromosomes). ■

Suggested Reading

Campbell & Reece, *Biology* (6th ed.), chapter 15.

Freeman, *Biological Science*, chapter 10.

Purves et al., *Life* (7th ed.), chapter 10.

Shine and Wrobel, *Thomas Hunt Morgan: Pioneer of Genetics*.

1. How did the description of chromosomes and their movements by Sutton and Boveri both lead to the rediscovery of Mendel's work and, eventually, contribute to the much later discovery of the double helix by Watson and Crick?

2. Color-blindness is a recessive sex-linked trait in humans. If a woman is color-blind, can you predict whether her daughters will or will not be color-blind? What about her sons?

Charles Darwin and "The Origin of Species"
Lecture 17

An important consequence of the fact that genetic variation is introduced with each successive generation as organisms reproduce is that this variation provides the substrate for evolutionary change in populations.

At almost the same time that Mendel was working out his laws of inheritance, Charles Darwin was completing his masterwork *On the Origin of Species by Means of Natural Selection*, the book in which he proposed a radical new theory—natural selection—as a mechanism to account for the change of species over time. This lecture begins with an overview of 19th-century views on geological history, natural theology, and evolution. It then describes the long journey—both physical and intellectual—that led Darwin to the final articulation of his theory. The lecture ends with a summary of Darwin's argument for how natural selection acts on populations and leads to evolutionary change. Over the last several lectures, we have examined how traits are transmitted from parents to offspring in a way that both maintains continuity of information across generations and introduces genetic variation.

An important consequence of genetic variation is that it provides the substrate for evolutionary change. When considered over the time span of Earth's history, the most significant manifestation of genetic variation is the evolutionary transformation of life from the simplest early cells to the enormous complexity and diversity of living things we observe today. Scientists consider the idea of evolution as established fact today, but such was not the case only 150 years ago. The insights of the naturalist Charles Darwin, summarized in his 1859 publication *On the Origin of Species*, began our modern understanding of evolutionary biology.

Charles Darwin was born in 1809 in Shrewsbury, England. Darwin's father desired his son to study medicine, but Darwin himself had little interest in the subject and proved to be an unsuccessful student. Darwin's real passion lay in natural history—the description of plants and animals in their natural habitats. He aspired to join the clergy, because natural history was a typical pursuit of clergymen at the time, who saw such activities as a way to illustrate the glory of God through his creation. In 1831, Darwin took a position as ship's naturalist on H.M.S. *Beagle*, which was to embark on a five-year voyage of exploration around the globe. One of Darwin's jobs was to collect plant and animal specimens from all over the world.

The prevailing view in the early 19th century was that all organisms were formed by a "special creation," such as that described in Genesis, and that species remained immutable. This was a Greek and a Christian idea and had dominated Western thinking for more than 2,000 years. The rapid progression of research in the biological and geological sciences began to yield data that did not support the view that the Earth and the species it contained were immutable. Geologists realized that the Earth was much older than religious doctrine suggested and that geological features underwent radical transformations over time. They also realized that physical forces at work in nature could explain current physical features, as explained by Charles Lyell's theory of gradualism.

The rapid progression of research in the biological and geological sciences began to yield data that did not support the view that the Earth and the species it contained were immutable.

Comparative anatomists noticed that animals that looked very different shared many of the same basic parts, even if those parts differed in their details. For example, the forelimbs of birds and mammals are different, but they clearly share the same set of bone types. The existence of homologous structures can be understood if species were transformed from a common ancestor. Structures without apparent function—*vestigial structures*—could also be understood best as leftovers of a gradual process of change.

Paleontologists identified fossils of species that were no longer living, demonstrating that species are not constant, at least to the extent that some species that existed previously on Earth no longer exist today. It was also obvious that some fossil species resembled modern species, suggesting that

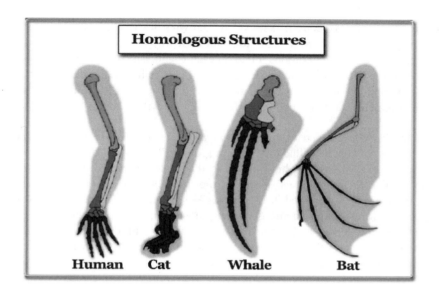

Homologous Structures

Human   Cat   Whale   Bat

the living form descended from the fossil form. This situation was common enough to be stated as the *Law of Succession*, which said that modern species descended from fossil species through a series of intermediates.

Based on these kinds of evidence, several theories of evolution had been proposed before Darwin's work; most notable was Jean-Baptiste Lamarck's theory of acquired characteristics, which suggested that changes caused by use or disuse of an individual's body parts could be passed on to successive generations of offspring. Lamarck was correct in his argument for evolution, but the evolutionary mechanism he proposed was fundamentally flawed. Our modern understanding of genetics, in particular as described in the Central Dogma, makes it clear that information cannot flow from proteins back to DNA. Lamarck also was correct to point out that the environment plays an important role in evolution.

Darwin's work on the *Beagle* provided him with abundant evidence for geological change, homologies among species, and relationships between fossil and living forms. Particularly illuminating were species occurring on island groups, including the Galapagos Islands, where Darwin observed groups of species (such as the so-called "Darwin's finches") that were all quite similar but differed from island to island in a way that seemed particularly well suited for the conditions found on each island. The differences between groups on different islands made sense if all groups had descended from the same common ancestor but had, since that time, adapted to their particular environment. Darwin called this pattern "descent with modification."

After Darwin returned from his trip in 1836, he spent more than 20 years working on what he called the "species problem." In 1844, Darwin prepared a short essay describing his solution to this problem, but he was reluctant to publish as he continued to gather more evidence to support his ideas. Darwin's hand was forced in 1858 when Alfred Russell Wallace, a naturalist working in the South Pacific, sent him a manuscript that essentially spelled out the same theory as Darwin's. After consulting with colleagues, Darwin had both his and Wallace's papers published simultaneously. Darwin provided a detailed and more completely supported exposition of the theory in *On the Origin of Species by Means of Natural Selection* the following year.

Darwin's contribution was not to propose that evolution occurred but, instead, to suggest a specific mechanism by which evolution could occur. He called this mechanism "evolution by natural selection." The essential elements of the theory of natural selection are really quite simple.

- There is variation among individuals of a species, and some of this variation is heritable.

- In general, more offspring are produced by species than can survive.

- Given that there are more offspring than resources can support, there is competition among individuals for resources available to them to grow, survive, and reproduce.

- Some variations will be more successful than others in allowing individuals to take advantage of these resources in a particular environment. These more successful individuals will be "naturally selected" to survive longer and leave more offspring that share successful adaptations for that environment.

- Over time, natural selection will cause species to evolve adaptations that are particularly well suited for survival and reproduction in a given environment.

Darwin's book created an enormous stir in Victorian England, largely because of the extension of the theory to human evolution and the suggestion that God was not necessary to account for all natural features. Darwin's evidence made clear that evolution does occur; his theory of natural selection was also generally accepted, although scientists continued to debate its details for many years. ■

Suggested Reading

Campbell & Reece, *Biology* (6th ed.), chapter 22.

Darwin, *On the Origin of Species*.

Freeman, *Biological Science*, chapter 21.

Questions to Consider

1. How does Darwin's theory of evolution by natural selection differ from earlier views of evolution?

2. Darwin's book *On the Origin of Species* includes extensive material on the breeding of domesticated species. Why do you think this kind of information was important for Darwin to develop his argument?

Natural Selection in Action
Lecture 18

It is well established that wing color is a heritable trait in butterflies and moths. Therefore, the historical change in wing color observed in this population may be consistent with the hypothesis that the shift represents an evolutionary change.

This lecture presents several examples that demonstrate the process of evolution by natural selection in action, including data from both field studies and laboratory experiments. Some examples illustrate the different ways in which selection can act on populations of organisms. Other examples, such as the evolution of antibiotic resistance in bacteria, illustrate the practical significance of understanding mechanisms of evolutionary change in our world. The lecture also introduces a definition of *Darwinian fitness*.

Two additional points need to be made about natural selection. Natural selection acts only on existing, heritable variation. If there is no variation for a particular trait, natural selection cannot act on that trait. This is why variation from mutation and genetic recombination is so important. Although natural selection acts on individuals, its consequences occur in populations. Individuals do not themselves evolve; evolutionary change is measured as change to the average characteristics of a group. Darwin's theory of evolution by natural selection has been well documented, both in field studies of naturally occurring evolutionary change and in laboratory studies in which the evolution of organisms can be manipulated (*artificial selection*).

A primary example comes from a classic study of color change over time in a species of moth. For generations, scientific collectors have filled museum cases with specimens of butterflies and moths, creating extensive collections that include many representatives of the same species occurring in different locales or occurring at the same locale in different years. One particularly complete collection is of the peppered moth, *Biston betularia*, collected near Manchester, England, over a period of 150 years. Moths collected before the 1850s have mostly pale wings, with rare examples of darker individuals. Fifty years later, however, 98% of the moths collected have dark wings, with only a few pale individuals. Given that wing color is well known to be heritable in butterflies and moths, this pattern suggests an evolutionary change in the population over time. This would predict that the change increased the survivability of the moth group; that is, that natural selection was "selecting" darker moths.

H. B. D. Kettlewell, a physician and avid moth collector, suggested in 1955 that the change in color resulted from natural selection caused by increasing industrialization in Manchester. Peppered moths usually rest on tree trunks covered with light-colored lichens. The light color blends in well with this background, presumably providing camouflage from predators. With the onset of the industrial revolution, the tree trunks in parks around Manchester became increasingly dark because of soot deposition. As the trunks became darker, the common, lighter moths became increasingly easy for visual predators, such as birds, to spot, whereas the rare, dark moths became more camouflaged. Kettlewell suggested that differential predation on the two color types resulted in greater survival and reproduction of the dark moths, causing an overall change in the relative frequencies of dark moths in the population. To test his idea, Kettlewell released equal numbers of dark and light moths into dark and light forests and observed bird predation on the moths. He found that moths that blended into the environment were eaten much less often than moths that stood out. The peppered moth example was considered at the time to be the first conclusive demonstration of natural selection in the wild. In recent years, however, scientists have argued that Kettlewell's work does not hold up because of his methods.

Moths collected before the 1850s have mostly pale wings, with rare examples of darker individuals. Fifty years later, however, 98% of the moths collected have dark wings, with only a few pale individuals. Given that wing color is well known to be heritable in butterflies and moths, this pattern suggests an evolutionary change in the population over time.

However, this example introduces two key points about evolution by natural selection. First, it is important to emphasize that natural selection results from differential reproduction among individuals in a population. Moths with different colored wings survived in different proportions, but what really matters is that one color type reproduced more than the other color type as a result of this differential survival. Second, the moth example illustrates the importance of the environment for understanding natural selection. Dark moths survive and reproduce better in dark environments, while light moths survive and reproduce better in light environments. The adaptive value of a trait depends on the environment. Natural selection can cause change only if the more well adapted individuals leave greater numbers of offspring than poorly adapted individuals. If natural selection acts after different individuals produce similar numbers of offspring, it will have no effect.

We are now in a position to formally define *Darwinian fitness*. A common shorthand for natural selection is the phrase "survival of the fittest," which implies direct competition among individuals in a group. This is not necessarily the case in evolution! For an individual to be considered more fit than its peers, the number of offspring it produces must be high *relative* to those peers. Ten offspring is very low for a fruit fly, for example. Fitness is also not an intrinsic property of an individual—it depends on that individual's reproductive performance *in a given environment*. Thus, *Darwinian fitness* is the *relative* reproductive success of an individual *in a given environment*.

Many other, more quantitative, examples of natural selection in action have been observed in both the field and the laboratory. Peter and Rosemary Grant have studied Darwin's finch populations in the Galapagos Islands since 1973. One small population of a single species of Darwin's finch, the medium ground finch, has been especially important in the Grant's work. The Grants and other researchers have shown that the size of a finch's beak depends on the size of the seeds it must crack open and eat. Within the population they study, though, the Grants have found considerable variation in beak size. Finding out whether beak size is heritable is made somewhat difficult by the range of factors that might influence it. Using a large sample set, the Grants found that beak size is largely genetic and, thus, heritable.

All evidence pointed to a natural-selection process working on beak size, but the Grants obtained convincing evidence of this after a severe drought starved to death more than 80% of the finch population they were studying. The Grants observed that the individuals that survived the drought had larger beaks than those that died. As it turned out, one of the more drought-resistant plants produced large hard seeds that small-beaked birds could not open. After the drought passed, members of the renewed finch population had markedly larger beaks than before. The Grants have since found that droughts and wet years tend to increase and decrease beak size, respectively, in the finch population as a result of the size of seeds that are available.

Humans have inadvertently selected pathogens and pests for increasing resistance to the methods we use to control them. Therapeutic antibiotics, if used correctly, will kill all pathogens in a host, for example, those that cause tuberculosis. Incomplete antibiotic treatment, however, will kill only some pathogens, leaving intact those individuals that are slightly more resistant. These resistant bacteria then reproduce, making the population more resistant overall. The same problem of unintended selection is increasingly common in the evolution of pesticide-resistant insects. ∎

Suggested Reading

Freeman, *Biological Science*, chapters 21 & 38.1.

Hooper, *Of Moths and Men*.

Weiner, *The Beak of the Finch*.

Questions to Consider

1. Biologists state that Darwin's theory of natural selection is proven by many examples of natural selection occurring in the wild and in the laboratory. Do you find this kind of evidence convincing? If not, what evidence would be convincing to you?

2. Why is evolutionary theory becoming increasingly important to modern medical research?

Reconciling Darwin and Mendel
Lecture 19

The rediscovery of Mendel's work led to greater skepticism about natural selection as being an important mechanism in evolution. Why is this? This was because Mendel's mechanism for inheritance seemed to contradict Darwin's ideas about natural selection.

This lecture begins by discussing the apparent conflict between Mendel's work and Darwin's theory of natural selection. The resolution to this conflict was achieved eventually through the *modern synthesis*, which depended on formal methods for modeling gene frequency changes in populations. The lecture goes on to illustrate how the gene pool of a population can be determined for a simple trait. This exercise leads to a discussion of how evolution, formally measured as a change in the relative frequency of genes across generations, can be modeled with a few simple equations. The lecture continues by describing the *Hardy-Weinberg equilibrium*, which predicts that evolution will not occur in a sexually reproducing population. The resolution to this apparently paradoxical conclusion comes from understanding that assumptions underlying the Hardy-Weinberg equilibrium are typically violated in natural populations.

After Darwin's *Origin of Species* was published in 1859, the scientific community generally accepted the fact of evolution. The mechanism that Darwin proposed— natural selection—was also accepted at first but lost favor when Mendelian genetics reemerged in the early 20th century. One reason Darwin's ideas about natural selection lost favor was that Darwin had not suggested a convincing mechanism by which heritable

After Darwin's *Origin of Species* was published in 1859, the scientific community generally accepted the fact of evolution. The mechanism that Darwin proposed—natural selection—was also accepted at first but lost favor when Mendelian genetics reemerged in the early 20th century.

traits might be transmitted from parents to offspring. Mendelian genetics did provide a mechanism for trait transmission, one that corresponded to the movement of chromosomes, which were just beginning to be identified as physical carriers of genetic information. Mendelian genetics seemed to be at odds with Darwin's thinking, however. Darwin emphasized gradual change in traits that showed continuous variation in a population. By contrast, Mendel and his followers successfully modeled the transmission of discrete, dichotomous traits. The Mendelians argued that natural selection for very small differences among traits could not account for the patterns of trait transmission they studied.

The eventual resolution of these two perspectives, which is referred to as the *modern synthesis*, came much later, in the 1930s and 1940s. One key to the modern synthesis was the realization that not all traits followed Mendelian rules of inheritance for single genes. Most notably, traits exhibiting continuous variation, such as height, depend on several or, potentially, many genes, all acting in concert. Another key to the modern synthesis was the development of formal methods (in a field called *population genetics*) to model gene frequency change in populations.

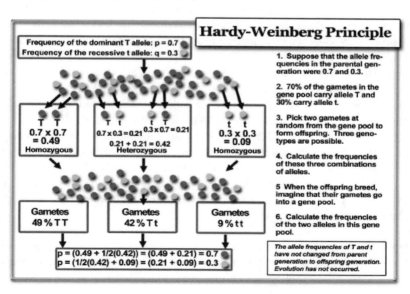

Hardy-Weinberg Principle

Frequency of the dominant T allele: p = 0.7
Frequency of the recessive t allele: q = 0.3

$$T\ T$$
$$0.7 \times 0.7 = 0.49$$
Homozygous

$$T\ t \quad t\ T$$
$$0.7 \times 0.3 = 0.21 \quad 0.3 \times 0.7 = 0.21$$
$$0.21 + 0.21 = 0.42$$
Heterozygous

$$t\ t$$
$$0.3 \times 0.3 = 0.09$$
Homozygous

Gametes
49 % T T

Gametes
42 % T t

Gametes
9 % t t

$$p = (0.49 + 1/2(0.42)) = (0.49 + 0.21) = 0.7$$
$$p = (1/2(0.42) + 0.09) = (0.21 + 0.09) = 0.3$$

1. Suppose that the allele frequencies in the parental generation were 0.7 and 0.3.

2. 70% of the gametes in the gene pool carry allele T and 30% carry allele t.

3. Pick two gametes at random from the gene pool to form offspring. Three genotypes are possible.

4. Calculate the frequencies of these three combinations of alleles.

5 When the offspring breed, imagine that their gametes go into a gene pool.

6. Calculate the frequencies of the two alleles in this gene pool.

The allele frequencies of T and t have not changed from parent generation to offspring generation. Evolution has not occurred.

The relationship between genotype and phenotype is normally not as straightforward as the discussion of Mendelian genetics might make it seem. The first set of complications arises from the fact that alleles can interact in more complex ways than in Mendel's pea plants. Snapdragon flowers that are homozygous for red and white colors, for example, will have an F1 generation with all pink flowers, because the heterozygous genotype for color has its own unique phenotype. This kind of interaction is called *incomplete dominance*. Many traits have more than two alleles, such as in the human ABO blood-type system. Types A and B are both dominant over O, but codominant to each other. *Codominance* means that both alleles are expressed equally. Genes can also interact with each other, as in *epistasis*, where the expression of one gene depends on an entirely different gene. For example, mice have alleles for brown or black fur, but an entirely different gene controls whether any pigment is deposited into the fur in the first place. The third and most ubiquitous set of complications is the result of the environment on gene expression. There are few if any cases where the environment does not play a role in gene expression.

The final cause of the complexity of this relationship is that for many heritable traits, phenotypical expression depends on the cumulative effect of many different genes. Instead of being discrete, dichotomous traits, they are continuously variable and must be measured (quantified) on some scale—hence their name, *quantitative traits*. Skin color in humans is a quantitative trait. There is evidence that skin pigmentation is affected by at least three genes, each with two alleles, one for darker skin and one for lighter skin. A person with six dark alleles will have the darkest skin; a person with zero dark alleles will have the lightest skin, and a person with three dark alleles will be somewhere in between. Although this is a simplification (there are obviously more than seven gradations of skin color), it shows the additive effect of multiple genes. The realization that the cumulative action of multiple genes, each following Mendelian principles, could produce continuously variable expression paved the way for the synthesis of Mendelian genetics with Darwinian natural selection.

How can we begin to expand genetic models to account for the evolution of traits in populations? In this context, a *population* is a group of individuals of the same species, all of which may mate with each other. The aggregate genetic makeup of this population is called its *gene pool*, which consists of all the alleles for all the genes for all the individuals in the group. In Mendelian genetics, the possible genotypes of offspring depended on the alleles present in the parents. In population genetics, the genotypes of future generations depend on the gene pool as a whole and on the relative frequencies of all alleles in the pool. In population genetics, evolution is a change in the relative frequencies of alleles in a gene pool for a particular population.

As an example, the ability to roll the human tongue is a trait controlled by a single gene; it illustrates how we can determine allele frequencies in a gene pool based on our knowledge of phenotypes and the relationship between phenotypes and genotypes. In a typical human population, about 91% of individuals can roll their tongues, and about 9% cannot. These percentages are the frequencies of phenotypes in the population. Each human has two alleles for this gene; thus, for a population of 100 individuals there are 200 alleles in our gene pool. It is hard to determine the relative frequencies of alleles directly, because "rollers" can have either the TT or Tt genotype, given that the tongue-rolling allele (T) is dominant over the non-rolling allele (t). "Non-rollers," though, can have only the tt genotype; using this information, we can calculate the relative frequencies of all other alleles: 70% of the total alleles would be T alleles and 30% would be t alleles.

The Hardy-Weinberg equation uses simple probability theory to compute the relative proportions of T and t alleles in the offspring of this population. It says that mating essentially draws alleles from the gene pool at random. The probability of an offspring having a particular two-allele genotype is calculated by multiplying together the probabilities of picking either allele. For example, the probability of a TT genotype is 0.7 x 0.7 = 0.49, or 49%. The Hardy-Weinberg equation predicts that 49% of our population will have the TT genotype, 42% will have the Tt genotype, and 9% will have the tt genotype. Because T is dominant, the TT and Tt genotypes can both roll their tongues. We can see that the equation works (49% + 42% = 91%).

This equation allows us to predict allele frequencies in successive generations of offspring, but we will reach a point where the frequencies will not change from generation to generation. This point is called the *Hardy-Weinberg equilibrium.* This equilibrium seems puzzling at first, because it suggests that no evolutionary change can occur. Genetic recombination only shuffles existing alleles and, thus, has no effect on the relative frequencies found in a gene pool.

The answer to this paradox is that the Hardy-Weinberg equation, like any model, rests on a number of specific assumptions. Identifying these assumptions and understanding when and how they are violated in natural populations provides a framework for predicting when and how evolution will occur. ■

Suggested Reading

Campbell & Reece, *Biology* (6th ed.), chapter 23.

Freeman, *Biological Science*, chapter 22.

Freeman and Herron, *Evolutionary Analysis* (2nd ed.).

Purves et al., *Life* (7th ed.), chapter 23.

Questions to Consider

1. Darwin did not know of Mendel's work, but if he had, how would this have influenced his ideas about evolution, if at all?

2. The "information" in a molecule of DNA is information about the sequence of amino acids that make up a protein. What is the nature of the "information" found in a population's gene pool?

Mechanisms of Evolutionary Change
Lecture 20

In population genetics terms, we have defined evolution as a change in the relative frequencies of alleles for a trait over time. But the Hardy-Weinberg equilibrium suggested that allele frequencies generally don't change across subsequent generations of a sexually reproducing population. What, then, if anything, does this tell us about evolution? Hardy-Weinberg seems to imply that evolution doesn't occur.

This lecture picks up the discussion of how assumptions of the Hardy-Weinberg equilibrium are violated in natural populations and how these violations are responsible for the occurrence of evolutionary change. An important point of this discussion is that natural selection, as described by Darwin, is not the only cause of evolution. Instead, a number of other factors can cause changes in the gene pool of a population, the most notable of these being genetic drift, or random fluctuations in the gene pool due to small population size. The lecture concludes by pointing out that

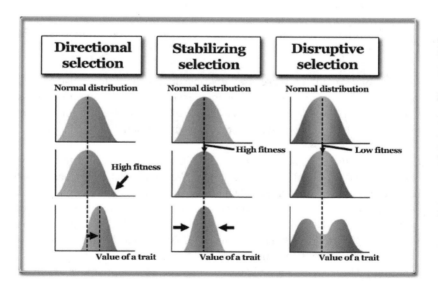

natural selection can be a stabilizing force, maintaining the current phenotypic profile of a population, as well as a directional force or a diversifying force, changing the average phenotype.

We learned last time that the frequencies of alleles in a population's gene pool will remain unchanged over generations—that is, evolution will not occur—if a population is in Hardy-Weinberg equilibrium. The Hardy-Weinberg equilibrium only holds, however, if its critical assumptions are met. By looking at these assumptions in more detail and understanding how they might be violated, we can gain insight into the mechanisms responsible for evolution. The Hardy-Weinberg equilibrium rests on five assumptions.

- There must be no mutation occurring in the population.

- There must be no immigration into or emigration out of the population.

- The population must be large.

- Individuals in the population must mate randomly.

- Reproductive success must be random for individuals in the population.

Clearly, some or all of these assumptions do not hold for most natural populations. In particular, natural selection ensures that reproductive success is not random. However, looking at violations of the other assumptions shows that natural selection is not the only mechanism of evolutionary change.

Violations of the Hardy-Weinberg assumptions are not equally likely, nor will they produce equal genetic variation. We know that mutations occur frequently, creating new alleles, which violates the first assumption. But although mutation can cause natural selection to act on a population in significant ways, it will only affect a gene pool directly if a single gene is subjected to a particularly high mutation rate. The random nature of mutation means that the overall mutation rate would have to be enormous for this to happen. The case of individuals moving between populations is called gene flow and can directly affect the gene pool if it consistently involves individuals with specific alleles. In nature, however, movement is more or less random and, therefore, has a weak effect on allele frequencies, though it does reduce genetic differences between populations.

The case of individuals moving between populations is called gene flow and can directly affect the gene pool if it consistently involves individuals with specific alleles.

Violations of the large population assumption can skew allele frequencies because of the sampling error inherent in small populations. Genetic drift represents genetic change caused by small populations. Natural populations are often small; thus, genetic drift is thought to be a major evolutionary force. Genetic drift can affect large populations, as well, if the population goes through a genetic "bottleneck," such as near extinction. Other bottlenecks can include the migration of small groups away from the larger population (the founder effect). The last two assumptions are often violated, because mating and reproductive success are rarely random. Natural selection is the only evolutionary force that leads to the evolution of adaptations; mutation, migration, and genetic drift changes are not necessarily adaptive. Change in allele frequencies in a gene pool is the underpinning of Darwin's theory of natural selection and what connects natural selection to Mendelian genetics.

The different ways in which natural selection affects traits in populations are referred to as modes of selection. All three modes are observable in the wild and reproducible in the lab. The distribution of quantitative traits typically forms a bell-shaped curve, also referred to as a normal distribution. Most individuals fall somewhere in the middle of the trait's continuum, while relatively few individuals occupy the extremes. The way natural selection affects this bell curve depends on which individuals in the distribution have the greatest relative fitness. In the Darwin's finch example, birds at one end of the bell-shaped curve had higher fitness than all other birds. These more fit individuals had a selective advantage that caused the average to move toward one end. This mode of selection, which causes the average value of a characteristic in a population to shift toward one end of the bell curve, is called directional selection. Evolutionary biologists have suggested that directional selection is actually not very common and occurs only when the environment changes. Stabilizing selection occurs when individuals with an average value for a trait have the highest fitness. Individuals at both extremes are selected against, and the bell curve narrows, reducing the amount of variation, instead of shifting to one end.

Disruptive or diversifying selection forms, over time, a bimodal distribution, with more than one distinct peaks. For example, the black-bellied seed-cracker has a bimodal distribution, with small-beaked birds and large-beaked birds but few in between. Thomas Bates Smith discovered that the beak sizes of newborn birds do form a bell-shaped curve, but birds with medium-size beaks typically die because the seeds these birds eat fall into two distinct size classes. Birds with medium-sized beaks are not as efficient at eating either size of seed as birds with larger or smaller beaks are. ∎

Suggested Reading

Campbell & Reece, *Biology* (6th ed.), chapter 23.

Freeman, *Biological Science*, chapter 22.

Freeman and Herron, *Evolutionary Analysis* (2nd ed.).

Purves et al., *Life* (7th ed.), chapter 23.

Questions to Consider

1. Why is genetic variation necessary for evolution to occur?

2. Why does natural selection lead to adaptation, whereas genetic drift does not, even though both processes lead to evolution?

What Are Species and How Do New Ones Arise?
Lecture 21

In this lecture and in the next, we are going to look at what is known about how new species arise. As you might guess, the answer has something to do with biological information, essentially involving the separation and diversification of a single gene pool into two. In this sense, our discussion of speciation takes our analysis of biological information up yet another level in the hierarchy of life—from the level of populations, to the level of distinctly different species.

This lecture begins with the problem of defining what is meant by a *species*. The biological species concept, which defines species on the basis of reproductive isolation, is used most commonly by biologists in spite of its theoretical and practical difficulties. Alternative definitions are introduced, with a discussion of the advantages and disadvantages of each.

The lecture then turns to the question of how new species arise. Allopatric speciation represents the most straightforward case, in which an ancestor species becomes divided by a physical barrier into two separate populations that are prevented from exchanging genetic material.

The dominant view of contemporary biologists, descent with modification, suggests that all living and extinct species descended from a common ancestral species that lived more than 3 billion years ago.

The dominant view of contemporary biologists, descent with modification, suggests that all living and extinct species descended from a common ancestral species that lived more than 3 billion years ago. If this is true, evolutionary mechanisms must have somehow led to the creation of new, distinct species (*speciation*)—and frequently, to account for the variety of living species. Though speciation is an established fact, its mechanisms are not fully understood, and it remains an active area of research.

Organisms often appear to fall into distinct groupings. We intuitively think of these groupings as *species* (from the Latin meaning "kind" or "type") representing well-defined categories of living things. The problem of defining and classifying species, however, is not as easy as it first appears. A single species might occur in distinct forms—a Chihuahua and a German shepherd, for example. Different species may be virtually indistinguishable from each other, as with willow and alder flycatchers. Evolutionary biologists are particularly interested in the problem of how new species arise. To address this question, we first must have some way of objectively defining a species.

The most commonly used framework for defining species is the *biological species* concept first articulated in 1942 by Ernst Mayr, one of the notable evolutionary biologists of the 20th century. Mayr defined a species as a population or group of populations that can successfully interbreed in nature and produce viable and fertile offspring but cannot successfully interbreed with members of other species. Thus, the ability of two organisms to reproduce sexually provides the foundation of the biological species concept. An equivalent way to say this is that a biological species is the most inclusive grouping of organisms for which the exchange of genetic information is possible. By this concept, barriers to the exchange of genetic information separate species—this is called *reproductive isolation*.

The biological species concept is generally accepted in practice, but it does not account for some important cases. Many otherwise distinct species sometimes hybridize and produce viable, fertile young in geographic regions where they overlap. Many groups of organisms reproduce sexually only infrequently or not at all. In these groups, the biological species concept simply cannot be applied. Paleontologists interested in extinct species known only from fossils obviously cannot use information about successful interbreeding to define species.

There are several alternatives to Mayr's biological species concept. The *morphospecies* concept is an older idea that emphasizes differences in physical characteristics alone. It is based on the assumption that physical differences are generally the result of genetic differences arising from genetic information. It is widely used by paleontologists because they have no other way to identify fossil species, but it suffers from subjectivity in the choice of relevant characteristics used to distinguish species. The *phylogenetic species* concept is a recent idea that emphasizes the use of modern statistical tools to determine patterns of shared ancestry among a group of organisms, then defines species on the basis of these evolutionary patterns. Both concepts can be applied to any group of organisms, living or extinct, but assumptions behind the morphospecies concept may not apply, while scientists typically do not have the data they need to use the phylogenetic concept fully. In practice, biologists use a combination of different approaches, depending on which group they are working with, the questions to be answered, and the information available.

Having defined what we mean by *species*, we can now turn to the more difficult problem of understanding how new species have arisen over evolutionary time. On examining the fossil record, we see two different patterns of speciation. Evolutionary forces acting on a species over evolutionary time may so transform that species that we would classify the living form as a distinct species compared to fossil forms. This sort of evolutionary transformation is called *anagenesis* and is presumably caused by natural selection, genetic drift, or other factors leading to cumulative changes. Alternatively, one ancestor species may give rise to two or more descendent species through the process of *cladogenesis*, or branching evolution. Cladogenesis must be responsible for the enormous diversity of species observed on the planet.

Given the strong bimodal distribution of the black-bellied seed-cracker, a reasonable question is whether it comprises one species or two. The black-bellied seed-cracker is considered one species because large-beaked and small-beaked birds mate and produce viable offspring. Furthermore, birds with intermediate beaks are born; they just do not survive as well as the others. The large-beaked and small-beaked birds could diverge into two species only if they stopped mating with each other. As long as the exchange of genetic material is possible, the birds remain a single species. The seed-cracker example illustrates the essential requirement for speciation: that gene pools become isolated from each other. Once this happens, the isolated gene pools will develop along divergent lines through natural selection.

There are thought to be two main sets of conditions under which gene flow can stop and gene pools become isolated. These conditions correspond to two modes of speciation. *Allopatric speciation* involves the physical division of a gene pool by a barrier, such as a geographic feature. *Sympatric speciation* involves the division of a gene pool without physical or geographic separation. It is harder to envision this happening, and some biologists have been skeptical that it occurs at all.

Most work on speciation has focused on allopatric speciation, which is conceptually straightforward and relatively easy to illustrate. To understand allopatric speciation, first consider a population of a single species that has a relatively broad geographic distribution, such as a plant species spread across a plain. Now, imagine that two subpopulations become separated by a geographic barrier, such as a rise in sea level. The plants could then live only on the separated highlands. Other geological events, such as the upthrusting of a mountain range, the movement of a glacier, or even continental drift, could also divide a population.

When a physical barrier divides a geographically continuous population, it is called a *vicariance event* and the new, disjunct distribution is called a *vicariance distribution*. Allopatric speciation can also occur when a subpopulation moves across a physical barrier and becomes isolated. This is called a *dispersal event*, with a resulting *dispersal distribution*. Darwin's finches are an example of serial colonizations of each Galapagos island. Once subpopulations become separated by a physical barrier, their new environments are usually at least slightly different. Natural selection will, therefore, cause the gene pools of isolated subpopulations to change over time. Depending on the size of the subpopulations, genetic drift can play a large role in evolutionary change. It tends to be a large factor in dispersal events, for example. The isolated gene pools may diverge to the point that the subpopulations can no longer mate successfully, even after the physical barrier is removed. At this point, we would consider the two subpopulations to have become distinct species. ■

Suggested Reading

Campbell & Reece, *Biology* (6th ed.), chapter 24.

Freeman, *Biological Science*, chapter 23.

Purves et al., *Life* (7th ed.), chapter 24.

Schilthuizen, *Frogs, Flies, and Dandelions: Speciation—The Evolution of New Species*.

1. Does the difficulty that biologists have in defining what it means to be a "species" represent a challenge to Darwin's theory of evolution by natural selection? Why or why not?

2. Just because two populations have separate gene pools with no gene flow between them does not mean they will eventually become two different species. What other conditions are necessary for speciation to occur?

More on the Origin of New Species
Lecture 22

The basic idea behind allopatric speciation is that once gene flow is blocked by some physical barrier, then gene pools of the now-isolated populations can begin to diverge due to natural selection or genetic drift. At some point these gene pools may be sufficiently divergent that individuals from the two populations can no longer mate and produce viable offspring. It's at this point when we might say that two new species had arisen from an original ancestor.

This lecture continues the discussion of how new species arise. Sympatric speciation occurs in the absence of physical separation of populations and, thus, requires different mechanisms for preventing gene flow between sets of individuals. The lecture also discusses how, once the process of speciation has begun, barriers may arise that further reduce gene flow between incipient species, thus enforcing reproductive isolation. It ends by exploring the idea that natural selection might act to enhance reproductive isolation through the process of reinforcement, in which characters involved in mating diverge even further when recently evolved species come back into contact. The lecture ends by considering an alternative theory of the mode and pace of evolution and outlining what evolution does *not* do.

Sympatric speciation mechanisms are less well understood than allopatric speciation mechanisms. In fact, evolutionary biologists continue to debate whether or not physical separation is a necessary first step in the speciation process. Sympatric speciation occurs when there is no physical separation between individuals that become reproductively isolated. One sympatric speciation mechanism involves an accident during meiosis that results in the formation of diploid gametes. If diploid gametes fuse, the resulting polyploid zygote will have four copies of the parental chromosomes. Sometimes, such individuals survive and are able to produce their own gametes. However, such individuals can no longer reproduce with normal diploid individuals, because gamete fusion would produce triploid offspring, which would almost certainly be sterile. A polyploid individual is completely isolated from a diploid population. Polyploid individuals could successfully mate with each other, but more likely is the possibility that the polyploid individual would mate with itself. Speciation through polyploidy is common in plants because many species can reproduce by self-fertilization, obviating the need to find a sexual partner with a similar genetic abnormality. Botanists estimate that 70% of all flowering plants are, in fact, polyploid.

Another speciation mechanism involves interspecies hybrids that are sterile but can fertilize themselves. These hybrids can reproduce but will be reproductively isolated from both parent species. Modern wheat, for example, is the result of two hybridizations and is a polyploid that contains the genes of three wild grains. Natural selection may also act strongly enough to prevent gene flow between populations. In the case of the soapberry bug, the introduction of a new species of soapberry tree produced a bimodal distribution of beak size, similar to the black-bellied seed-cracker. However, because the soapberry bug also lays eggs on the host plant, the combination of natural selection for beak size and the association of feeding with mate choice may eventually restrict gene flow enough to produce two different species.

Once gene flow between two populations is blocked, new species will result only if genetic divergence leads to an incompatibility that preserves reproductive isolation.

Once gene flow between two populations is blocked, new species will result only if genetic divergence leads to an incompatibility that preserves reproductive isolation. There are several mechanisms for preserving reproductive isolation. Prezygotic barriers prevent the gametes of two individuals from ever fusing with each other. They include behavioral mechanisms, such as mating location specificity; mechanical limits that physically prevent individuals from mating; and incompatible physiological differences that prevent fertilization. Postzygotic barriers prevent zygotes from becoming viable organisms. They are largely caused by the fact that hybrid offspring may not be fertile or, even if fertile, may be less fit than normal individuals. Although these reproductive isolation mechanisms block gene flow between species, they are not themselves responsible for speciation.

If two populations of two recently evolved species come to overlap in space, reproductive isolating mechanisms will reduce gene flow in spite of the fact that individuals from the two species are in close proximity again. Our discussion to this point has assumed that isolating mechanisms arise as a byproduct of genetic divergence. Natural selection, though, can act to enhance reproductive isolation. Individuals that entirely avoid producing hybrid offspring might have a fitness advantage, so we might expect natural selection to enhance the effectiveness of isolating mechanisms. Selection is less likely to enhance postzygotic isolating mechanisms because natural selection, by definition, would not likely act to *reduce* offspring viability or fertility. Selection might act to enhance prezygotic isolating mechanisms through the process of *reinforcement,* so named because it reinforces differences that arose initially when populations were isolated from each other.

The best evidence for reinforcement comes from *Drosophila,* different species of which have ranges that overlap to differing degrees. Jerry Coyne and Allen Orr worked with fruit fly species that were closely related but varied in whether they lived in the same area as other species (*sympatry*).

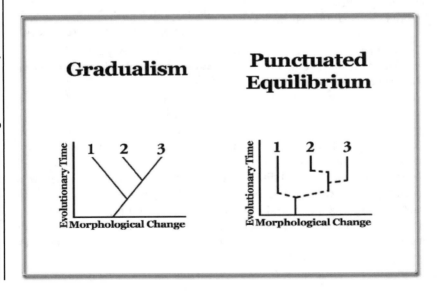

The prediction was that closely related flies living in sympatry should be less likely to mate than equally closely related flies living farther apart. Coyne and Orr found that sympatric species were less likely to hybridize, supporting the hypothesis that natural selection reinforces reproductive isolation.

The implication of the way we have talked about evolution so far is that changes accumulate slowly over time. This theory of a slow, steady evolution is called *gradualism*, and was the view espoused by Darwin. More recent evidence suggests that there can be long periods of little change interrupted by rapid, abrupt evolutionary changes. This alternative is called *punctuated equilibrium* and was first proposed in 1972 by Niles Eldridge and Stephen Jay Gould. The "rapid" changes of punctuated equilibrium are still relatively long, long enough to involve the same kinds of mechanisms for evolutionary change we have discussed, such as genetic drift occurring in small populations or natural selection. Eldridge and Gould's main point is that speciation itself stimulates evolutionary change and that once this process is complete, new species undergo relatively little evolutionary change for long periods.

Although evolution is often seen as a continual progression, it does not produce "perfect" organisms, or even "better" organisms, in any absolute sense, for three reasons. Evolution does not act on a blank slate but must work with an organism's existing features. Adaptations are often compromises between competing selective pressures, as in the case of an animal that would benefit from being brightly colored enough to attract mates but not so bright that it attracts predators. Not all evolution is adaptive—genetic drift is an important mechanism of evolutionary change and is essentially random. ∎

Suggested Reading

Campbell & Reece, *Biology* (6th ed.), chapter 24.

Freeman, *Biological Science*, chapter 23.

Purves et al., *Life* (7th ed.), chapter 24.

Schilthuizen, *Frogs, Flies, and Dandelions: Speciation—The Evolution of New Species*.

1. The case of the soapberry bug might be argued to be an example of allopatric speciation occurring on a very fine spatial scale. Can you defend this position?

2. Some have argued that evidence for punctuated equilibrium presents an inherent challenge to Darwin's theory of evolution by natural selection. Do you agree or disagree with this view, and why?

Reconstructing Evolution
Lecture 23

As the result of speciation processes operating over billions of years, we find ourselves in a world in which the information content of life, represented by the DNA of all living things, has become diversified and organized into millions and millions of different packages. Millions of different species, each carrying its own variant of that information and each having its own unique form and place on the planet.

Having addressed the question of how new species might arise, this lecture now turns to the question of how biologists organize the enormous diversity of living things. Older views on classification based on apparent similarities among groups of organisms suffer from the fact that these similarities may arise through convergent evolution. The lecture introduces *phylogenetic systematics*, a newer approach for reconstructing evolutionary history and relationships among a group of organisms based on

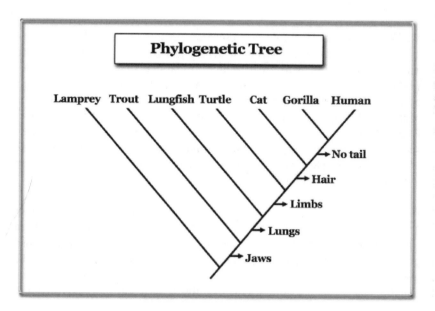

statistical analysis, and shows the utility of this approach for understanding historical patterns of evolution.

Over the history of the Earth, the biological "information" in living things has diversified into millions of different species with complex and unique adaptations, each possessing DNA molecules with sequences of nucleotides that reflect those adaptations. How can we sort out and make sense of this enormous diversity? More important, how can we determine the evolutionary history of a group of organisms, allowing us to better understand when and how particular traits arose?

One reason to organize living things in a systematic fashion is that it provides insight into evolutionary patterns and processes. Another reason for understanding not only the systematic relationships among organisms but also the history that led to those relationships is that it is becoming increasingly clear that understanding evolutionary relationships provides insight into problems in medicine, agriculture, and conservation. In biology, the most relevant and useful way to classify living things is by their evolutionary history.

We have an intuitive feel for how to separate organisms into different groups, and this classification is the oldest activity we would consider biological science. Aristotle went to great trouble to classify all living forms on his *scala naturae*, and *taxonomy*—the naming and classification of organisms by type—remained a dominant field in biology in Darwin's time. The area of modern biology concerned with classification in an evolutionary context is called *systematics*. Classifying, for example, two sparrows into separate species is an easy task. If given sparrows plus a duck and a vulture, we would easily group the sparrows together as being more similar to each other than to the duck and the vulture.

However, we would incorporate the sparrows, duck, and vulture in a larger group if then shown a dog, a cat, and a lion, because the birds are more similar to each other than to the other animals. We probably would also group the cat and the lion together as being different from the dog among the mammals. If given a fruit fly, we would probably group all the other animals together in a group that excludes the fruit fly, because these animals are more similar to each other than to the fly. There are two important characteristics of this intuitive classification scheme.

- It is based on shared similarities, such as skeletal features and body type.

- It is hierarchical, meaning that we have more and less inclusive groupings; for example, the cat and the lion are grouped together compared to the dog, but the dog, cat, and lion are all grouped together compared to the birds.

We usually classify organisms hierarchically, with the lowest levels containing very similar organisms and the higher levels containing progressively less similar organisms that are still more similar to each other than they are to other groups.

Carolus Linnaeus (Carl von Linne), an 18th-century Swedish botanist, formalized a hierarchical classification system that works much the same as the approach we just took and is still used by biologists today. Linnaeus's system starts with species and groups similar species into *genera* (singular *genus*), similar genera into *families*, similar families into *orders*, and so forth up to *classes*, *phyla*, and *kingdoms*. In the Linnaean system, each organism received a series of names that not only identifies it but places it in the hierarchy of nested groups. Linnaean taxonomy works well for classifying organisms in most cases (although there are many notable exceptions), but it does not tell us anything about the evolutionary histories and relationships of groups of organisms. The evolutionary history of a group of species is called its *phylogeny*.

Classical approaches to taxonomy and systematics assumed that similarities between species reflected evolutionary relationships between them. However, this is not necessarily the case. First, not all similarities are the result of descent from the same ancestor; rather, they may reflect a common set of selective pressures on unrelated species. This is known as *convergent evolution*. For example, dolphin flippers and fish fins are similar but evolved from completely different original structures. Structures that are similar because of convergent evolution are called *analogous structures*. Structures or features that are similar because of common ancestry are called *homologous structures*. Determining which structures are homologous and which are merely analogous can be quite difficult. Second, even homologous structures do not always help us to determine evolutionary relationships. Cats, lions, and dogs share many characteristics that are not useful because they are all shared identically among these organisms. Only homologous structures that are shared by some but not all species in a group provide useful information.

Phylogenetic systematics was introduced in the 1960s by Willi Hennig, a German entomologist who realized that the evolutionary history of a group of organisms would be reflected in changes to the observable structures or features of those organisms. In this approach, structures or other features we are examining are referred to as *characters*, which can have different states. Hennig's work used morphological (shape-based) characters, but modern characters are often DNA sequences. Hennig argued that some characters will change in some species but not in others, and that the differences would yield information about those species' relationships. Each species represents a mix of primitive characters held in common with ancestor species and derived characters that differ from the ancestor species. Note, however, that organisms themselves are not "primitive" or "derived." Hennig realized that the characters useful for determining evolutionary relationships among organisms would be those derived characters that are shared to differing degrees among species. These are called *shared derived characters*.

> **Phylogenetic systematics was introduced in the 1960s by Willi Hennig, a German entomologist who realized that the evolutionary history of a group of organisms would be reflected in changes to the observable structures or features of those organisms.**

A simple example illustrates how shared derived characters can be used to generate a phylogeny. Modern systematists, however, use computers and vast amounts of data to generate probabilities of the degree to which species are related to each other.

Character Matrix

Characters

	Jaws	Limbs	Hair	Lungs	Tail	Shell
Lamprey	-	-	-	-	+	-
Trout	+	-	-	-	+	-
Lungfish	+	-	-	+	+	-
Turtle	+	+	-	+	+	+
Cat	+	+	+	+	+	-
Gorilla	+	+	+	+	-	-
Human	+	+	+	+	-	-

Taxon

- Seven species (a lamprey, a trout, a lungfish, a turtle, a cat, a gorilla, and a human) share six characters (jaws, limbs, hair, lungs, tail, and shell) to varying degrees. We can generate a matrix that shows how species do or do not share characters.

- An important assumption is that the characters used are homologous, which of course, is not always easy to determine.

- We also must choose a species that we assume to be the most primitive, which is called the *outgroup* (in this case, the lamprey).

- The character states of the outgroup then are defined as the primitive states of those characters, and any deviation is considered a derived state. For example, because lampreys have no hair, the presence of hair is the derived state for that character.

- By comparing patterns of shared derived traits, we can identify species that are evolutionarily closer to each other. For example, gorillas and humans share 5 derived traits, while cats and humans share 4. We conclude that humans are closer to gorillas than to cats—that is, they share a more recent common ancestor.

Performing this type of analysis with many characters and for many organisms generates a branching tree. Each species occupies the tip of a branch and is joined to other species at forks (or "nodes"), which occur higher or lower on a branch, depending on how closely related the species are. The vertical dimension of the tree represents evolutionary time, and branching points at similar vertical levels imply relationships between species. This may seem obvious, but it also means that, for example, lungfish are more closely related to humans than to trout! Phylogenetic systematics transformed taxonomy by providing a framework for deciding how species are related to each other. When using genetic characters, this framework enables us to look at the evolutionary histories of both populations and species and, thus, represents information at the highest level of biological hierarchy. ■

Suggested Reading

Blunt, *Linnaeus: The Compleat Naturalist*.

Campbell & Reece, *Biology* (6th ed.), chapter 25.

Purves et al., *Life* (7th ed.), chapter 25.

Questions to Consider

1. Linnaeus used a hierarchical classification system to organize all known species. Can you think of another, non-biological example of a hierarchical classification system?

2. Why is it incorrect to say that any living species is truly "primitive" in the common sense of that word?

Lecture 23: Reconstructing Evolution

The History of Life, Revisited
Lecture 24

> "...all living things have much in common, in their chemical composition, their germinal vesicles, their cellular structure, their laws of growth and reproduction. ... Therefore, I should infer from analogy that probably all of the organic beings which have ever lived on this earth have descended from one primordial form, into which life was first breathed." —Darwin, *Origin of Species*

This lecture takes a final look at the concept of information and evolution in biology by returning to the question of how an original, primordial life form might have given rise to the enormously complex biodiversity observed on the planet today. Drawing on background covered earlier in the course and anticipating material to be discussed later, the lecture provides a brief tour of the major events that have occurred in the evolution of life on Earth, including the evolution of complex cells and the evolution of multicellular organisms, suggesting how these events may have contributed to the patterns of life we see today. Darwin's view of descent with modification led him to the conclusion that there existed in the remote past an organism that is the universal common ancestor to all life. The information encoded in that very first DNA still exists in some form today, even though it has been copied and modified an unfathomable number of times, and could, theoretically, be traced all the way back.

The first living organism must have arisen sometime between 3.9 and 3.5 billion years ago, based on geological and fossil evidence. The oldest fossil organisms are 3.5 billion years old; these organisms already resemble modern prokaryotes, suggesting that life evolved much earlier. The first entity we might call "living" was a single cell with a membrane, an RNA-based genetic system, and the ability to extract energy and nutrients by breaking down organic molecules it absorbed. After RNA was established, DNA took over the information-storing role. The major effects of natural selection on such an organism must have been to refine the information-storing mechanism and to establish cooperation among different kinds of biomolecules.

The fossil record makes clear that early Earth was teeming with prokaryotic cells following the existence of the first cell. It is also clear that life existed only as prokaryotic cells for at least 1.5 billion years. The two major lineages of prokaryotes, bacteria and archaea, diverged before the evolution of eukaryotic cells. The differences between bacteria and archaea are subtle and mostly involve biochemical properties. The vast majority of prokaryotes are bacteria, and archaea now tend to live in extreme environments, such as hot springs or extremely salty water. Early prokaryotes also evolved an enormous variety of biochemical (metabolic) pathways with which to capture, store, and use energy. This was basically the evolution of the proteins needed for these pathways to work. Nearly all of the metabolic pathways in modern cells evolved before eukaryotes even appeared.

A transforming event in the history of life was the evolution of biochemical pathways that captured energy from sunlight and stored it in simple sugars, a process known as *photosynthesis*. Because photosynthesis tapped into an endless source of energy, it was an enormously successful adaptation. The most important thing about photosynthesis in the present context is that the most efficient photosynthetic pathways generate oxygen as a waste product. Over the course of about 1 billion years, this increased Earth's atmospheric oxygen from almost zero to nearly modern levels. Oxygen is highly reactive and tends to break down organic molecules. Increasing oxygen levels caused many organisms that had originally evolved in the absence of oxygen to go extinct.

Some groups of organisms adapted to increased oxygen levels; the most notable adaptation was the evolution of biochemical pathways of cellular respiration, which use oxygen to extract the energy stored in organic molecules much more efficiently. Cells had essentially found both a new source of fuel and a better way to burn the fuel they had. Another positive result of oxygen accumulation was the eventual development of an ozone layer in the upper atmosphere. Ozone, a modified form of oxygen, absorbs damaging UV radiation from the Sun and permitted organisms to live on land for the first time. Eukaryotic cells first arose about 2.1 billion years ago from an archaean ancestor. At some point in history, cells began to "eat" each other by engulfing other cells in their membranes (*endocytosis*). As competition for resources increased, endocytosis began to serve as an efficient way to gain many resources at once.

The endosymbiotic theory of eukaryotic evolution suggests that at least two important organelles developed from endocytosis that resulted not in cell death, but in a symbiotic relationship between the engulfing cell and the engulfed cell. Before this could happen, however, cell membranes had to become more flexible, which also facilitated the evolution of other membrane-bound chambers within existing cells. This development may have given rise to the eukaryotic nucleus, which enabled increasingly large and complex genomes to evolve. For an engulfed cell to evolve into an organelle, there must have been a selective advantage for both of the original cells. The endosymbiotic theory suggests that the advantage to the engulfed cell was the nutrient-rich environment of the inside of the engulfing cell, while the engulfing cell benefited from the engulfed cell's more efficient metabolic pathways. Mitochondria and chloroplasts are organelles specialized for cellular respiration and photosynthesis, respectively, and likely to have arisen as described by the endosymbiotic theory. Three pieces of evidence support this theory: Mitochondria and chloroplasts share structural features with prokaryotes; each has a separate genome and reproduces separately from its host cell; and both are bacteria, while eukaryotes evolved from archaea. Though they carry their own genes, mitochondria and chloroplasts have evolved along with their hosts and could not now survive on their own. Although archaea and bacteria are separate lineages, the evolution of eukaryotic cells recombined them in an integrative way.

If we reduced the entire history of the Earth to a single calendar month, multicellular organisms would have appeared around the 24th day. From that point, life evolved rapidly.

The evolution of eukaryotic cells around 2 billion years ago caused an explosion of diversification, and evolutionary change sped up, eventually creating multicellular organisms. Eukaryotic cells diversified into a range of single-celled protists, which are abundant today. Eukaryotic cells, however, also gave rise to the evolution of multicellular organisms. Phylogenetic analysis suggests that the first multicellular organism arose perhaps 1.5 billion years ago, but the first potential fossil found is 1.2 billion years old. More convincing multicellular fossils do not appear until about 600 million years ago.

Multicellularity permitted a huge range of diversification as a result of cellular specialization. Selective pressures could act only on parts of an organism, and specialized cells could become very well adapted to their tasks. Multicellularity also allowed large, complex organisms to develop. Organisms that were large enough could develop internal environments that enabled them to survive in harsh conditions and external adaptations to those conditions. The most significant consequence of multicellularity was the development of cells specialized for sexual reproduction and the associated process of meiosis. Sexual reproduction introduced a much greater amount of genetic variation into populations of organisms. If we reduced the entire history of the Earth to a single calendar month, multicellular organisms would have appeared around the 24th day. From that point, life evolved rapidly. Once specialized cells and features arose, however, mechanisms had to develop to protect them from the wide range of new conditions in which life could exist. ∎

Suggested Reading

Campbell & Reece, *Biology* (6th ed.), chapter 26.

Gould, *The Book of Life: An Illustrated History of the Evolution of Life on Earth.*

Liebes et al., *A Walk through Time: From Stardust to Us: The Evolution of Life on Earth.*

Questions to Consider

1. Why can life no longer spontaneously arise on the modern Earth, whereas it could on the primitive Earth?

2. How does the idea that all organisms today, including ourselves, share genetic continuity with the first "organism" that ever existed on the planet change your view of life? Your view of your own existence?

From Cells to Organisms
Lecture 25

The second segment of the course, which we are about to begin, is centered on the theme of "Development and Homeostasis." As I will explain in more detail later, in this part of the course we are going to look at how complex living things get put together in the first place.

We begin by setting up two major questions: First, how do single cells proliferate and form complex multicellular organisms with a diverse array of different cell types? Second, how do different cell types in a complex multicellular organism coordinate their activities in such a way as to maintain the integrity and function of the organism as a whole? The first question brings us to a discussion of developmental biology, while the second brings us to a discussion of homeostasis and the physiological mechanisms organisms use to protect and maintain an internal environment. Development and Homeostasis refers to how complex living things are put together, how their parts coordinate with one another, and how they maintain their functions in the face of challenging environments.

The Information and Evolution theme began at the molecular level and ended at the point in time where multicellular organisms first evolved. A key point from the first third of the course is that, in order for life as we know it to exist, living things must be able to store and transmit "information" about their own structures to reproduce. In fact, the majority of this information is information about the structures of proteins. Another important point is that DNA, the molecule that stores biological information, is helpless on its own. This leads to a paradox: DNA stores information about how to build proteins—which can't be "read" without proteins. It is uncertain how this paradox was originally solved by living things. After looking at DNA, we examined how it is transmitted from parents to offspring through mitosis and meiosis. This led to another key point: Mutations and genetic recombination during meiosis constantly introduce genetic variation into offspring; this variation leads to evolution by natural selection.

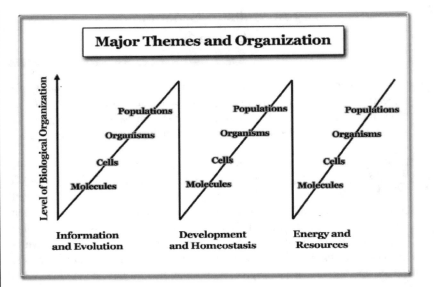

Major Themes and Organization

Level of Biological Organization

Populations
Organisms
Cells
Molecules

**Information
and Evolution**

Populations
Organisms
Cells
Molecules

**Development
and Homeostasis**

Populations
Organisms
Cells
Molecules

**Energy and
Resources**

Darwin's theory of natural selection transformed our understanding of biology by illustrating that how living things work is a consequence of history and organic evolution. Not all evolution, however, is the result of natural selection, nor does it always produce adaptations. We concluded by examining how speciation has led to the vast variety of modern and ancient life, then looking at ways to organize this diversity. This led to the conclusion that the genetic information in every organism that has ever existed is simply a modification of the genetic information in the first single-celled living organism.

The development of multicellular organisms created the opportunity for an internal environment to allow the evolution of specialized cells. *Development* refers to growth and change over time, while *homeostasis* is the coordinated interaction of the parts of an organism to create a stable internal environment. Multicellular organisms are thought to have arisen independently several times, perhaps as early as 1.5 billion years ago, probably from colonial forms of single-celled organisms.

The members of a group of green algae called the *Volvocales* vary from single, isolated cells to hollow balls of cells (*Volvox*) that comprise hundreds of different cells. This progression raises the question of where to draw the line between a cell colony and a multicellular organism. Most biologists agree that the division between a group of cells and a multicellular organism is where different cells develop distinct functions and can no longer survive on their own. In *Volvox*, for example, special reproductive cells get nutrients from other cells, not the environment, and the other cells cannot reproduce on their own.

Once cells clustered together, evolution could act on different parts of the cluster in different ways, eventually producing distinctly different cell types.

Two adaptations were necessary for the evolution of multicellular organisms. The first adaptation was simply the ability of cells to stick together. This may have been selected for a variety of reasons, such as that a greater mass of cells is less likely to be moved by water currents. For this to happen, cell membranes must have developed the ability to adhere selectively to their own kind. The second adaptation had to do with the ability of a single cell to change its structure and function in order to survive harsh conditions. This adaptation must have involved the evolution of genetic mechanisms that would later allow cells to specialize within a larger organism.

Once cells clustered together, evolution could act on different parts of the cluster in different ways, eventually producing distinctly different cell types. Any kind of cellular specialization, however, raises three questions. How can the offspring of specialized reproductive cells produce the range of cell types in a new organism? How can the different complex parts of multicellular organisms communicate with each other? How can an internal organism's internal environment be maintained in a state that meets the needs of the organism's different parts? ■

Suggested Reading

Campbell & Reece, *Biology* (6th ed.), chapter 40.

Freeman, *Biological Science*, chapter 27.

Harold, *The Way of the Cell: Molecules, Organisms and the Order of Life*.

Purves et al., *Life* (7th ed.), chapter 41.

Questions to Consider

1. Is *Volvox* a multicellular organism or a colony of specialized single-cell organisms? How might you argue this point either way?

2. Many single-celled organisms are eukaryotic, meaning that their single cell contains many different kinds of specialized organelles. Is the concept of homeostasis relevant to such organisms? Why or why not?

Lecture 25: From Cells to Organisms

Control of Gene Expression I
Lecture 26

Indeed, differences in the way cells function often relate to differences in the way cells are shaped. Muscle cells are elongated, for example. Brain cells will often have long extensions protruding from them that serve as a kind of cellular wire—we will look at that later in the course—and so forth. Different cells are different shapes. They look different.

This lecture begins by illustrating how cells differ in the proteins they express. The same cell may express different proteins at different times in its life, and in multicellular organisms, different types of cells typically express different suites of proteins. Given that all cells in an organism have the same set of genes, how do these differences in protein expression arise? The lecture outlines the history of the original experiments done by Jacques Monod and François Jacob in the late 1950s and early 1960s using bacteria to discover the basic mechanisms of gene regulation.

Though we have discussed cell specialization, we have not examined what makes cells different from each other. Differences in cell function often produce different cell shapes, but the critical difference is the different protein mix each type of cell contains. Though many thousands of proteins are coded

Differences in cell function often produce different cell shapes, but the critical difference is the different protein mix each type of cell contains.

for in a typical eukaryotic cell, most cells contain only a fraction of that number at any one time. This is the case even in single-celled bacteria. This situation makes sense because making proteins is expensive and many proteins do not store well. This leads to the question of how cells control protein production.

We know that making proteins requires the transcription of DNA into mRNA, then the translation of mRNA into proteins; thus, we could alternatively ask why all genes in a cell are not always transcribed and translated. The general answer is that cells regulate gene expression by controlling the conditions necessary for transcription and translation.

The complexity of gene expression means that there are many possible points where cells can control it. In addition to transcription and translation, the initial mRNA transcript must be processed before it is translated, and the final polypeptide must often be further modified by enzymes before it is functional. Cells could theoretically control gene expression at any of these points, but the majority of gene regulation happens at the level of transcription—specifically, by controlling mRNA synthesis. This is the case primarily for efficiency; it "costs" cells less to prevent the process from starting in the first place.

Control of transcription mechanisms involves genetic "lock-and-key" mechanisms, which work differently in prokaryotes and eukaryotes. To a first approximation, the "switch" that turns transcription on and off is a lock-and-key mechanism. The lock is a specific sequence of nucleotide bases on the DNA that is distinct from but often located physically adjacent to the gene it controls. Each gene has one or more of these regulatory regions, which normally occur "upstream" from the gene. The key is usually a protein with the right shape (including not only physical shape but the correct physical and chemical properties of amino acids) to fit the DNA lock. In general, only one protein will bind to a particular regulatory region.

In order to start transcription, RNA polymerase must bind to promoter sites on the DNA molecule. The binding of RNA polymerase to a promoter is not specific; thus, regulatory regions and proteins generally act in two ways to control gene expression. In prokaryotic cells, regulatory regions typically lie in between promoter sites and genes. Regulatory proteins bound to regulatory regions physically block RNA polymerase from reaching the gene. This represents *negative control* and is typical of prokaryotic cells.

The other type of control depends on the fact that RNA polymerase cannot always bind efficiently to the promoter by itself. In this case regulatory proteins interacting with regulatory regions affect the ability of RNA polymerase to bind to a promoter. In the most general case, regulatory proteins (called "transcription factors") facilitate the binding of RNA polymerase,

The Central Dogma

Replication — DNA
Transcription → RNA
Translation → Protein

resulting in *positive control*, though these proteins can have either a positive or negative effect on binding in specific cases. These types of controls create two contrasts: physical blockage of RNA polymerase versus an effect on its ability to bind to a promoter region on the DNA, and negative control versus positive control.

Though the lock-and-key mechanism for gene regulation can be compared to turning on a car, there are some important differences. The "driver" (RNA polymerase) is not selective as to which "car" it chooses. RNA polymerase simply tries to transcribe every gene. Some genes will be expressed only if the key is not in the regulatory lock. Some genes require a combination of many different keys to be expressed, and some keys must be in their locks, while others must be out.

In the late 1950s and early 1960s, Jacques Monod and François Jacob investigated how gene regulation works in prokaryotes. The bacteria *Escherichia coli* (*E. coli* for short) requires several enzymes to metabolize lactose. Biochemists discovered in the early 20th century that *E. coli* produces these enzymes only when lactose is available, suggesting that lactose induces enzyme production.

This observation led Jacques Monod and François Jacob to the question of how lactose could induce gene expression; they found mutant forms of *E. coli* that differed in how they expressed lactose-digesting enzymes. Two kinds of mutants were unable to digest lactose; in one case, an enzyme involved in lactose breakdown itself was defective, while in another case, an enzyme that brings lactose into the cell was defective. These mutations fit into the expected pattern: A mutation in a gene causes a coding error that produces a dysfunctional protein, which cannot do its job. A third kind of mutant always produced lactose-digesting enzymes, regardless of whether lactose was present or not. This type of mutation produced a gain of constant function rather than a loss of function. Monod and Jacob inferred that this third type of mutant must have a mutation in some protein involved in controlling gene expression, not in the genes coding for the enzymes themselves.

Monod and Jacob's idea was revolutionary at the time, because it pointed to a protein whose sole function was to regulate the expression of other genes. In *E. coli*, the regulatory protein seemed to inhibit enzyme production. After some debate, physicist Leo Szilard prevailed with the idea that the regulatory protein acted as a repressor that normally prevented production of the lactose-digesting enzymes. Szilard's model suggested that lactose acts as an inducer by disabling the repressor protein; that is, expression of the lactose-digesting enzymes is under negative control. ■

Suggested Reading

Campbell & Reece, *Biology* (6th ed.), chapter 18.

Freeman, *Biological Science*, chapter 14.

Jacob, *The Statue Within: An Autobiography*.

Judson, *The Eighth Day of Creation: Makers of the Revolution in Biology*.

1. Is turning on a car an example of positive control or negative control?

2. Why was it surprising to Jacob and Monod to find a mutation of a gene that caused a functional protein that is normally absent in a cell to be produced?

Control of Gene Expression II
Lecture 27

In the late 1950s, an American biochemist named Arthur Pardee came to Paris to work with Jacob and Monod, and it was collaboration among these three researchers that led to a confirmation of Szilard's hypothesis. The work that they did is usually referred to with the somewhat fanciful name of the PaJaMo Experiment, which is taken from the first two letters of each scientist's last name.

This lecture extends the idea of protein-DNA interaction in gene expression to the more complex architecture of eukaryotic genes, emphasizing the role of multiple interacting regulatory factors. The same basic principles apply in eukaryotic cells as we saw in prokaryotic cells, but with many added layers of complexity that correspond to additional layers of control. The lecture begins by reviewing the basic mechanisms we learned last time, adding other details of the structure of gene regulatory regions on DNA. The lecture then proceeds to outline differences in the organization of prokaryote and eukaryote genomes that require additional regulatory mechanisms to come into play. The lecture ends with a summary of the elements that eukaryotic cells use to turn on and off the expression of their genes.

The PaJaMo experiment confirmed Leo Szilard's hypothesis of a repressor protein. In the late 1950s, Pardee began working with Monod and Jacob, and the three eventually confirmed Leo Szilard's hypothesis of negative control for the genes for lactose-metabolizing proteins in *E. coli* bacteria. Their experiment (usually called *PaJaMo*, from the last names of each scientist) was intended to separate the effects of lactose as an inducer from the effects of the repressor protein on the expression of two enzymes, β-galactosidase and galactoside permease. In practice, they focused on β-galactosidase.

The PaJaMo experiment took advantage of the process of *conjugation*, in which bacteria transfer genetic material to each other through extra-chromosomal pieces of DNA, called *plasmids*. Bacteria are normally haploid, but bacteria that receive plasmids become diploid for any genes contained on the plasmids.

Pardee, Monod, and Jacob used bacteria with mutations in both the *lacI* (repressor protein) and *lacZ* (β-galactosidase) genes as recipients in a conjugation experiment. As donors, they used normal bacteria. Before conjugation, the recipient cells could not produce β-galactosidase. However, because they also had defective repressor protein genes, if they received a normal β-galactosidase gene, they would express it. In conjugation, the recipients received functional genes for both proteins and should then have acted like normal cells. What the scientists actually observed was that after conjugation, the recipient cells produced β-galactosidase even in the absence of lactose, but only for a few hours. After those few hours, β-galactosidase would be produced only in the presence of lactose, as is typical of a normal cell. The three scientists eventually realized that the two genes were transcribed at different rates. Because the *lacZ* gene is transcribed much more quickly than the *lacI* gene, it took a few hours for enough of the repressor protein to be made to shut down β-galactosidase production.

The PaJaMo experiment took advantage of the process of *conjugation*, in which bacteria transfer genetic material to each other through extra-chromosomal pieces of DNA, called *plasmids*.

In 1961, Jacob and Monod published a proposed summary model of gene expression. Genetic mapping had shown that the genes for β-galactosidase, galactoside permease, and a couple of other enzymes all occur in a single long sequence on the bacteria's chromosome. The functional coding regions of these genes are preceded by a single promoter site. Jacob and Monod's model proposed that there was a regulatory region, called the *operator*, between the promoter and the first coding region. The operator is where the repressor protein would bind to physically prevent RNA polymerase from transcribing the coding regions. Subsequent studies have shown that this is the case. Lactose binds directly to the repressor protein, changing its shape in a way that makes it unable to bind to the operator. RNA polymerase is then free to transcribe the group of lactose-metabolizing proteins.

Jacob and Monod referred to the entire genetic unit—the promoter, the operator, and the coding regions—as an *operon*. Because their operon dealt with the metabolism of lactose, it was called the *lac* operon. The *lacI* gene that codes for the repressor protein is not part of the operon but occurs nearby on the chromosome, somewhat "upstream" of the operon. We now know that *E. coli* has many other operons and that the binding of regulatory proteins to operators is a common control mechanism.

Prokaryotic and eukaryotic gene regulation differ in important ways, for several reasons. Gene regulation in eukaryotes is different in many ways from gene regulation in prokaryotes, but two differences are immediately applicable. Prokaryotes characteristically have functionally related groups of genes that share a single promoter region and a single control mechanism. In eukaryotes, each individual gene typically has its own promoter and control regions. The way that regulatory proteins affect RNA polymerase is both different and much more complex in eukaryotic cells compared to prokaryotes.

Jacob and Monod's demonstration of the way prokaryotes work, though, was an important breakthrough for both types of cells. Among other things, it proved that some proteins exist solely to control the expression of other genes. The interactions between the repressor protein and the operator, and between the repressor and an inducer, such as lactose, are not the only influences on transcription. Another regulatory region in the *lac* operon helps RNA polymerase bind to the DNA strand and, thus, provides a measure of positive control over gene expression in the same way as is common in eukaryotes.

Gene regulation differs for eukaryotes and prokaryotes because, among other factors, the genomes of eukaryotes are generally much larger than those of prokaryotes. In addition, eukaryote genomes are separated into several linear pieces (i.e., different chromosomes) and contain introns that are not transcribed. There are also large stretches of repetitive DNA whose function is not currently known. Eukaryote genomes are also tightly packaged as a complex of DNA and proteins called *chromatin*, whereas prokaryote DNA is unpackaged. Though they are different, gene expression in eukaryotes follows some of the general principles identified by Jacob and Monod.

Eukaryotic gene regulation is more complex than gene regulation in prokaryotes. The most obvious difference from prokaryotes is that eukaryotic DNA is packaged in chromatin, which must somehow be unwrapped to allow RNA polymerase in. Recent research suggests that chromatin may play its own regulatory function instead of just being a supportive and protective framework.

Although it is unclear how chromatin might be unpacked in a gene-specific way, once the DNA is unpackaged, we are presented with the same question as in prokaryotes: How is the activity of RNA polymerase controlled to regulate gene expression? Each eukaryotic gene is associated with three kinds of regions on the DNA strand: the coding region, a promoter, and one or more regulatory regions. Certain regulator proteins must be present, and sometimes certain other proteins must be absent, for a gene to be transcribed. In addition, at least some regulatory proteins are highly selective about the DNA sequence to which they bind. In eukaryotes, the presence or absence of regulatory proteins influences the ability of RNA polymerase to bind to a promoter. These proteins are generally called *transcription factors*. A very large number of regulatory proteins may be involved in regulating transcription.

Some regulatory proteins are generic and required for any gene to be transcribed; they are called *basal transcription factors*. A number of basal transcription factors must bind to RNA polymerase, forming a *transcription initiation complex*, for RNA polymerase to do its job. Other transcription factors affect the transcription of only one or a few genes; these are called *regulatory transcription factors*. Because these interact with the initiation complex, transcription involves not only protein-DNA interactions but also protein-protein interactions.

Regulatory regions are normally adjacent to or even part of the promoter, but in eukaryotes, they might be very far away—up to 20,000 base pairs distant—from the genes they affect. Distant regulatory proteins are called *enhancers* because they seemed to enhance, rather than directly affect, transcription. It now appears that the DNA strand will actually bend back on itself, bringing enhancers into proximity to the genes they control. As in prokaryotes, regulatory proteins can have either a positive or negative effect on transcription; however, in eukaryotes, all regulation involves the binding of RNA polymerase and the initiation complex, rather than simple physical barriers. ■

Suggested Reading

Campbell & Reece, *Biology* (6th ed.), chapters 18 & 19.

Freeman, *Biological Science*, chapters 14 & 15.

Jacob, *The Statue Within: An Autobiography*.

Judson, *The Eighth Day of Creation: Makers of the Revolution in Biology*.

Questions to Consider

1. Would the "Pa-Ja-Mo" experiment have supported Szilard's hypothesis of negative control in the lac operon if the lacZ gene and the lacI gene were transcribed at the same rate? Why or why not?

2. Having many regulatory proteins controlling the transcription of a gene seems unnecessarily complex, just like using many keys to start a single car. What are some possible advantages of this added complexity?

Getting Proteins to the Right Place
Lecture 28

Remember that eukaryotic cells are characterized by having many internal compartments; compartments that we call *organelles*. The significance of this compartmentalization, you will recall, is that it allows the cell to sequester different substances or different biochemical processes and keep them separate from the rest of the cell.

Simply producing the right proteins at the right time is only the first step to regulating cell function on the molecular level. This lecture introduces the equally important problem of how proteins find themselves in the right places inside or outside a cell. The lecture briefly reviews cell structures associated with protein synthesis, including ribosomes, the endoplasmic reticulum (ER), and the Golgi apparatus. It then describes the signal hypothesis proposed by Günter Blobel, which suggests that the initial few amino acids of a protein being synthesized determine whether that protein will be produced in the cytoplasm or in the ER. The lecture ends by describing other kinds of address labels used to sort proteins and by describing how inclusion-cell disease is caused by malfunctioning protein-sorting mechanisms.

Normal cell function, however, depends not only on having the proper set of proteins, but also on having those proteins occurring in proper locations in the cell.

We have seen how the particular suite of proteins found in a cell can be determined by turning on or off the transcription of genes coding for those proteins. Normal cell function, however, depends not only on having the proper set of proteins, but also on having those proteins occurring in proper locations in the cell. For example, the proteins involved in DNA replication and transcription must find their way into the nucleus of a eukaryotic cell, other proteins must find themselves in the cytoplasm on the cell, others are embedded in the cell's membranes, and yet others must be exported outside the cell. Thus, another issue that must be considered in order to understand how cells specialize is how proteins become localized in the cell after they are synthesized.

One possible way for proteins to localize would be random diffusion; however, there are two major problems with this idea. Even in a space as small as a cell, random diffusion would not be very efficient. Some proteins might end up in the right places, but it would take a long time to happen. An even more serious problem is that many of the places proteins need to go are within organelles or subunits of organelles and, thus, are surrounded by biological membranes. Most molecules, especially such molecules as proteins, cannot cross membranes by themselves. To overcome these problems, cells have evolved a variety of protein-trafficking mechanisms.

Eukaryotic cells are characterized by having many internal compartments, called *organelles*, that allow the cell to separate different substances and processes. One set of organelles is called the endomembrane system, and it has several components. The series of flattened chambers that spreads throughout a cell is called the *endoplasmic reticulum* (ER), which is interconnected inside. Toward the edges of the cell, these chambers appear to break apart, which is actually the budding off of a number of *vesicles* from the ER. Beyond the ER is a stack of separated, pancake-like chambers, called the *Golgi apparatus*, which both receives vesicles from the ER and buds off its own vesicles.

The overall picture is of two sets of membrane-enclosed chambers with small transport vehicles moving between them and moving outward from the Golgi apparatus. The ER also has bumpy areas as seen under the microscope, called *rough ER*, which are rough because many ribosomes are attached to the ER surfaces. *Ribosomes* are large complexes of RNA and protein that construct other proteins. Ribosomes may also be found free in the cytoplasm of the cell. The microscopic anatomy of the endomembrane system has long suggested that at least one of its functions is to process, package, and transport proteins once they have been synthesized. In the 1950s, experiments in which radioactive amino acids were added to a cell in short pulses, then followed over time, confirmed the hypothesis that proteins move from the rough ER to the smooth ER and then to the Golgi apparatus, where they are packaged for transport to the outside of the cell and other places.

The role of the endomembrane system in processing and transporting proteins raises the question of how proteins are directed into the ER. In the early 1970s, Günter Blobel proposed the *signal hypothesis*, which suggests that a sequence of amino acids at the beginning of a polypeptide serves as an address tag that directs a synthesizing ribosome to move to the ER. It is possible to synthesize proteins, even proteins normally secreted into the ER, in a cell-free environment. However, proteins synthesized this way are about two dozen amino acids longer than the same protein synthesized by an intact cell, consistent with the signal hypothesis. Blobel suggested that these extra amino acids are normally removed by the ER because their only function is to direct ribosomes to the ER. This idea was confirmed by adding intact ER to a cell-free solution, which resulted in proteins of the same length as normally synthesized by the cell.

Many experiments since have supported Blobel's hypothesis and have shown how the address tag works. All protein synthesis begins in the cytoplasm with free ribosomes. If an address tag occurs at the beginning of the polypeptide, the ribosome stops synthesis. The address tag then attaches to a signal-recognition particle, which docks the ribosome into the ER membrane. Synthesis then restarts, with the synthesized protein directed inside the ER. The information in the address tag ultimately resides in the DNA itself, though these amino acids have nothing to do with the protein's function.

Proteins synthesized in the ER have many destinations, and similar kinds of address-tag mechanisms are responsible for this additional sorting. Proteins move progressively through the ER and into the Golgi apparatus via vesicles. In the Golgi apparatus, different kinds of carbohydrates (sugars) are attached to proteins (*glycosylation*) to form *glycoproteins* (literally "sugar proteins"). The added sugar components can aid protein function or folding; they also often act as an address tag that determines the protein's ultimate destination.

Proteins destined for lysosomes are an example of this kind of addressing. *Lysosomes* are organelles filled with digestive enzymes that break large molecules into smaller pieces so that other organelles can process them. These digestive enzymes are transported from the Golgi apparatus in vesicles. Sugars attached to enzymes destined to be transported to lysosomes bind selectively to proteins on the membrane of the Golgi apparatus. These proteins, in turn, bind selectively to other proteins found on the lysosome membrane, so vesicles from the Golgi apparatus will selectively bind to lysosomes if they have lysosomic enzymes inside. This two-part addressing system, in which proteins have labels that attach to vesicles which themselves have labels, ensures that proteins normally find their proper destinations.

Inclusion-cell (I-cell) disease is an example of a disease caused by dysfunctional protein addressing. It occurs in about 1 out of every 650,000 births. I-cell disease causes skeletal abnormalities, severe mental retardation, and usually death by age 10. In I-cell disease, lysosomes lack a critical enzyme that allows them to break down waste products. The lysosomes fill up and ultimately destroy the cells containing them. I-cell disease is caused by a single recessive mutation, which suggests that it is caused by a dysfunctional enzyme. Another logical guess would be that the mutation has disabled a crucial transcription factor. However, I-cell patients manufacture the enzyme correctly; it simply never leaves the Golgi apparatus, or is secreted outside the cell. Instead, I-cell disease is caused by the lack of an enzyme responsible for attaching a specific carbohydrate address tag. This missing address tag prevents the digestive enzyme from becoming packaged in a vesicle that will deliver it to the lysosome. ■

Suggested Reading

Alberts et al., *Essential Cell Biology* (2nd ed.), chapter 14.

Freeman, *Biological Science*, chapter 5.

Purves et al., *Life* (7th ed.), chapter 12.

Questions to Consider

1. Palade's work demonstrating that proteins are transported through the endomembrane system required him to use cells that mostly produce proteins destined to be secreted outside the cell. Why was this important for Palade's experiments to succeed?

2. I-cell disease and similar recessive genetic diseases are a primary motivation for genetic counseling of potential parents. What is your view of the social and medical benefits and drawbacks of genetic counseling?

Genetic Engineering and Biotechnology
Lecture 29

> If our predecessors in the 20th century were living in the electronic age, I think that it can truly be said that we in the 21st century are living in the genetic age. This is an appropriate point in this course to take this detour, because we have now learned most of what we need to know to understand what genetic engineering and biotechnology are all about.

This lecture begins by describing how the fundamental mechanisms cells use to replicate and transcribe DNA provided researchers with insight into how to modify genes, how to transfer genetic material from one organism to another, and how to rapidly sequence genes. These tools provide the basis for genetic engineering and biotechnology, which are rapidly transforming our lives. The lecture ends with examples showing how genetic engineering and biotechnology have been applied in medicine and agriculture.

In many ways, the promise of biotechnology began with Watson and Crick's first description of the DNA double helix, because many of the fundamental tools we use to analyze and manipulate genes today depend on the complementary base pairing rules they described. Advances in genetic engineering and biotechnology over the last several decades have had as much to do with developing techniques for conveniently or quickly working with DNA as with new conceptual understanding.

Genetic engineering involves the production of recombinant DNA. We have seen recombinant genotypes and phenotypes in meiosis, where the term simply referred to new mixtures of traits from two different parents. *Recombinant DNA* has a similar meaning, with two important differences. When creating recombinant DNA, we determine by choice which DNA will be included. Meiotic recombination, on the other hand, works by chance. The second difference is that we can combine DNA from completely different organisms if needed or desired.

The discovery in the 1960s of a particular class of bacterial enzyme called *restriction endonucleases* (or *restriction enzymes*) was a crucial first step in learning how to manipulate genes. Restriction enzymes are defense mechanisms bacteria use to break down the DNA of viruses, thus preventing viruses from infecting a bacterial cell. They cut DNA apart at sequences called *recognition* or *restriction sites*. Restriction sites are typically only a few bases long. The two strands at a restriction site usually are palindromic, which on DNA means that the same base sequence occurs on both strands in reverse directions (e.g., GAATTC on one strand with CTTAAG on the other). This is the case because of complementary base pairing.

The bacteria's own DNA is protected from the action of its restriction enzymes, because in the bacteria, the sequences the enzyme recognizes are chemically modified by adding methyl groups (methylated). Because restriction enzymes cut between two particular bases in a restriction sequence, each cut piece now has a short section of single-stranded DNA extending beyond the double-stranded portion of the molecule. The exposed bases on these "sticky ends" will align through base pairing with any strand that has the appropriate complementary sequence, providing a way to recombine cut pieces of DNA.

The second major advance in biotechnology was the ability to introduce recombinant DNA into a new organism.

The key to creating recombinant DNA is the fact that the sticky ends of any fragments of DNA cut by the same restriction enzyme—regardless of which organism the DNA came from—will be complementary to each other. DNA ligase, the enzyme that stitches together Okazaki fragments during DNA replication, can be used in the lab to stitch together the sticky ends of DNA pieces, creating new recombinant DNA. Hundreds of restriction enzymes have been discovered, each recognizing a different DNA sequence and, thus, each cleaving DNA at different points along the overall length of the molecule.

The second major advance in biotechnology was the ability to introduce recombinant DNA into a new organism. Early work used prokaryotes as

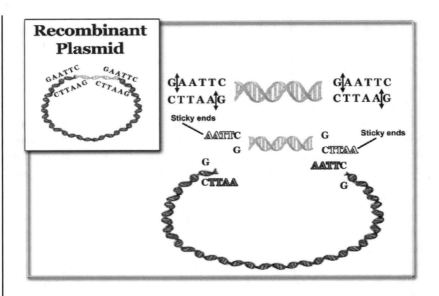

Recombinant Plasmid

GAATTC
CTTAAG
Sticky ends

GAATTC
CTTAAG
Sticky ends

AATTC
G

G
CTTAA

G
CTTAA

AATTC
G

hosts for recombinant DNA, because bacteria normally transfer short pieces of DNA from one to another. Bacteria transfer DNA through conjugation, in which small pieces of DNA, called *plasmids*, are transferred from one cell to another. Restriction enzymes can cut open a plasmid and allow the insertion of a piece of genetic material that has been clipped out with the same restriction enzyme. The plasmid containing the added genetic material can then be inserted into new host cells using the natural process of conjugation. A genetically modified bacterium will use its own DNA synthesis machinery to make more copies of the recombinant gene as it divides and will use its own protein synthesis machinery to produce the protein coded for by the inserted gene.

This method works, but it has some practical problems. First is the difficulty of determining whether the appropriate plasmid has been created, because restriction sites occur frequently, resulting in many DNA fragments. It may also be difficult to identify bacteria that have incorporated the desired plasmid. One way to do this is by incorporating not only the desired gene but also an easily identified genetic marker or reporter gene. A major problem is that introducing eukaryotic genes into prokaryotic organisms also requires adding a prokaryotic promoter mechanism. In addition, eukaryotic genes have introns that must be removed. This is normally done by using mRNA and reverse transcriptase to create artificial genes that lack introns (complementary DNA or "cDNA").

Other methods of inserting foreign DNA into both prokaryotic and eukaryotic cells have in common the use of a vector that transports DNA into cells, where it is expressed, if not incorporated into the genome. For example, one method involves creating small artificial chromosomes with desired characteristics that function as normal chromosomes in host cells. This has been successful with yeast, and considerable progress has been made with an artificial human chromosome. Creating transgenic organisms becomes increasingly difficult as the host organism becomes more complex, but the routine insertion and expression of foreign DNA into any organism may not be far away.

A third major advance in DNA technology has been the development of methods to determine rapidly the sequence of bases in a molecule of DNA. The most visible consequence of the development of sequencing methods has been the ability to sequence the entire genomes of some organisms, including humans. Excluding bacteria, about a dozen genomes have been completely sequenced to date. In many cases, this kind of detailed knowledge is what makes possible much of the genetic engineering we have discussed.

Although practical applications are still being developed, genetic engineering and biotechnology have already led to important commercial and medical benefits. The broadest definition of biotechnology is simply the manipulation of organisms to make useful products. Selective breeding of plants and animals is, in this sense, an old form of biotechnology, but it is quite slow.

The first and most widely used application of biotechnology has been to produce proteins that previously could be obtained only through tedious or costly means. Insulin used to treat diabetes could previously be harvested only from tissues taken from cows and pigs. This process is costly, it is difficult to purify the insulin, and the insulin did not function properly in some patients because the animal protein differs from the human form. Insulin is now produced commercially by bacteria that have had the human insulin gene added to their genomes, allowing them to produce the human form of the protein abundantly and relatively cheaply.

In the United States, almost three dozen transgenic crop plants are in common commercial use. Plants may be modified for insect or drought resistance, or increased nutritional value. However, many critics argue against the use of transgenic food species because of the unintended consequences gene manipulation might have—for example, overproduction of pesticides or other toxic compounds or the decimation of a wild species by a genetically modified one. These possibilities are real and will need to be weighed against the benefits of transgenic organisms, especially as population pressures cause an increased demand for food. ■

Suggested Reading

Campbell & Reece, *Biology* (6th ed.), chapter 20.

Enriquez, *As the Future Catches You: How Genomics and Other Forces Are Changing Your Life, Work, Health and Wealth.*

Freeman, *Biological Science*, chapter 17.

Purves et al., *Life* (7th ed.), chapter 16.

Stock, *Redesigning Humans: Our Inevitable Genetic Future.*

Questions to Consider

1. Do you believe the claim that making a recombinant organism is fundamentally the same as the selective breeding of domesticated species? Why or why not?

2. If you agree that some organisms should be genetically modified (such as bacteria to produce insulin), then do you think there are some organisms that should *not* be modified? Why or why not?

How Cells Talk—Signals and Receptors
Lecture 30

In multicellular organisms, the predominant environment experienced by most cells are the other cells that surround them. Thus, the cells in multicellular organisms really should be seen as sort of social entities. They are constantly talking to each other. They are constantly sending signals and receiving signals and changing the way they behave in response to those signals.

This lecture is the first of two that turn to the question of how molecular messages control cell function. All cells respond to external signals, and it is especially important for the different kinds of cells in multicellular organisms to communicate with each other in order to coordinate their activities. This lecture presents an overview of the issues involved in cell signaling and introduces the role of the hormone epinephrine in the fight-or-flight response as a context for discussing the basic components of a cell signaling system. The lecture then goes on to describe mechanisms of signal reception, which generally provide an indirect molecular connection between the outside and the inside of the cell.

The last several lectures have shown how the unique collections of proteins that characterize different kinds of cells (and different kinds of cell functions) are the products of highly regulated mechanisms for controlling the expression of genes and for delivering proteins to the right place. Cells do not exist in isolation, however. Even single-celled organisms constantly receive and respond to external cues that affect cell function. The *lac* operon system provided an example in which lactose in the environment regulates gene expression. Another way to describe lactose in this system is as a *signal* that *E. coli* responds to in an adaptive fashion, meaning that *E. coli*'s ability to detect and respond to lactose ultimately increases its fitness.

In multicellular organisms, the most common kinds of signals are those produced by other cells. Given that most cells in a multicellular organism are surrounded by other cells, it makes sense that cells would need to communicate with each other to perform different functions. Signaling is essential not only among groups of cells but also between cells that are next to each other, much like musicians in an orchestra. Cell-cell signaling is essential in development, where signals direct how cells differentiate their function and find their correct position in the organism, and in homeostatic maintenance, where signals convey information necessary to coordinate activities of cells that have diverse functions in different parts of the organism.

Cell signaling involves three components, or stages. *Reception* is exactly what it says—the way in which a cell detects a signal in its environment. In *transduction*, signals are converted from their original form into a form the cell can "understand" and respond to. In other words, an external signal must be converted into an internal signal. *Response* involves anything the cell does in reaction to a signal, which mostly involves the action of proteins.

Given that most cells in a multicellular organism are surrounded by other cells, it makes sense that cells would need to communicate with each other to perform different functions.

The fight-or-flight response provides a context for understanding the principles of chemical signaling on the cellular level. When a person is startled or scared, he or she feels fear and excitement and his or her body experiences several objective changes, such as higher blood pressure, increased blood glucose, and increased oxygen consumption by the brain. This coordinated complex of responses is called the *fight-or-flight response.* The fight-or-flight response is caused largely by the effect of the hormone epinephrine (also called adrenaline), which is released by the adrenal glands into the bloodstream and quickly transported throughout the body.

Epinephrine's effect on the liver is an example of a common signal reception process. Epinephrine, like most cell signals, cannot enter the cell by crossing the cell membrane directly. In general, the phospholipid bilayer of cell membranes does not allow large or electrically charged molecules to cross. Thus, the signal must exert its action indirectly, by interacting with proteins embedded in the cell membrane that span the membrane from inside to

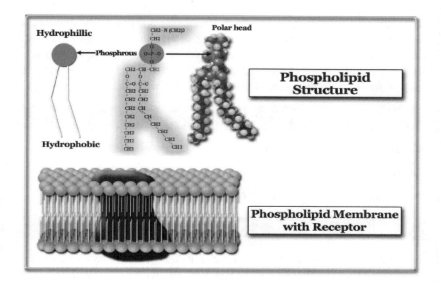

Hydrophillic

Phosphrous

Hydrophobic

Polar head

Phospholipid Structure

Phospholipid Membrane with Receptor

outside. These membrane proteins are called *receptor proteins*. Chemicals that interact with receptor proteins are called *ligands*. A ligand will bind to a specific site on a receptor protein, which generally changes the shape of the entire receptor protein. Although receptor proteins interact with ligands in a highly specific way, receptors can be grouped into several broad classes.

Epinephrine receptors are G-protein–linked receptors, which are very large proteins with seven helical regions connected by short loops. On the outside of the cell, one of these loops has a binding site for epinephrine. When epinephrine binds to this site, the entire receptor changes shape, including the part inside the cell. A protein called G protein is located near the G-protein–linked receptor on the inside of the cell. When the receptor changes shape, G protein moves closer to the receptor, binding a molecule of GTP and activating the G protein. The activated G protein moves away from the receptor and interacts with an enzyme called adenylyl cyclase, changing its shape and activating it. Adenylyl cyclase catalyzes the production of cyclic AMP (cAMP), which is the messenger that will ultimately trigger the cell's internal response to epinephrine.

The important point to gather from this sequence is that a signal external to a cell has triggered an internal signal, even though the external signal could not enter the cell itself. Other classes of receptors use other mechanisms to trigger a cellular response, but in almost all cases, the connection between the extracellular signal and the intracellular response is indirect. ■

Suggested Reading

Alberts et al., *Essential Cell Biology* (2nd ed.), chapter 15.

Campbell & Reece, *Biology* (6th ed.), chapter 11.

Purves et al., *Life* (7th ed.), chapter 15.

Questions to Consider

1. Can you develop an argument for why the very first cells that every existed must have been able to communicate with each other?

2. Why do most extracellular signals *not* cross the cell membrane directly, and why might this be an advantage to the cell?

How Cells Talk—Ways That Cells Respond
Lecture 31

The primary response of liver cells when they receive epinephrine is to break down glycogen molecules into individual molecules of glucose. Glucose produced this way is in a useful form that can be released into the bloodstream, providing the rest of the body with a quick source of energy.

This lecture continues the discussion of mechanisms by which extracellular signals can control cell function. The lecture begins by explaining the basic ideas behind signal transduction pathways, emphasizing how these pathways amplify signals and provide additional levels of control and coordination. Signal transduction often involves the *phosphorylation* of proteins, which is a common mechanism for turning proteins on or off. A few small molecules that are not proteins as well as ions also play important roles in cell signaling by acting as *second messengers* inside the cell. The response of cells to signals may involve turning on or off the activity of existing proteins or may regulate gene expression if the end product of a signal transduction pathway acts as a transcription factor in the nucleus.

The binding of a ligand to a receptor protein changes the shape and, thus, the activity of the receptor, but this is usually only the first step in a cascade of events that converts the original signal into a molecular form that brings about a functional cellular response. Such a cascade is called a *signal transduction pathway* or a *signal transduction cascade*. We know that one functional response to epinephrine is to cause liver cells to convert sugars from the complex storage form of glycogen to a simpler form (glucose) that is released into the bloodstream, to provide a quick source of energy. The conversion of glycogen to glucose in the liver depends on the activity of an enzyme called glycogen phosphorylase. Therefore, the binding of epinephrine to a receptor must cause a change in the activity of an enzyme.

Enzyme activity can be regulated in several ways. Epinephrine could affect an enzyme ultimately by regulating the expression of its gene; if more of the enzyme is synthesized, the overall activity level in the cell will be higher. This type of control does take place. Another method of control, however, would be to activate inactive copies of the enzyme.

Although it is expensive for cells to build proteins, it also takes a certain amount of time, which may be far too long for the cell to wait (certainly too long for the fight-or-flight response). In cases where a faster response is adaptive, cellular mechanisms have evolved to activate existing proteins. One important method involves *phosphorylation* (the addition of a phosphate group). Phosphate groups are highly negatively charged, and their addtion generally has a profound effect on a protein's shape. In particular, proteins will typically occur in an inactive form without a phosphate group and in an active form with one. The function of many types of enzymes is simply to phosphorylate other enzymes; the general name for such an enzyme is a *protein kinase*. Protein kinases are so important that 1 of every 100 eukaryotic genes may code for one. The sequential phosphorylation of a series of protein kinases is an important, common mechanism in signal transduction cascades. In the case of epinephrine, cAMP triggers a series of proteins to sequentially phosphorylate each other, from protein kinase A to phosphorylase kinase to glycogen phosphorylase, with the last being the enzyme that converts glycogen to glucose.

Signal transduction pathways have several advantages over a more direct mode of activation. First, the signal becomes amplified by the cascade, because each step progressively activates a larger number of molecules.

Although it is expensive for cells to build proteins, it also takes a certain amount of time, which may be far too long for the cell to wait (certainly too long for the fight-or-flight response).

In this way, a very small number of signal molecules can quickly lead to the activation of a very large number of functional molecules. One calculation suggests that a single molecule of epinephrine will cause 100 million molecules of glycogen phosphorylase to be activated.

Another important consequence of a signal cascade is that the activation of different proteins in the cascade can produce multiple functional outcomes. For example, one of the phosphorylation steps in epinephrine response deactivates glycogen synthase, which normally synthesizes glycogen. Thus, not only will epinephrine enable the break down of glycogen into glucose, but it will also disable the creation of new glycogen. Signal cascades also allow cross talk among different pathways; instead of acting in a linear fashion, most cascades are networks with multiple inputs and outputs. In epinephrine response, the initial blood glucose level may be very high and the production of more glucose may actually be disadvantageous. Other signaling cascades can modulate glucose production to avoid damage. In general, the interaction of kinases with other signal molecules creates a much higher level of control and feedback than would otherwise be possible.

Special sets of small nonprotein molecules also play key roles in signal transduction pathways. cAMP, for example, is produced by adenylyl cyclase and activates the first protein kinase in the epinephrine signal transduction pathway. In this position, cAMP is the first intracellular signal resulting from the extracellular signal of epinephrine. cAMP and other molecules of its type are referred to as *second messengers* because they are the next in line after the original external signal (i.e., the first messenger). IP_3, DAG, and calcium ions also serve as second messengers in cells. Calcium ions are notable both because they are so simple and because they bind to a protein called calmodulin to carry out their second messenger function.

The response of cells to signals involves either turning on or turning off the activity of proteins already present in the cell, or turning on or off the synthesis of new proteins through the control of gene expression. The rapid production of glucose in the liver is an example involving an enzyme that exists in an inactive form in the cell, which is rapidly activated by the signal transduction pathway stimulated by the epinephrine signal. The epinephrine kinase pathway, however, also activates in the nucleus a transcription factor that controls the expression of the glycogen phosphorylase gene. Once activated, this transcription factor contributes to longer-lasting response by facilitating the synthesis of more enzyme molecules.

Signals affect the activity of only certain cells; further, different kinds of cells responding to the same signal can have completely different responses. Whether or not a cell responds to a signal depends entirely on whether it expresses the protein that serves as the receptor for that signal. The same receptor found in different types of cells may activate different kinds of signal transduction pathways with different functional endpoints. The diversity of proteins found in different kinds of cells explains the diversity of cell responses to signals; at the same time, the fact that different cells may share some common types of proteins accounts for diverse responses to a common signal, such as epinephrine. ■

Suggested Reading

Alberts et al., *Essential Cell Biology* (2nd ed.), chapter 15.

Campbell & Reece, *Biology* (6th ed.), chapter 11.

Purves et al., *Life* (7th ed.), chapter 15.

Questions to Consider

1. The "fight-or-flight" response involves one molecular signal affecting many different kinds of cells in the body. Can you think of a different kind of response that might involve a molecular signal affecting only one or a small number of cell types?

2. Many signal transduction pathways activate transcription factors as well as enzymes. What role would this play in regulating the activity of a cell?

From One Cell to Many in an Organism
Lecture 32

The question we're going to begin to address today is: "How do you get from a single-celled zygote to a complete organism?" This is a very simple question to ask; but, as it turns out, it is a very difficult one to answer.

This lecture describes the two basic puzzles of development, then outlines the earliest attempts to solve these puzzles. It then provides an overview of the factors that influence development, the process by which development occurs, and the early developmental outcome common to all organisms. Sexual reproduction involves the production of haploid gametes, which come together to form a diploid zygote—a single cell that will develop into a full organism.

The question of how a zygote develops into a complete organism has been at the center of biology since before Darwin's time. It is not surprising that this question should be so central, given the magnitude of the problem. A vertebrate animal, such as a human, may be composed of up to 10^{14}—one hundred trillion—cells! These cells may be specialized into hundreds of distinctly different cell types, each with one or more unique functional roles to play in the organism. Furthermore, these many kinds of specialized cells must occur in the right proportions and must be found in the right positions in the organism.

The process of development raises two broad questions, or puzzles. The first question is one of diversity. All organisms start from a single cell, and by and large, those cells all look pretty much the same. Yet zygotes from different species develop into organisms as diverse as oak trees and earthworms or sea urchins and giraffes. In addition, each of these organisms has many different kinds of cells, each performing different functions and each occurring in different proportions and positions in the organism. How do both the diversity we observe between species and the diversity we observe within a single species arise from a single, relatively uniform cell?

The second question is one of consistency. In spite of the potentially enormous complexity of a completely developed organism and in spite of the intricate developmental processes involved, things go wrong relatively rarely in development. For example, every giraffe zygote develops into a slightly different giraffe, but giraffes as a whole are remarkably alike. How is this consistency in development maintained?

The answers to both questions must be found in the same set of developmental mechanisms. The most fundamental question, then, is what dictates the way a single cell turns into many different kinds of cells. The Greek philosopher Aristotle originally proposed that organisms must develop from a single uniform cell. This view is referred to as *epigenesis*.

All organisms start from a single cell, and by and large, those cells all look pretty much the same. Yet zygotes from different species develop into organisms as diverse as oak trees and earthworms or sea urchins and giraffes.

The alternative view—also ancient—was that an egg cell included an entire organism in miniature. This is known as *preformation*. Preformation became the dominant view among scientists by the 18th century, largely because it required no special mechanisms or mysterious "force" to create the parts of an organism. Preformation had its difficulties, most notably the problem of how an entire miniature organism could fit into something the size of a single cell. This was not originally seen as much of a problem, because modern cell theory did not mature until the second half of the 19th century.

s microscopes improved in the 18th and 19th centuries, however, biologists, including Caspar Friedrich Wolff, began to describe the development of organisms in detail, and it became apparent that fertilized eggs did not contain entire organisms. Preformationists could always claim that these kinds of observations were simply not adequate because of the limitations of the microscopes. Nonetheless, the weight of evidence from early embryologists eventually held sway, and by the late 19th century, the idea of epigenesis became universally accepted.

The acceptance of epigenesis, however, raised the fundamental question of how a single cell is able to give rise to many different kinds of cells. Early embryologists could only propose that there must be some unknown force of nature (the "essential force") that would control development. As biologists in the late 19th and early 20th centuries began to understand how the cell worked, especially the process of mitosis and genetic mechanisms, the idea of an essential force was quickly replaced by more specific theories of developmental mechanisms.

Several sets of factors influence development. The earliest embryologists did not know about genes or genetics, but we know today that the zygotes of different species have different genomes; thus, it seems reasonable that genomic differences must underlie both diversity and consistency in development.

The emergence of the structure of an organism clearly depends on genetic information, but genes alone cannot fully account for all aspects of development. One obvious reason this is true is that development in multicellular organisms does not simply produce a large group of identical cells. A zygote has a given set of genes that is accurately copied and transmitted to its daughter cells. If genes were solely responsible for development, every daughter cell would be the same because we expect them to have the same genes. We know that different cells can express different genes, but what ultimately is responsible for determining which genes are expressed?

Clearly, something external to the genome must be responsible for differences that arise among cells in the development of a multicellular organism. Factors external to genes that affect gene expression may be collectively referred to as the *environment*. Gene expression may be modulated by environmental factors that are completely external to the developing organism, such as temperature and nutrition. These factors can affect development to the extent of producing completely different forms under different conditions, as in the case of the moth *Nemoria arizonaria*.

Although the external environment clearly influences the development of organisms, two other sets of factors control the orderly progress of development. Though outside the organism's genes, these environmental factors are internal to the organism. The first crucial environmental factor is the cellular contents of the fertilized egg. These stored factors are called *cytoplasmic determinants*, or *maternal determinants* because they necessarily come from the mother. The second crucial environmental factor is interactions among cells. Cell-to-cell interactions become increasingly important as cells become more specialized and assume their proper positions and proportions. The end result is that the development of a complex organism is due not just to the organism's genetic blueprint, but also to the way the environment— defined on several levels—influences the expression of that blueprint.

Development depends on three main processes. The first process is *cell division*—clearly, for a single cell to produce the many cells that make up an organism, it must divide properly and in the proper amounts. The second process is *differentiation*, in which cells become specialized, developing specific structures and functions. Differences in gene expression play an essential role in differentiation.

The third main process of development is called *morphogenesis*, which literally means "creation of form." Morphogenesis refers to a set of mechanisms that change the shape and organization of an organism's structure. One morphogenetic mechanism involves cells changing their shape. Changes in cell shape cause tissue layers to bend and fold, creating more complex shapes out of simpler ones. A second morphogenetic mechanism is cell movement. Cells move by reaching out cellular protrusions that then drag the rest of the cell along. Molecules on the surfaces of cells, such as glycoproteins, help cells adhere selectively to other cells during movement. A third morphogenetic mechanism involves cells that are pre-programmed to die (a process called *apoptosis*). Programmed cell death is important, for example, in creating the spaces between our fingers and toes.

The specific details of development vary greatly from species to species; however, the earliest events in development always create asymmetries that establish the basic body plan of the organism. In plants, the fundamental asymmetry is along the vertical root-shoot axis; in animals, the most fundamental asymmetry is along the head-to-tail (anterior-posterior) axis. ■

Suggested Reading

Campbell & Reece, *Biology* (6th ed.), chapters 21 & 47.

Freeman, *Biological Science*, chapter 18.

Gilbert, *Developmental Biology* (7th ed.).

Purves et al., *Life* (7th ed.), chapters 19, 20, & 21.

Questions to Consider

1. Russian nesting dolls might be used as an analogy for one of the assumptions of the preformation hypothesis of development. Can you explain what this assumption is and why this analogy is apt?

2. We often hear news reports of scientists having discovered "the gene" for some trait. How are such reports misleading?

Patterns of Early Development
Lecture 33

Of course, there are considerable differences among different kinds of animals, and the details of how development proceeds. But at the same time—and fortunately for our discussion—the very earliest stages of development share much in common across all sorts of animals—from sea urchins to fruit flies, and from frogs to humans.

This lecture examines the four earliest stages of development—fertilization, cleavage, gastrulation, and organogenesis—and outlines the processes involved in each. After fertilization, each stage involves a set of simple processes repeated over and over to produce the great diversity of cell types and structures found in a complex multicellular organism, and ultimately the diversity we observe across different kinds of organisms. The specific processes and patterns of development differ greatly among different groups of animals, but all animals share much in common in the early stages of development.

The first step in the development of a sexually reproducing organism is *fertilization*—the creation of a zygote from the fusion of a female gamete and a male gamete. Fertilization is more complex than the random joining of gametes; the ability of a sperm to penetrate an egg depends on an intricate set of cell-signaling mechanisms. Fertilization initiates a series of events that cause the zygote to become inherently asymmetric—that is, to have an asymmetric distribution of protein and messenger RNA (mRNA) in the cytoplasm. In some organisms, this asymmetry is visually apparent because it is associated with an equally asymmetric distribution of yolk that can be observed under a microscope or, sometimes, with the naked eye.

To classical embryologists, the yolk-containing end of a zygote is known as the *vegetal pole*, while the end with less yolk is known as the *animal pole*. This distinction leads to a useful picture of a zygote as a globe with north and south poles. Though the zygotes of many animals do not contain visible yolk, they do have an asymmetric distribution of protein and mRNA. This asymmetry is one of the sources of information that may cause the zygote's daughter cells to diversify.

After fertilization, the zygote undergoes a rapid series of cell divisions called *cleavage*. Cleavage is simply a form of mitosis; the resulting daughter cells are called *blastomeres*. The cell divisions that occur during cleavage follow a very orderly pattern with respect to cell orientation. As in normal mitosis, a dividing cell separates along the plane formed by the chromosomes during metaphase (the *metaphase plate*). If a zygote is pictured as a globe and the first division of cleavage divides it along a longitudinal axis, the two blastomeres will have the same north-south orientation as the zygote. However, blastomeres also may divide along the "equator" of their globes (along an equatorial axis), producing daughter cells with a different orientation.

If a zygote is pictured as a globe and the first division of cleavage divides it along a longitudinal axis, the two blastomeres will have the same north-south orientation as the zygote.

The details of which cells divide along which axis are unimportant, and different groups of animals follow different patterns. The important point is that the first series of cell divisions during cleavage does follow a specific pattern of orientations. This specific pattern of cell orientations is important during cleavage because, depending on their orientations, blastomeres may or may not preserve the asymmetry of the parent cell. The regular pattern of orientations in the first several divisions of cleavage establishes another level of asymmetry in the developing organism, with some blastomeres having the same relative arrangement of proteins and mRNAs (cytoplasmic determinants) as their parents and other blastomeres becoming distinctly different.

Another characteristic of cleavage is that there is no net increase in the volume of cytoplasm between cell divisions. The cells, therefore, become progressively smaller with each division, and there is little or no increase in the size of the embryo. Because there is no growth, cell division also occurs at a very rapid rate. One final feature of cleavage is that, in general, the genes of the developing organism are not expressed. DNA is replicated but not transcribed, which suggests that cleavage must be controlled by the proteins and mRNAs—the cytoplasmic determinants—found in the zygote.

After some number of cleavages has occurred, the developing organism turns into a solid ball of small cells called a *morula*. A fluid-filled cavity then develops inside the ball of cells, forming a hollow ball of cells called a *blastula*. The inner space of this hollow ball is called the *blastocoel*, and the sheet of cells that surrounds it is called the *blastoderm*.

The next key stage in early development is called *gastrulation*, during which the cells of the developing organism fold into more complex shapes and begin to assume different developmental fates. Gastrulation varies even more among groups of animals than fertilization or cleavage, but gastrulation in all animals shares a common set of mechanisms.

During gastrulation, morphogenesis becomes particularly important. Gastrulation involves three major morphogenetic phases. First, some cells move from the surface of the blastula to its interior. Second, as a consequence of this migration, three distinct layers of different kinds of cells are formed in the embryo. Third, by the end of gastrulation, the blastula has become an embryo, with an internal digestive cavity that is connected to the outside and that defines the anterior-posterior axis of the animal.

The sea urchin provides a convenient model for describing gastrulation. Gastrulation in sea urchins begins at the vegetal pole, where the cells flatten and form the vegetal plate. A number of cells from the vegetal plate (called *mesenchyme cells*) detach from the blastoderm and enter the blastocoel as loose cells. The cells in the vegetal plate change shape and begin to buckle inward. The inward-extending sheet of vegetal plate cells forms a deep pouch inside the blastocoel called the *archenteron*, which is connected to the outside by a hole (the *blastopore*). The closed end of the archenteron eventually extends all the way to the outer wall of cells on the other side and forms a second opening, creating a tube that will become the sea urchin's gut.

The final product of gastrulation is an embryo with a primitive gut and three distinctive cell layers. The *ectoderm* is the outermost layer; it is derived

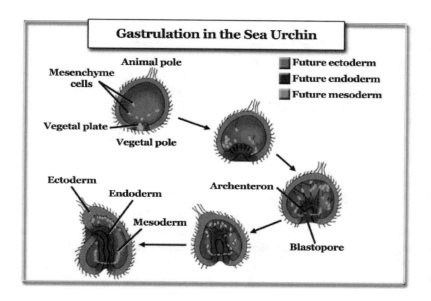

Gastrulation in the Sea Urchin

Animal pole
Mesenchyme cells
Vegetal plate
Vegetal pole

Future ectoderm
Future endoderm
Future mesoderm

Ectoderm
Endoderm
Mesoderm

Archenteron

Blastopore

from those cells of the original blastoderm that remained on its outside through the entire process. The innermost layer is the *endoderm*; it is the layer formed when cells at the vegetal plate extended to the inside of the blastoderm as the archenteron formed. Finally, there is a third layer of cells, called the *mesoderm*, located between the ectoderm and endoderm. The cells of the mesoderm are derived from mesenchyme cells that detached from the original hollow ball and migrated into the blastocoel.

These three layers (also called the *embryonic germ layers*) give rise to distinctly different kinds of tissues in the adult animal. In vertebrates, the ectoderm obviously gives rise to the outer layer of the skin (or epidermis) and derivatives of the epidermis, such as hair and nails. It also gives rise to much of the nervous system, the lining on the inside of the mouth and the cornea and lens of the eyes, and many glands found in the skin. The mesoderm gives rise to the skeletal system, muscles, circulatory system, gonads, and some internal organs, such as the kidneys and the heart. The endoderm gives rise to the inner linings of the digestive and respiratory systems, as well as other internal organs, such as the liver and pancreas.

The formation of rudimentary limbs, appendages, and organs that follows gastrulation is referred to, in general, as *organogenesis*. The specific events that occur during organogenesis differ radically from animal group to animal group, giving rise to the enormous diversity in body structure among different kinds of animals. In spite of this diversity, all these morphogenetic movements, to a large extent, simply represent the folding and bending of the three embryonic tissue layers established during gastrulation. The establishment of internal structures, such as organs, and external structures, such as limbs, involves a series of *invaginations* ("in-pocketings") and *evaginations* ("out-pocketings") of the different germ layers.

To picture the developments of organogenesis, imagine slicing an embryo from "north" to "south"—this would be equivalent to slicing crosswise through a hollow tube that has three concentric layers running along its length. In organogenesis, different layers at different points along the length of this tube are bent and folded inward to form invaginations or outward to form evaginations. For example, in vertebrate animals, one of the earliest structures to form is an additional tube running along most of the length of the embryo that will eventually become the spinal cord and brain. This tube is called the *neural tube*, and it is formed as an invagination of the ectoderm. The important point is that the essentially simple process of morphogenetic movement is repeated over and over again, with different variations and in different places, to create the rudiments of all the organs and appendages of a complex animal body. ■

Suggested Reading

Campbell & Reece, *Biology* (6th ed.), chapter 47.

Freeman, *Biological Science*, chapter 19.

Gilbert, *Developmental Biology* (7th ed.).

Purves et al., *Life* (7th ed.), chapter 20.

1. In some snails, whether the shell coils to the left or right is known to depend on a single gene. Can you explain how it is possible for individuals that are homozygous for the right-coiling allele of this gene to have a left-coiling shell and vice versa, as is commonly observed?

2. Why is it essential for animal development that animal cells are flexible?

Determination and Differentiation
Lecture 34

A fertilized egg, or a zygote, is said to be *totipotent*. This term simply means that it has the full potential to give rise to the entire organism, including all of the different cell types and structures. But the potential of individual cells to specify an entire organism generally diminishes as development proceeds. That is, totipotency is lost.

This lecture examines how developmental processes not only create many cells but also cause those cells to differentiate into many different types of cells. A zygote can give rise to any type of cell, but its daughter cells eventually cannot. Several theories have been advanced to explain why, how, and when the fate of a cell becomes more restricted, with that cell only able to develop into a specific type. Experiments designed to test these theories eventually led to the recent development of cloning and point to the great promise of stem cell research. The lecture concludes by outlining the two gene regulation mechanisms that control differentiation and discussing the first, *cytoplasmic segregation*.

As development proceeds, however, the potential of individual cells to specify an entire organism generally diminishes. In some organisms, snails for example, the two blastomeres that result from the very first cleavage division already have lost the potential to develop into the whole organism on their own.

In other organisms, the blastomeres resulting from the first few cleavages can be separated, and each will then develop into an entire normal organism. In mammals, for instance, each of the cells in the eight-cell stage (after three cleavage divisions) can develop independently into a complete adult. At some point in the development of all organisms, however, the potency of the blastomeres arising from cleavage begins to be reduced. After some number of cell divisions, individual blastomeres can no longer develop into complete adults. As a cell's potency is reduced, its fate becomes more restricted. This restriction of cell potential is called *determination*. In developmental biology, determination means commitment—cells become committed to specialize in a particular way.

A cell may be determined long before it shows any specialization in its biochemical, physiological, or morphological properties. Determination is not a sudden occurrence in the life of a cell, however; it is a stepwise process. Even after blastomeres have lost their potential to develop into a whole organism, they may still be able to develop into several different kinds of cells. Although their potential has become restricted, the fate of these blastomeres is not entirely determined. At some later stage, however, the progeny of these cells will have an even more restricted set of possible outcomes. Determination represents a progressive restriction of a cell's developmental potential. When a cell finally achieves its developmental endpoint, it is said to have *differentiated*. Most of the cells in an adult organism are highly differentiated, with distinct physical, biochemical, and physiological properties that enable them to perform specific functions.

Several theories have attempted to explain cell determination and differentiation. We know today that all cells in an organism have the same genetic material and that determination and differentiation must have something to do with how those genes are turned on and off. Before biologists knew about genetic mechanisms, however, it seemed equally possible that determination and differentiation happened as a result of cells receiving a progressively limited set of genes over the course of development. August Weismann, in his germ plasm theory, assumed that there must be some sort of "determinants" that were passed on as cells divided. Weismann suggested that a fertilized egg contained all the determinants needed to direct the development of an entire organism. He called this complete set of instructions the *germ plasm*. Weismann proposed that as cells divide during cleavage, they receive different subsets of the germ plasm.

> **A cell may be determined long before it shows any specialization in its biochemical, physiological, or morphological properties. Determination is not a sudden occurrence in the life of a cell, however; it is a stepwise process.**

However, this theory presented a difficulty: If the cells of an adult organism were created by dividing up the entire germ plasm, how could that adult reproduce itself? Weismann suggested that, at the very beginning of development, a small group of *germ line cells*, each with an entire copy of the germ plasm, is set aside for reproduction.

A few years after Weismann published his theory in 1883, Wilhelm Roux fertilized frog eggs in the lab and allowed them to go through the first division of cleavage. He then killed one of the resulting two blastomeres. Roux observed that the remaining cell was unable to develop into a complete frog, which seemed to support Weismann's germ plasm theory. There was a problem with this experiment, however; although Roux killed one cell, the dead cell stayed in contact with the living cell. We know now that proteins on cell surfaces act as signals during development, so the presence of the dead cell may have affected the development of the remaining living cell.

In the early 1890s, Hans Driesch performed a similar experiment but physically separated the two cells. When separated, the two blastomeres would each develop into complete adults. Many biologists in the 1890s and early 1900s performed similar experiments, with the general result that blastomeres often retained totipotency for at least the first few divisions of cleavage. Though these experiments ruled out the germ plasm theory in the strictest sense, they did show that blastomeres eventually lost totipotency.

Only in the 1950s did it start to become possible to test whether differentiated cells all retain the same genetic material, by transplanting the nucleus of a differentiated cell into an egg cell. However, the crudity of the technique at first made it difficult to find a definitive answer.

In 1997, Ian Wilmut and colleagues successfully transplanted a nucleus from a six-year-old female sheep into an enucleated egg taken from another female. The egg with the transplanted nucleus was then implanted into the uterus of a third female. The result was the birth of the world's most famous lamb, Dolly. Dolly grew up normally and was even able to produce offspring of her own, demonstrating conclusively that the nuclei of even the most differentiated cells in an adult organism retain an entire set of genetic material and finally putting the germ plasm theory to rest.

Of course, the reason many people have heard of Dolly is because she was the first example of a mammal being cloned, through the process of nuclear transplantation. Clones are, by definition, genetically identical individuals. Since Dolly was cloned in 1997, many other mammals, such as mice, cats, cows, and other farm animals, have been cloned successfully. In theory, there is no reason why humans could not eventually be added to this list.

Determination and the developmental potential of cells also lead into another much-discussed topic—stem cell research. A stem cell is any cell that remains relatively undifferentiated in an organism. Though most cells in an adult organism are highly differentiated, some tissues need frequent replacement or repair and retain cells that can still divide and differentiate into different cell types. One reason stem cell research is so interesting is its potential application to medicine. The long-term goal of this research is to use stem cells to replace damaged cells in such systems as the brain, where cells are not normally replaced.

Though adult stem cells are relatively undifferentiated, they generally retain the ability to differentiate into only a few types of cells. The stem cells that have the most potential to differentiate are found, instead, in very young embryos. Embryonic stem cells can be very close to retaining totipotency. The difficulty is that embryonic stem cells must be derived from human embryos, specifically from surplus embryos donated by infertile couples. This potential use of human embryos involves serious ethical and political considerations that are still under debate.

Because the genomes of differentiated cells remain the same, differences between cell types must be the result of gene regulation mechanisms. We have seen that the presence or absence of transcription factors is ultimately what controls gene expression; therefore, we must ask what causes differences in the distribution of transcription factors in different cells in the developing organism.

The distribution of transcription factors in a cell's cytoplasm is called the cytoplasmic environment. Two main mechanisms affect the cytoplasmic environment during development. The first of these mechanisms is called *cytoplasmic segregation*. Because of the asymmetry of the zygote, maternal

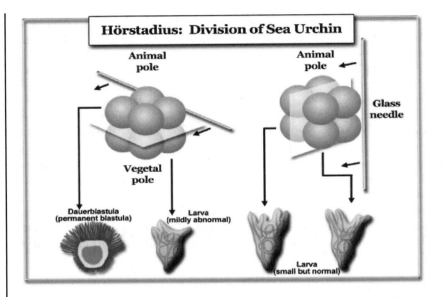

Hörstadius: Division of Sea Urchin

Animal pole

Animal pole

Glass needle

Vegetal pole

Dauerblastula (permanent blastula)

Larva (mildly abnormal)

Larva (small but normal)

determinants may be divided differently among blastomeres during early cleavage, depending on the orientation of cell divisions. These determinants are largely responsible for controlling the earliest phases of development, and cells with different complements of determinants will follow different developmental trajectories. The second mechanism is called *induction*, which refers to the influence of neighboring cells on the development of an embryonic cell. Induction becomes especially important in later stages of development, as the structure of the developing organism becomes increasingly complex.

In many organisms, cytoplasmic determinants, not the expression of the organism's own genome, play the largest role in the very earliest stages of development. The mRNAs and proteins already stored in the egg by the mother are responsible for controlling cleavage and the formation of the blastula. Blocking transcription factors in a developing organism will generally make no difference until the gastrulation phase. The asymmetric segregation of maternal determinants during cleavage is responsible for determining the fundamental organization of the developing embryo. Classic experiments done on sea urchins in the late 1920s by the Swedish biologist

Sven Hörstadius illustrate this point. Sea urchin blastomeres (or even zygotes) divided along the longitudinal axis will develop normally; those divided along the equatorial axis will develop into misshapen larvae or not develop at all. This is because a longitudinal division preserves the original distribution of cytoplasmic determinants, whereas an equatorial division does not. ■

Suggested Reading

Campbell & Reece, *Biology* (6th ed.), chapters 21 & 47.

Editors of *Scientific American, Understanding Cloning.*

Freeman, *Biological Science*, chapter 18.

Gilbert, *Developmental Biology* (7th ed.).

Purves et al., *Life* (7th ed.), chapters 19 & 20.

Questions to Consider

1. Weismann's germ plasm theory proved to be wrong, but could it have been right? What reasons can you think of for why cells should not simply divide up genes for different functions as development progressed?

2. What, in your view, are the drawbacks of stem cell research?

Induction and Pattern Formation
Lecture 35

Today we are going to turn to the process of induction, in which the developmental fate of cells is determined by signals that they receive from the cells around them. Our discussion of induction will then lead us to begin to consider how the complex morphology of an organism emerges in development through a process called *pattern formation*.

Cytoplasmic segregation is the main mechanism underlying differentiation in early development, but the mechanism of induction becomes increasingly important in later stages. In later phases of development, the fate of a cell depends more on its position in the embryo than on the nature of that cell's own cytoplasm, because signals received from other cells become a dominant influence on gene expression. The importance of induction in development was discovered long before mechanisms of cell signaling and gene expression were understood. In the early 20th century, Hans Spemann developed a technique for transplanting tissues from one embryo into another and performed a series of transplants on newts.

Because Spemann was interested in progressive determination, he transplanted tissues from embryos of different ages to see how this altered the fates of these tissues. For example, tissue that would normally become neural ectoderm would be transplanted to a region of a different embryo that would become epidermis. Spemann discovered that, if the transplant was done early enough, the transplanted piece of tissue would develop according to where it was transplanted instead of where it came from. For example, the transplanted neural ectoderm tissue became normal epidermal tissue.

However, Spemann found this result only if the transplant was done relatively early. If transplanted at a later time, tissue would not be determined by its locale but by its region of origin. Neural ectoderm tissue transplanted late enough would still become neural ectoderm tissue. Spemann's work not only illustrated progressive determination, but it also showed the importance of location on determination, which is presumably caused by signals received from neighboring cells.

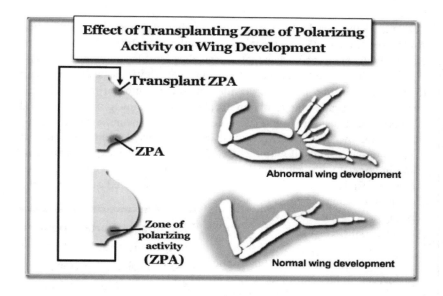

Effect of Transplanting Zone of Polarizing Activity on Wing Development

Transplant ZPA

ZPA

Abnormal wing development

Zone of polarizing activity (ZPA)

Normal wing development

Spemann's most important experiment was done in 1924, in collaboration with his young student Hilde Mangold. They were interested in a region of the newt blastopore that appeared to become determined very early, and they predicted that this tissue would not change its fate even when transplanted very early in development. Mangold found, as predicted, that the transplanted tissue did not change its developmental fate; more surprisingly, she also observed that at the point where the transplanted tissue was attached, a new, second embryo arose. This second embryo was composed of cells derived from both the transplanted tissue and the original host. The transplanted cells had somehow altered the developmental fate of the cells around them.

In addition to dramatically illustrating how cells in one tissue can affect the developmental fate of the cells around them, this result indicated that particular regions in a developing embryo play a disproportionately important role in organizing the development of tissues around them. Spemann referred to these regions as *organizers*. Not all induction involves highly localized organizers, but since their discovery, many other organizers have been identified.

The lens of the vertebrate eye provides another example of how induction contributes to the development of a complex structure. The lens is an extremely differentiated tissue that is specialized to transmit and focus light. It develops from ectodermal tissue—the same germ layer tissue that gives rise to skin and hair. In a frog embryo, for example, a region of the developing nervous system called the forebrain develops from an invagination of neural ectoderm tissue near the head-end of the animal. This neural ectoderm tissue bulges out at the sides to form optic vesicles, which will eventually form the nervous tissue associated with the eye. The optic vesicles expand until they come in contact with ectodermal cells on the outside of the embryo. When the optic vesicles come in contact with the undifferentiated outer ectoderm, the region of contact begins to thicken, forming a lens placode, which is the precursor to the lens itself.

It is possible to demonstrate that optic vesicle tissue induces the outer ectoderm to form the lens placode and, ultimately, the lens by removing the vesicle or inserting a sliver of plastic between it and the ectoderm. In both cases, the lens fails to develop. This result also indicates that some molecular signal must pass from the optic vesicle to the ectoderm. Another feature of induction illustrated by lens development is that induction is often reciprocal. Once the lens has formed, it induces the optic vesicle to further differentiate into the optic cup, one part of which develops into the retina. The lens also induces other ectodermal cells on the outside of the embryo to become the cornea of the eye.

The most important point to be made is that induction often involves sequences of reciprocal interactions among different tissues in the developing organism.

The most important point to be made is that induction often involves sequences of reciprocal interactions among different tissues in the developing organism. For example, the specific placement of the lens depends on the precise position of the optic vesicle; thus, it makes sense that the optic vesicle should induce lens formation.

The determination and differentiation of cells into functionally different cell types is only one part of what is needed to build the complex structure of a multicellular organism. The front and rear legs of a cat are made of the same kinds of cells and tissues but are very different in shape and, of course, work in different ways. The difference between these two kinds of limbs is a consequence of their tissues' arrangement in space, not the different kinds of tissues they contain. The development of the spatial organization of the parts of an animal is called *pattern formation*.

Pattern formation involves induction, but all the examples we have seen involved direct contact between the interacting tissues. In some cases, however, signals spread more widely through the developing organism; because these signals may diffuse across wide stretches of tissue, they create signal gradients within those tissues. These gradients of molecular signals can then provide developing cells with information about their relative position in the embryo; these cues are also called *positional signals*.

The development of a chicken wing provides a useful example illustrating the functioning of positional signals. Vertebrate limbs begin as undifferentiated limb buds, small expanses of tissue protruding from the main axis of the trunk of the developing embryo. Each bone, muscle, and other component of a limb will arise, in a precise three-dimensional arrangement, from this lump of ectodermal and mesodermal tissue.

Embryonic tissues in a wing bud somehow receive information indicating what part of the limb they should turn into, depending on where they are located in that limb. One model suggests that particular regions of the limb serve as organizers that provide information about relative position to developing cells by secreting diffusible molecular signals. The relative orientation of parts of a chicken wing is similar to that of a human hand in that both have important asymmetries along the proximal-distal (fingertips-to-wrist), anterior-posterior (thumb-to-little finger), and dorsal-ventral (palm-to-back of the hand) axes. In chickens, differentiation along the proximal-distal axis appears to be controlled at least in part by an organizer region located on the outermost tip of the developing wing bud. This region is called the *apical ectodermal ridge*, or AER.

The AER secretes several proteins that act as growth factors by inducing cell division. If the AER is surgically removed, the limb stops growing; if it is transplanted elsewhere, a new limb will be induced there. Even more significantly, if the AER is removed at different times, it does not simply produce smaller limbs; instead, the limbs will lack distal parts. This suggests that the AER produces a molecular signal that helps specify position along the proximal-distal axis. The AER does not appear to work alone but in conjunction with an area of tissue immediately beneath it called the *progress zone*. Reciprocal signaling between these regions is responsible for patterning along the proximal-distal axis. The exact mechanism by which the progress zone and AER specify the proximal-distal axis is still the subject of considerable research and debate.

A second major limb-bud organizer region, and a better-understood one, is the *zone of polarizing activity*, or ZPA. The ZPA is located near the base of the limb bud, on the posterior side. One model suggests that the ZPA produces a molecular signal that diffuses throughout the limb bud. This hypothesis was tested experimentally by transplanting the ZPA from one chick to an incorrect position on the developing wing of another chick and observing the results. A second ZPA added to the anterior margin of a wing bud produced two sets of digits, which were mirror images of each other along the anterior-posterior axis (like two human hands joined at the thumbs).

When a substance diffuses away from a fixed source, the concentration of that substance is higher closer to the source and diminishes steadily as you move away from the source. The concentration of ZPA-produced signals is particularly high on the posterior side of the limb bud and increasingly lower in the anterior direction; this concentration gradient "tells" cells where they are in the limb bud along the anterior-posterior axis. Cells near the transplanted ZPA received positional information indicating that they were on the posterior side and, thus, were induced to produce posterior structures. Though it is clear that signals produced by cells induce development, much is still unknown about how other cells receive these signals and how these signals influence gene regulation, even in a well-understood system, such as a chicken. ■

Suggested Reading

Campbell & Reece, *Biology* (6th ed.), chapter 47.

Freeman, *Biological Science*, chapter 19.

Gilbert, *Developmental Biology* (7th ed.).

Purves et al., *Life* (7th ed.), chapter 20.

Questions to Consider

1. The ability to introduce markers that uniquely label cells and their progeny has revolutionized experimental developmental biology. Based on Spemann's work, can you explain why?

2. Biologists suggest that a large evolutionary change in the morphology of structures such as limbs might occur as the result of a small change in the activity of an organizer during development. Can you explain how this might work?

Genes and Development
Lecture 36

What we are going to do in this last lecture on development is to look at pattern formation in an organism in which the genetic mechanisms underlying the development are fairly well understood. The organism we will look at is the fruit fly, *Drosophila*, an organism that we encountered earlier in our course when we talked about genetics.

Many aspects of *Drosophila* development are unique, but the general mechanisms are similar to those involved in the development of many animals, including vertebrates. The lecture begins with a discussion of how the segmented construction of insects illustrates the basic principles of pattern formation and then discusses the original experiments that identified the genes responsible for *Drosophila* pattern formation. The lecture then describes one set of *Drosophila* genes that act as master switches in pattern formation, as part of a regulatory cascade of interacting genes. The lecture concludes by discussing *homeotic genes*, which act as localized master switches triggering the development of specific structures, and that illustrate deep genetic similarities in developmental mechanisms among very different types of organisms.

The *Drosophila* fruit fly is an ideal study organism for several reasons, including its role as an example of pattern formation. Fruit flies, like all insects, are highly segmented—their bodies have an obviously modular construction. Segmentation is most obvious in the larval stage, which is a juvenile period, such as the caterpillar stage in the development of butterflies. The larval form of a fruit fly is a small grub, which has obvious rings marking the segments along its anterior-posterior (head-to-tail) axis. When the larva later develops into an adult, these segments specialize into different regions of the head, the thorax, and the abdomen. In this way, segmentation establishes the functional differences that develop along the anterior-posterior axis.

The early development of *Drosophila* differs from that of other organisms we have discussed. In *Drosophila*, cytokinesis—the final separation of daughter cells—does not occur during the first 10 or so rounds of initial nuclear replication. The result is one cell with many nuclei (a multinucleated cell). As these nuclei continue to divide, they line up along the walls of the cell, leaving no nuclei in the center. Suddenly—at about the 13th round of division—cell membranes partition all the nuclei into very small individual cells. The result is a hollow oval of small cells that is approximately the same size as the original zygote. This hollow ball of cells is called a blastula, just as in sea urchins and frogs. As the *Drosophila* blastula undergoes gastrulation and the embryo develops, body segments begin to appear, with obvious differences between the head and the tail ends. These segments at first look similar, but even adjacent segments will develop in different ways.

This description of *Drosophila* development raises two questions concerning pattern formation. First, how does a segmented structure arise from an unsegmented one? Second, how do segments at different points along the anterior-posterior axis develop into the different structures appropriate for their positions?

The answer to both these questions involves the differential expression of genes. Many different genes control segmentation and the emergence of the anterior-posterior axis in a *Drosophila* embryo. The majority of these genes are regulatory genes—their products are transcription factors that turn on and off the expression of other genes. These genes are expressed sequentially, which builds patterns from the original asymmetry of the maternal determinants in the *Drosophila* egg.

Experiments in the 1970s identified genes responsible for pattern formation in *Drosophila*. Two developmental geneticists, Christiane Nüsslein-Volhard and Eric Wieschaus, set out to identify genes involved in pattern formation in *Drosophila* by exposing them to mutagens and examining which mutations appeared to affect pattern formation. This project was ambitious and difficult, but Nüsslein-Volhard and Wieschaus were able to identify more than 1,000 genes that affect development, about 120 of which specifically affect pattern formation.

One of the first mutations the researchers described was of a gene they named *bicoid*, which means "two-tailed." Bicoid mutant larvae lack heads—

they are essentially two tails attached to each other at the middle. When Nüsslein-Volhard and Wieschaus performed genetic crosses with individuals carrying the mutant gene, they found that bicoid larvae display a pattern of inheritance called *maternal effect inheritance*. This means that the phenotype of the offspring depends entirely on the genotype of the mother, rather than on whether the larva inherits the mutant gene itself.

Maternal effect inheritance is caused by cytoplasmic determinants added to the egg by the mother. The protein produced by the bicoid gene is normally distributed asymmetrically along what will become the anterior-posterior axis of the larva. Because the cells that produce bicoid mRNA come into contact with only one end of the egg, there is a much higher concentration of the mRNA on that end than on the other end of the egg.

If bicoid mRNA is injected into the head end of an egg with the bicoid mutation, the embryo develops a normal head. Similarly, if bicoid mRNA is injected into the tail end of a normal egg, the egg develops into a two-headed larva.

The bicoid gene performs its role in pattern formation by coding for a transcription factor that influences the expression of other genes. The protein produced by the bicoid gene activates other genes that ultimately involve the development of head structures. The end of the embryo with a high concentration of bicoid protein becomes the head, and the end with a low concentration of bicoid becomes the tail. Bicoid, however, is not the only "switch" that turns on genes involved in making a *Drosophila* head. Instead, bicoid and other maternal determinants control a cascading sequence of other genes, which in turn, produce other transcription factors. A single factor such as the asymmetric distribution of the bicoid protein coordinates the activities of the many genes involved in constructing a head by activating a cascade of additional switches, each of which specifies and controls the expression of other genes.

In a developing *Drosophila* embryo, the initial gradient of bicoid establishes the basic segmentation pattern by regulating the activity of *segmentation genes*, which come in three classes: *gap genes*, *pair-rule genes*, and *segment polarity genes*. Bicoid and other maternal determinants regulate the activity of the gap genes, which organize large areas into basic subdivisions along the anterior-posterior axis, setting up a slightly more complex grid of signals along this axis. The gene products of the gap genes, in turn, regulate the expression of pair-rule genes, which divide the embryo into pairs of segments. Pair-rule gene products are also transcription factors that regulate the activity of segment polarity genes—which themselves produce transcription factors. This cascade of transcription factors produces an increasingly refined and complex pattern of gene expression.

The pair-rule gene called the *even-skipped gene*, or *eve* for short, illustrates this cascade. The *eve* gene's protein is normally expressed in seven discrete bands along the length of the embryo. The *eve* gene itself is preceded by a very complex regulatory region that contains seven different regulatory sequences. The regulatory sequences can be activated independently, and each is responsible for the production of one discrete band of the *eve* gene's protein product along the axis of the developing embryo. At the stage in development where pair-rule genes are beginning to be expressed, there is a very complex set of gradients of transcription factors along the axis of the embryo. At any place along the embryo where one of *eve*'s regulatory sequences finds the right combination of proteins, *eve* is turned on.

The second band of *eve* expression (*eve* stripe 2) corresponds to the regulatory region called the stripe 2 module. One simplified model suggests that this module includes binding sites for two regulatory proteins that activate transcription and binding sites for two regulatory proteins that repress it. The relative concentrations of these four proteins determine whether or not transcription occurs, and this combination of concentrations occurs only at one narrow region along the embryo's head-to-tail axis. In this way, a regulatory cascade produces gradients of several

The similarity of homeotic and *Hox* genes illustrates a deep commonality in the basic developmental genetic pathways of animals and suggests that a basic genetic "toolbox" evolved very early and has been used in similar ways to create the varied body plans of all organisms.

transcription factors that together regulate gene expression in a highly localized fashion.

The differentiation of relatively uniform segments into diverse parts depending on their location along the head-to-tail axis is mediated by the activity of another set of genes called *homeotic genes*. Once segmentation genes have established body segments, homeotic genes specify the types of appendages and other structures that each segment will form. Mutations in homeotic genes produce extremely bizarre morphological transformations, because they cause the development of structures in the wrong places on the animal, such as the development of a leg on a head segment that would ordinarily have produced an antenna.

Like segmentation genes, homeotic genes code for transcription factors that, in turn, regulate the expression of many other genes. Therefore, homeotic genes are best thought of as master switches that control the expression of many other genes in a localized way. The *Hox* genes in vertebrates are remarkably similar in function and location to the homeotic genes found in *Drosophila*—so close that a mutant fruit fly can receive the appropriate *Hox* gene from a chicken and develop properly. This is remarkable considering that insects and vertebrates have not had a common ancestor for hundreds of millions of years. The similarity of homeotic and *Hox* genes illustrates a deep commonality in the basic developmental genetic pathways of animals and suggests that a basic genetic "toolbox" evolved very early and has been used in similar ways to create the varied body plans of all organisms. ■

Suggested Reading

Campbell & Reece, *Biology* (6th ed.), chapter 21.

Freeman, *Biological Science*, chapter 20.

Gehring, *Master Control Genes in Development and Evolution: The Homeobox Story*.

Gerhart and Kirshner, *Cells, Embryos and Evolution: Toward a Cellular and Developmental Understanding of Phenotypic Variation and Evolutionary Adaptability*.

Gilbert, *Developmental Biology* (7th ed.).

Purves et al., *Life* (7th ed.), chapter 19.

1. Gene expression in development often involves a cascade of interacting transcription factors. How is this similar to and different from the way intracellular signal transduction pathways work in cell signaling?

2. How does the fact that very different kinds of organisms, such as chickens and flies, share genes that are remarkably similar, such as homeotic genes, change the way you might think about defining a "species"?

Homeostasis
Lecture 37

The advantage of having a more complex organization is obvious. Different cells and different tissues can specialize in an organism, such that each has its own particular job to do, and each can be optimized to do that particular job particularly well. But there is a potential downside to being complex. The more parts and the more kinds of parts an organism has, the harder it is to get them all to work together correctly.

This lecture begins by discussing the dependence of biochemical reactions and cellular processes in general on external conditions, and the effect of this dependence on organisms. Multicellular organisms often maintain a constant internal environment that buffers the majority of the cells and tissues in the organism against the shocks and changes of the external world, a process referred to as *homeostasis*. The lecture continues by examining mechanical and biological examples of homeostatic mechanisms and concludes by concentrating on one of the most important examples of homeostasis in animals—the regulation of body temperature.

All of the biochemical reactions necessary for cell function and life in general depend critically on the physical conditions in which they occur. Physical and chemical conditions, such as pH level, temperature, and salt concentration, affect the function of the enzymes that catalyze biochemical reactions. Temperature is especially critical, because biochemical reactions run at different rates depending on the temperature of their environment. Many reactions will stop completely if the temperature is too high, because enzymes lose shape at high temperatures and become dysfunctional.

Because these physical and chemical conditions are so important, cells would benefit by maintaining them within a narrow range of values to allow biochemical reactions and other cellular processes to work in an optimal fashion. In general, we expect natural selection to optimize cell function, but this is difficult if conditions affecting that function fluctuate widely. This argument can be extended to organisms in general—the many ways that organisms function depend on properly functioning tissues, organs, and so forth, which in turn, function best in a limited range of environmental conditions. However, organisms often live in environments where physical conditions are not optimal; furthermore, these conditions may constantly change.

Larger organisms have more ways to cope with changing and non-optimal conditions than smaller organisms. Relatively small or simple organisms often have a limited range of environments in which they can survive. For example, *Hydra* are small, simple invertebrates composed of only two cell layers. Because all cells are in contact with the environment, the physical conditions inside those cells are virtually identical to those outside. In more complex organisms, only a relatively small number of cells on exposed surfaces have direct contact with the environment. The majority of cells in a complex organism exist in an internal environment that provides a buffer against unfavorable external conditions, allowing the organism to occupy a broader range of environments. An internal environment can be an advantage only if it is adequately buffered against outside conditions. Much of the structure and function of complex, multicellular organisms is devoted to maintaining internal environments.

The maintenance of a constant internal environment by an organism is called *homeostasis*. Claude Bernard proposed the concept of homeostasis in 1865 in an influential book titled *An Introduction to the Study of Experimental Medicine*. Bernard argued that animals do not functionally live in their external environments but in an internal environment formed by the fluids that surround and bathe all tissues in the body. Bernard further suggested that the primary condition for freedom and independence of existence is the stability of the internal environment and that all vital mechanisms have only one object—keeping the internal environment constant. As Bernard suggested, maintaining homeostasis is a ubiquitous feature of the way organisms work. Common examples of homeostasis in

> **At low temperatures, the mouse's metabolic rate would vary inversely with temperature ... because the mouse would increase its metabolic rate to generate more heat.**

human physiology include maintaining constant body temperature, blood pressure, and blood sugar levels.

Homeostasis requires several mechanisms. First, an organism must be able to modify the parameter (pH, temperature, and so on) that will be under control. In addition, homeostasis requires a mechanism for obtaining information about that parameter to determine how much control to exert. Any mechanism that modifies some parameter of the internal environment is called an *effector*. Any mechanism that obtains information about the present state of a parameter is called a *receptor*. An organism must also have a *comparator* that compares the current value of the parameter to the desired value, calculates the difference between the two, and directs an effector to change the value of the parameter in the appropriate direction.

In addition to these mechanisms, two types of physiological information are necessary for homeostatic regulation. A *set point* is the desired value (or acceptable range of values) at which a regulated parameter is supposed to be maintained. *Feedback* refers to information from the receptor about the current state of the parameter under control.

Maintaining the temperature of a room is a useful non-biological example of homeostasis. A thermostat is a comparator that receives feedback from a thermometer (a temperature receptor) and compares it to a user-adjusted set point—the desired room temperature (for example, 68°F). The thermostat is also connected to an effector—the heating system for the room. When the temperature drops below 68°F, the thermostat detects the difference between the feedback and the set point and switches the heater on. When the room temperature increases to the set point, the thermostat switches the heater off. This example illustrates *negative feedback*, in which a change in the parameter triggers a response that counteracts the initial fluctuation. Homeostatic systems invariably involve negative feedback because it is stabilizing—it prevents small deviations from becoming larger.

In contrast, positive feedback occurs when an initial change leads the control system to cause an even greater change in the same direction. If a thermostat used positive feedback, a room temperature above 68°F would cause the heater to turn on and make the room even hotter. Positive feedback systems magnify an initially small perturbation, which makes them less useful in biological control systems (there are exceptions, however).

An important biological example of homeostasis is the control of body temperature in animals. Biological mechanisms that regulate temperature are called *thermoregulation mechanisms*. Organisms tend to perform thermoregulation in one of two general ways, which differ with the kinds of effectors available to modify body temperature. *Ectothermic* organisms change the temperature of their bodies mainly by absorbing heat from their surroundings. Most invertebrate animals, as well as such vertebrates as fishes, reptiles, and amphibians, are ectotherms. *Endothermic* organisms derive most or all of their body heat from the heat generated by their own metabolism (the cellular processes that break down sugars and other biomolecules to produce energy). Mammals and birds are notable endotherms, although some fish and even some insects are endothermic.

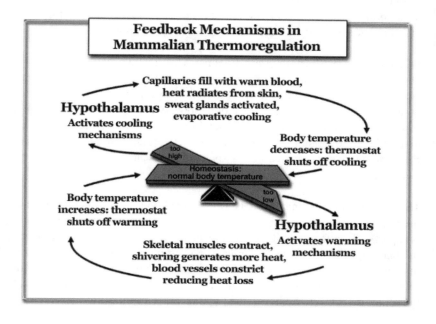

An ectothermic lizard and an endothermic mouse are about the same size. Placing both in separate sealed chambers and varying the ambient temperature in the chambers allows us to compare the two types of thermoregulation. As the chamber temperatures fluctuate from very cold to very hot, the mouse would maintain a constant high body temperature, while the lizard's body temperature would be about the same as the ambient temperature. The lizard's metabolic rate would increase proportionately with the ambient temperature, because it essentially reflects the rate of the biochemical reactions in its cells, which is tied to the ambient temperature.

At low temperatures, the mouse's metabolic rate would vary inversely with temperature—the lower the temperature, the higher the metabolic rate—because the mouse would increase its metabolic rate to generate more heat. At temperatures much higher than body temperature, the mouse's metabolic rate would rise again as it expended energy to lose excess heat. Lizards can control body temperature, however; in nature, the lizard would use a behavioral mechanism—moving into the sun when it was cold and moving into the shade when it was hot—to regulate its temperature.

Endothermic and ectothermic organisms use many other kinds of physiological mechanisms to modify body temperature. Many animals can control the amount of blood flowing to their skins, increasing (*vasodilation*) or decreasing (*vasoconstriction*) blood flow to increase or decrease heat loss potential. Animals lose water when breathing and, in some cases, from their skin; in low humidity, this water will evaporate and cool the animal. Evaporation can be increased by panting and, in some mammals, by sweating.

Thermoregulation in mammals is well understood. The effectors are the thermoregulation mechanisms we have just discussed. The comparator is a group of cells in the base of the brain in a structure called the *hypothalamus*. In many species, the hypothalamus is the primary temperature receptor; however, it also integrates information from other receptors, such as those found in the skin. If the temperature of the hypothalamus falls below its set point (about 98.6°F in humans), the hypothalamus triggers muscle shivering and vasoconstriction, which increase body temperature. If the temperature of the hypothalamus rises above its set point, it triggers vasodilation and sweating, both of which lower body temperature. ∎

Suggested Reading

Bernard, *An Introduction to the Study of Experimental Medicine.*

Campbell & Reece, *Biology* (6th ed.), chapters 40 & 44.

Purves et al., *Life* (7th ed.), chapter 41.

Schmidt-Nielsen, *How Animals Work.*

Questions to Consider

1. What are some other biological examples and non-biological examples of negative feedback and positive feedback?

2. Homeostasis buffers organisms from changing external environments, but even if all environments found on the planet were completely stable and unchanging, organisms would still require homeostatic control mechanisms to survive. Why?

Hormones in Animals
Lecture 38

Indeed, the ability to transmit physiological information from one tissue
or organ to another, sometimes over very long distances, is essential
for the very existence of complex multicellular organisms. How this
physiological signaling works raises an important set of questions
that we need to address if we are to appreciate fully how organisms
function.

In this lecture, we begin by examining the importance of cell-to-cell
communication in homeostasis and then discuss the two main systems
that transmit physiological information over longer distances within
the bodies of animals: the nervous system and the endocrine system. After
looking at the endocrine system in general, we discuss the types of hormones
(chemical messengers), their features, and their functions in an organism.
We conclude by noting that some hormonal mechanisms have remained
unchanged over a long period of evolutionary time and now occur in the
same form in a wide range of different organisms, even though they have
acquired different physiological functions.

Homeostasis depends on the ability of different biological components in an
organism—cells, tissues, or organs—to communicate with each other. For
homeostasis to work, receptors need to send information to a comparator and
the comparator needs to send information to effectors. Indeed, transmitting
physiological information from one tissue or organ to another, sometimes over
very long distances, is essential for the existence of complex multicellular
organisms. Although mechanisms for long-distance internal communication
have evolved in all multicellular organisms, they are most sophisticated in
animals. Because animals tend to be able to move, their external environment
can change rapidly, which means they especially need to be able to obtain,
process, and transmit information about the external environment in order to
respond in an adaptive fashion.

Two structurally and functionally overlapping systems of internal communication have evolved in animals. The *nervous system* is a high-speed, high-performance information transmission and processing system. Its cells are specialized to transmit electrical impulses over long distances and to send chemical signals between adjacent cells. The nervous system is most obviously involved in the immediate control of animal behavior.

The *endocrine system* is a slower information transmission system that involves cells and tissues that produce chemical signals called *hormones*, which are compounds specialized for long-range communication between tissues. The endocrine system also affects animal behavior, but it tends to have more global effects, and effects that are generally slower than those of the nervous system. Hormones also play a key role in the homeostatic regulation of many physiological factors and the control of developmental processes. Whereas nervous systems are solely found in animals, both plants and animals use hormones for internal communication.

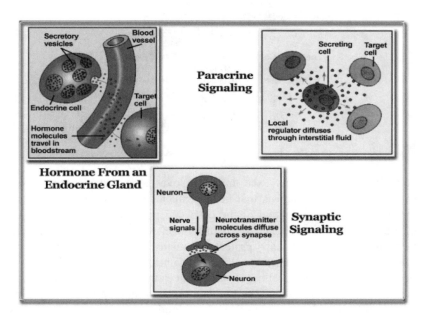

The endocrine system transmits chemical signals throughout the entire organism. Endocrine cells are usually assembled into organs called *endocrine glands*, which typically include some mechanism for releasing the hormones they produce directly into the circulatory system (bloodstream) for efficient delivery to the rest of the organism. Because they are released into the bloodstream, hormones exert their action over long distances, reaching targets throughout the body.

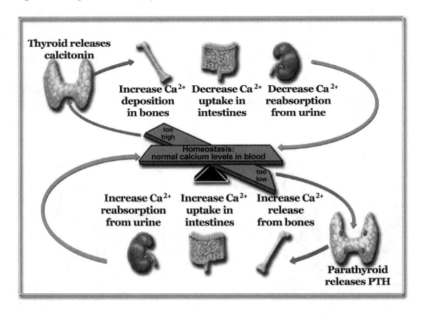

Not all chemical signals exert influence over long distances; paracrine signals are chemical signals that behave much like hormones but only in the immediate neighborhood of the cells that produce them. An example of a paracrine, or local regulator, is histamine, which causes inflammation (a tissue response that helps protect organisms from invasion by foreign materials or microorganisms). When a damaged tissue is inflamed, it becomes red, hot, and swollen. Histamine does this by causing small blood vessels (capillaries) in the tissue to dilate (expand) and become leaky. This allows protective blood proteins and white blood cells to leave the capillaries more easily and begin to repair the injured area.

Although local responses to histamine are protective, histamine responses sometimes can spread across the body, causing such problems as hay fever. A different kind of close-range chemical signaling is *synaptic signaling*, which involves the release of chemical signals called *neurotransmitters* from nerve cells. Although neural communication is long distance, synaptic signaling is specialized for close-range communication between pairs of cells that essentially touch each other. Although hormones, local regulators, and neurotransmitters are considered functionally separate classes of chemical signals, the lines separating them are not always distinct. For example, some chemicals function as hormones in one context and as neurotransmitters in a different context. In addition, these categories of chemical signals have many molecular mechanisms in common.

Although the number and diversity of hormones is enormous, they can be classified broadly into two major groups. Water-soluble hormones include peptides and other amino-acid derivatives; these are sometimes called *peptide hormones*. Lipid-soluble hormones are primarily types of steroids (a kind of lipid). The most notable steroids are the sex steroids, including androgens and estrogens, which are involved in the expression of secondary sex characteristics, the regulation of reproductive physiology, and the control of sexual behavior. Because water-soluble hormones are large electrically charged molecules, they cannot pass through cell membranes and must act by binding to receptors on the target cell's surface.

As discussed previously, one advantage of intracellular signal transduction is that a small signal can be greatly amplified. Hormones are generally released in small quantities that spread through the body, resulting in a very small concentration in target tissues. Signal transduction cascades amplify these weak signals significantly. In contrast to water-soluble hormones, steroids can pass through the cell membrane; therefore, steroid receptors are located in the cell's cytoplasm. Specific receptor molecules bind to the steroid once it enters the cell, forming a hormone-receptor complex that can then enter the nucleus and affect gene transcription.

The fact that hormones circulate to every cell in an organism brings into focus several features of their physiological action. First, although every cell in an organism may be exposed to the same hormones, only specific target cells will respond to a given hormone. This can be explained by the fact that only target cells have receptor proteins for a particular hormone, not because the hormones themselves specifically target particular cells.

Second, different kinds of cells can respond to the same hormone in different ways. Some hormones have highly specific functions and influence only a single kind of target cell, but other hormones have a variety of different effects on different kinds of target cells. When released into the bloodstream, epinephrine initiates a series of physiological responses—increasing heart rate, constricting blood vessels in the gut, and so forth—because different kinds of cells in different tissues have receptors for it, and the specific response of each cell depends on its type.

Whereas nervous systems are solely found in animals, both plants and animals use hormones for internal communication.

The third general feature is that many hormones function in antagonistic pairs; one hormone will have one effect on a system, while a different hormone will have the opposite effect. For example, calcitonin produces several effects that reduce the level of calcium in the blood, while parathyroid hormone increases calcium in the blood by producing exactly the opposite responses in the same tissues. Antagonistic control offers two advantages over a single hormone. The first advantage is speed—releasing an antagonistic hormone to stop or down-regulate the system is faster than waiting for the effects of a single hormone to disappear. The second advantage is precision—a system that depends on the ratio of one hormone to another can be precisely regulated even when the absolute concentrations of the hormones are very low, which is usually the case.

The fourth general feature is that different hormones may have the same effect on a particular kind of tissue. For example, epinephrine causes blood sugar levels to increase by increasing production of glucose; glucagon has exactly the same effect. The difference is that glucagon functions in long-term control of blood sugar levels, whereas epinephrine is involved in short-term emergency responses.

One quite remarkable feature of hormones is that virtually identical chemical signals are often found in widely divergent species. For example, a hormone called thyroxin is found in animals as different from one another as clams, frogs, and humans. Apparently, many fundamental chemical signals evolved very early in evolutionary history, then remained unchanged, in spite of the fact that the organisms using these compounds diverged and diversified. Even more interesting is the fact that, although the structures of these chemical signals have remained the same, their physiological functions have changed dramatically. Thyroxin seems to be associated with feeding in invertebrates; it helps control the transition from tadpole to adult in amphibians; and in mammals, it helps regulate cellular metabolism. It appears that because certain kinds of molecules are good at conveying information, their chemical structures do not change over evolutionary time; they simply acquire different physiological functions. ■

Suggested Reading

Campbell & Reece, *Biology* (6th ed.), chapter 45.

Purves et al., *Life* (7th ed.), chapter 42.

Schmidt-Nielsen, *Animal Physiology: Adaptation and Environment*, chapter 12.

Questions to Consider

1. One approach to treating a hormonal disorder could be to increase or decrease the amount of hormone in the bloodstream. Based on your knowledge of cell signaling mechanisms, can you think of a fundamentally different kind of approach that could be taken?

2. Antagonistic control is a common feature of hormonal regulation. Can you think of a non-biological example of antagonistic control?

What is Special about Neurons?

Lecture 39

The nervous system, which we will begin to discuss today, is a very different kind of signaling system, one that uses the transmission of electrical signals along what are essentially specialized cellular wires, to send information from one place to another specific place in the body.

This lecture begins our discussion of the nervous system by examining nerve cells—*neurons*—and the properties that enable them to transmit information over long distances at high speeds. We also look at the electrical properties of neurons and describe the ion concentration gradients and ion channels that create the neuron's *resting potential*. The lecture ends with a brief overview of how an *action potential* is triggered in a neuron.

One major functional difference between the endocrine system and the nervous system is the relative speeds with which they send information. Hormonal communication is relatively slow. Hormones, such as epinephrine, can act quite quickly, in a few seconds, but even that short time is much too slow for some information that has to be transmitted among the parts of a complex organism. For example, someone juggling three balls needs information to travel among muscle and eye receptors, the central nervous system (acting as a comparator), and muscle effectors much faster than is possible by hormones traveling through the bloodstream. The nervous system is responsible for such rapid transmission and processing of information in animals, and its specialized cells are called nerve cells, or *neurons*.

Neurons are similar to other cells in many ways, including many of their electrical properties, but they have three unique features. The first unique feature is that the voltage across a neuron membrane changes rapidly and in a controlled fashion. This change is called an *action potential*. The second unique feature is that this action potential can propagate over long distances. The third feature is that one neuron can influence the voltage of another neuron. The first and third of these features are the result of specializations of the neuron's cell membrane, specifically, membrane proteins that act as ion channels.

The second feature is largely a matter of the peculiar anatomy of nerve cells. The most obvious anatomical difference between neurons and other cells is that neurons have several long processes extending from the body of the cell. Often, one of these processes (the *axon*) is much longer than the others. Usually, a number of shorter processes, called *dendrites*, also extend from the cell body. The neuron described is generic; neurons come in many different shapes that relate to the way particular kinds of neurons receive and transmit information. Most neurons have an axon, however. At the most distal tip of the axon is a specialized region called the *synaptic terminal*, which typically connects with another neuron, either directly on the cell body or on the dendrites. This arrangement suggests that neurons transmit information from one to the other at this point of contact, which is the case. The specialization of neurons for long-distance transmission is largely a matter of cell structure; in contrast to the "broadcast" nature of hormones, neural information travels directly to the intended target along cellular "wires."

All living cells have an excess of negative electrical charge on the inside of the cell relative to the outside. As a result, there is an electrical potential difference—a *voltage difference*—across the membrane.

The electrical signals that neurons transmit are basically the result of differences in the concentrations of charged ions on either side of a cell membrane. All living cells have an excess of negative electrical charge on the inside of the cell relative to the outside. As a result, there is an electrical potential difference—a *voltage difference*—across the membrane. *Voltage* is a measure of potential energy available to move electrons or charged ions. A battery's voltage is an electric potential between its two terminals; if the positive and negative terminals are connected by a wire, electrons will flow from the negative to the positive terminal. This flow of electrons can be used to do work.

The voltage measured across the plasma membrane (in the range of about –60 mV for a typical neuron) is called the *membrane potential*. The membrane potential of a neuron at rest is called its *resting potential* and primarily results from two factors. The first factor is that the composition of charged ions differs between the extracellular fluid and the cytoplasm of the cell. The second factor is that different kinds of charged ions are able to cross the cell membrane to a greater or lesser extent.

Both the cytoplasm of the cell and the extracellular fluid that surrounds it contain various kinds of positively and negatively charged ions. Inside the cell, the principal *cation* (positive ion) is potassium (K^+), although there also is some sodium (Na^+). Outside the cell, these relative concentrations are reversed. The main *anions* (negative ions) inside the cell are various charged organic molecules, including proteins, amino acids, and phosphates. Outside the cell, chloride ions (Cl^-) are the major anions, although some chloride occurs inside the cell, as well. The key point is the relative concentration of charged ions, particularly K^+ and Na^+, inside and outside the cell. Normally, K^+ is high inside the cell and low outside; Na^+ is low inside the cell and high outside. Concentration differences alone do not account for the membrane potential, however; also important are the *permeabilities* of these ions—how freely ions can pass through the cell membrane.

Ions cannot pass directly through cell membranes but must pass through ion channels. Ions cannot pass directly though the cell membrane because they are electrically charged. Instead, they must travel through transmembrane proteins that act as channels. There are many kinds of ion channel proteins, but they can be categorized by a few defining properties. One property involves the kinds of ions that can pass through the channel. Many channels are highly selective (they allow only one kind of ion to pass).

Another defining property of ion channels concerns how ions move through them. Some ion channels are passive; ions cross them under the power of diffusion. In the absence of any other force, ions will diffuse from a region of high concentration to a region of lower concentration. This action is referred to as *moving down a concentration gradient*. For example, all other things being equal, K^+ would flow through passive K^+-selective channels from the inside of the cell to the outside. Passive membrane channels determine the extent to which an ion can diffuse through the cell membrane. For example, K^+ ions have much greater permeability than Na^+ across the membrane of a resting neuron; this largely reflects the fact that there are many more K^+ passive channels than Na^+ passive channels. Other types of ion channels are active; they actively pump ions against the concentration gradient, which requires energy. The most important ion pump in neurons is the *sodium-potassium pump*. It simultaneously pumps Na^+ ions outside the cell and K^+ ions into the cell (in both cases, *up the concentration gradient*). Over the long run, the sodium-potassium pump maintains the concentration gradients of K^+ and Na^+ against the movement of K^+ and Na^+ ions through passive channels.

A final defining property of ion channels is whether they are always open or can be closed. Ion channels that can be opened and closed are called *gated channels*. Several kinds of stimuli can open or close gated ion channels. The overarching theme is that the permeability of the cell membrane to a particular ion depends on the number of open channels allowing that kind of ion to pass. The more open channels, the more permeable the ion.

With this background, we can examine the resting membrane potential in more detail. The cell membrane is fairly permeable to K^+, and there is a strong concentration gradient across it, with K^+ high on the inside and low on the outside. We expect a net movement of K^+ ions out of the cell, running down their concentration gradient. Although the chemical gradient tends to push K^+ outside, an electrical gradient tends to pull K^+ inside. Because K^+ is a positive ion, it is repelled by excess positive charge outside the cell and attracted by excess negative charge inside the cell. At some point, the chemical force pushing K^+ out of the cell will exactly match the electrical force pushing K^+ back into the cell. At this point, the flux of K^+ ions will be in equilibrium—there will be an equal number moving into and out of the cell.

This equilibrium occurs at the voltage at which the electrical and chemical forces are equal and opposite (-85 mV for K^+)—thus, the presence of a concentration gradient for a charged ion across a membrane will create a voltage difference. The difference between the resting membrane potential for a typical neuron and the equilibrium potential for K^+ comes from the fact that Na^+ is also permeable. However, it is not nearly as permeable as K^+; even though both chemical and electrical gradients push it into the cell, only a relatively small number of Na^+ ions get inside.

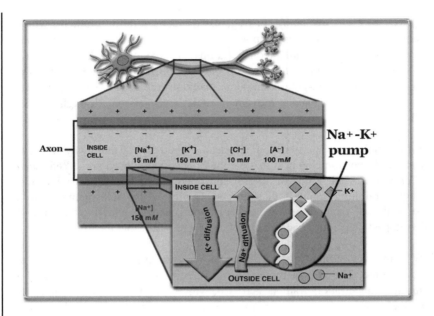

The membrane potential of a neuron can change. If the cell membrane suddenly becomes more permeable to Na⁺, the voltage across the membrane will become more positive (it will *depolarize*) as Na⁺ rushes into the cell. If the membrane potential of a neuron is depolarized above some threshold (about 15 or 20 mV more positive than the resting membrane potential for a typical cell), the inside of the cell suddenly becomes much more positive than the outside. The membrane voltage then drops (*repolarizes*) suddenly before returning to the normal resting membrane potential. This rapid change in voltage is called the *action potential*; it is the event that allows neurons to function as they do. ∎

Suggested Reading

Campbell & Reece, *Biology* (6th ed.), chapter 48.

Purves et al., *Life* (7th ed.), chapter 44.

1. The difference between the endocrine system and the nervous system in the way they transmit information is analogous to the difference between broadcast and cable television. What are some weaknesses of this analogy?

2. What do you think would happen to the resting membrane of a neuron if you experimentally *increased* the concentration of potassium (K^+) on the *outside* of the cell?

Action Potentials and Synapses
Lecture 40

> Last time we put an electrode into a neuron, we used it to measure the voltage across the membrane. But this time, we are actually going to use this electrode to add positive charges. In other words, you could run what we call *current* in or out of the cell through that electrode. "Current" simply means the flow of positive charges.

In this lecture, we review the initiation of action potentials and discuss how the anatomy of the neuron allows action potentials to propagate along the axon. Once a depolarization arrives at the axon terminal, the synapse provides a mechanism for an action potential in one neuron to depolarize another neuron, giving the nervous system its information-transmitting capability. We then examine the structure and function of synapses and neurotransmitters, the chemical signals found at synapses. Finally, we use this information to reexamine the physiological basis of common nervous system activities.

The action potential, which is a stereotypic pattern of depolarization, is one of the most important features of how neurons work. The voltage at which the action potential is triggered is called the *threshold* voltage. Unlike the graded potentials we looked at first, the action potential has a fixed amplitude and duration. It is an all-or-none event, and it happens the same way every time. The action potential is caused by rapid and reversible changes in ionic permeabilities across the cell membrane. These changes reflect the activity of voltage-gated ion channels that are normally closed but open when the voltage across the cell membrane depolarizes.

There are two types of voltage-gated channels, one selective for Na^+ and another selective for K^+. These channels differ in two important ways. First, the Na^+ channel responds very quickly to changes in membrane voltage, while the K^+ voltage-gated channel responds more slowly. Second, the Na^+ channel can stay open only for a relatively brief period of time—once it opens, it closes again regardless of the membrane potential. This property is called *inactivation*. The K^+ channel does not inactivate; it stays open as long as the membrane is depolarized.

The action potential is the result of the activity of K^+ and Na^+ ion channels. At the resting membrane potential, both the Na^+ and K^+ voltage-gated channels are closed and will not permit ions to pass. When the membrane begins to depolarize for any reason, the voltage-gated channels begin to open. The Na^+ channel opens quickly, however, while the K^+ channel opens much more slowly. As a result, the permeability of $Na+$ increases dramatically and Na^+ rushes into the cell. Na^+ entering the cell depolarizes it further, increasing the number of open Na^+ channels and, therefore, the amount of Na^+ entering the cell, which depolarizes the cell even more. This positive feedback cycle continues until all the Na^+ channels are open and Na^+ permeability is at its maximum. This is why, once triggered, the action potential is an all-or-none event.

If an action potential is triggered at one end of an axon, Na^+ will rush into this area because its permeability is greatly increased in this location.

The membrane potential repolarizes as rapidly as it depolarized, for two reasons. First, the Na^+ voltage-gated channels inactivate, decreasing the permeability of Na^+ back to its normal resting level. There appear to be two protein "gates" in this channel—one that opens with depolarization and another that closes a short time afterwards. Second, the K^+ voltage-gated channels begin to open. These channels are responding to depolarization, just like the Na^+ channels but more slowly. The Na^+ channels have already opened and started to close again by the time the K^+ channels open. The opening of these channels increases the movement of K^+ out of the cell, making the inside of the cell more negative.

When the cell membrane returns to its normal resting potential, the voltage that caused the K^+ channels to open is gone, but they remain open for a while longer because of their slow response. This causes the membrane to undershoot its resting membrane potential (become more negative than normal). In a millisecond or two, the K^+ channels close and the membrane potential returns to its normal resting level. After an action potential, there is a *refractory period* during which another action potential cannot be triggered. If the membrane is depolarized immediately following one action potential, another action potential will not be triggered. The refractory period is caused primarily by the fact that the inactivation gates of the Na^+ channels remain closed for a few milliseconds after the membrane has repolarized. The refractory period sets the maximum rate at which a neuron can generate action potentials.

Action potentials must be able to propagate to be useful as signals. The most important feature of membrane depolarization in nerve cells is that it can *propagate*, or move from one place to another along the axon. Action potentials propagate without any degradation; this ability enables the nervous system to transmit information over long distances.

The anatomy of neurons lends itself to long-distance communication, and the action potential travels down the cellular "wire" of the axon in a simple fashion. If an action potential is triggered at one end of an axon, Na^+ will rush into this area because its permeability is greatly increased in this location. This influx of Na^+ not only depolarizes the region around open channels, but it also causes adjacent areas to depolarize as well. If an adjacent segment of the axon is depolarized beyond its threshold, voltage-gated channels will open up and trigger an action potential in that segment. This process continues down the axon, like a row of standing dominoes falling over in sequence when the first domino in the row is tipped. However, propagation is really a continuous wave of depolarization down the axon, not a series of discrete events. As each section of an axon passes the threshold for an action potential, its response is just as strong as the first.

Action potentials typically travel in only one direction in a neuron—they are initiated at the cell body and travel away from it down the axon to the axon terminal. This is because the wave of depolarization leaves refractory segments in its wake, which cannot be immediately depolarized.

Synapses transfer depolarization between neurons. Once triggered, an action potential travels down the axon to the axon terminal, which typically terminates on the body or dendrites of another cell. The point of contact between these two cells is called a *synapse*. The transmitting cell is called the *presynaptic cell*, and the receiving cell is called the *postsynaptic cell*. Synapses allow depolarization in one cell to pass to an adjacent cell. It seems reasonable, therefore, that synapses would have channels that allow ionic current to pass directly from presynaptic to postsynaptic cells.

Electrical synapses do have intercellular channels, called *gap junctions*, which form a continuous cytoplasmic connection between two cells. Electrical synapses enable the action potential to pass unimpeded from one cell to the next, but they are relatively uncommon in vertebrates. Chemical synapses are by far the most common type. Chemical synapses have a very narrow space between the membrane of the presynaptic cell's axon terminal and the membrane of the postsynaptic cell. An action potential cannot cross this space; instead, it is the electrical signal converted into a chemical signal that crosses to the other cell, where it is converted back into an electrical signal.

Understanding the structure of chemical synapses is crucial to understanding their function. The presynaptic cell membrane has a large number of membrane-bound vesicles, each of which contains a quantity of a chemical signal called a *neurotransmitter*. There are many different kinds of neurotransmitters. When the depolarization of the action potential reaches the presynaptic terminal, these vesicles move to the cell membrane, fuse with it, and release their contents into the narrow space between the two cells. The mechanism by which the vesicles release their contents involves a set of calcium (Ca^{++}) voltage-gated ion channels. The postsynaptic cell membrane is covered with transmembrane proteins that act as highly specific receptors for neurotransmitters. Each receptor will specifically bind only with a particular type of neurotransmitter.

There are two general kinds of neurotransmitter receptors. In the first kind, the receptor molecule is itself an ion channel or part of an ion channel. When the neurotransmitter binds to the receptor, it causes a shape change in the channel. Because the neurotransmitter binds to the channel protein itself, this is called a *directly gated channel*. The second kind of neurotransmitter receptors are *indirectly gated*. In these cases, the neurotransmitter binds to a receptor that activates a second messenger system. In both cases, the effect of the neurotransmitter is to change ionic permeabilities on the postsynaptic membrane, which converts the chemical signal back to an electrical signal.

Some neurotransmitters may depolarize the postsynaptic membrane and bring the postsynaptic cell closer to its threshold; others may hyperpolarize the postsynaptic cell and make it less likely to fire an action potential. The effect a neurotransmitter has depends on which ion the receptor channel allows to pass and whether the neurotransmitter opens closed channels or closes open channels. Regardless of which effect a neurotransmitter has, enzymes or other mechanisms in the synaptic cleft quickly remove it after it is released; thus, the effect of one action potential reaching the presynaptic terminal is brief and precise.

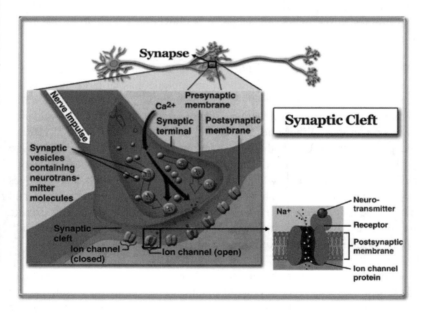

Though we have not examined in detail the type of information neurons convey, they essentially function by changing the permeability of Na^+ and K^+ ions across cell membranes. The nervous system responses as "simple" as juggling or as complex as love, fear, or remembering a face all stem from the action of ion channels. ■

Suggested Reading

Campbell & Reece, *Biology* (6th ed.), chapter 48.

LeDoux, *Synaptic Self: How Our Brains Become Who We Are.*

Purves et al., *Life* (7th ed.), chapter 44.

Questions to Consider

1. Why is it important that the strength of an action potential (i.e., the extent of depolarization) remain unchanged along the length of an axon?

2. What kinds of proteins do you think are most likely affected by mood-altering drugs?

Synaptic Integration and Memory
Lecture 41

We now understand something about how neurons can convey
information from one part of an organism to another, but there remain
two other critical features of how nervous systems work that we still
need to consider. Not only do we need to be able to transmit physiological
information, we also need to be able to process that information and to
store it.

This lecture begins by discussing the features of synapses that allow
information to be processed by nervous systems, as well as transmitted
through them. The many inputs to a typical neuron are evaluated and
acted on through the process of *synaptic integration*, which gives rise to
information processing of great complexity and speed. The lecture concludes
by examining one way such information appears to be stored, through the
permanent modification of the strength of a synapse; like nervous system
response, this information storage mechanism hinges on the function of
gated ion channels.

In addition to transmitting information, the nervous system must also
be able to process it. Several features of synapses form the basis of the
underlying mechanism of information processing in nervous systems. The
release of a neurotransmitter by the presynaptic cell at a synapse changes the
permeability of the postsynaptic cell membrane to different kinds of ions as
neurotransmitter-gated ion channels open or close. In this way, the chemical
signal generated when a depolarization arrives at a synapse is converted back
to an electrical signal in the postsynaptic cell.

Synapses are very small, localized structures, typically found on the dendrites
or cell body of a postsynaptic neuron. The change in postsynaptic membrane
potential caused by a synapse firing lasts only a few milliseconds at most. The
distance between the presynaptic and postsynaptic cells is only about 20 to
40 nanometers, and neurotransmitters cross this distance extremely quickly.
Neurotransmitter effects are equally brief, because the neurotransmitters are
broken down after release or taken back into the presynaptic cell.

Different kinds of synapses can be excitatory or inhibitory, depending on the kinds of ions that can travel through the postsynaptic gated ion channels and whether the effect of neurotransmitter binding is to open or close them. Excitatory synapses depolarize the postsynaptic neuron and thus cause it to become more likely to fire an action potential, while inhibitory synapses have the opposite effect.

The effect of a single synapse on the membrane potential of a postsynaptic cell is relatively small. The threshold for a typical neuron is on the order of 15 to 20 mV more positive than the resting membrane potential. A typical chemical synapse, however, will cause a change of only a few millivolts. Any given neuron typically receives many synapses from other neurons. Whether a neuron fires an action potential, then, depends on the summed activity of the neurons connected to it. This process is called *synaptic integration.*

In 1949, [Donald Hebb] proposed that memories could be modeled as changes in assemblies of cells.

Synaptic integration is the fundamental information-processing mechanism of the nervous system. The dozens, hundreds, or even thousands of synapses on a single neuron generally come from different input neurons, often from different parts of the nervous system. At any particular instant, the membrane voltage of a single output neuron is affected by many different inputs, some excitatory and some inhibitory. The basic mechanism by which these inputs are integrated is called *summation.* In a neuron with only excitatory inputs, the summed effects of several synapses may achieve a depolarizing effect that exceeds the threshold. Summation can occur across time and space.

Temporal summation (summation across time) refers to a single input synapse firing more than once and sufficiently rapidly that the depolarizing effects of the first firing have not worn off completely before the second firing occurs. The second depolarization adds to the first, bringing the membrane even closer to threshold. *Spatial summation* (summation across space) provides another level of complexity. In a neuron with two different excitatory synapses, neither synapse alone would be able to bring the postsynaptic cell to its threshold. If the two synapses fire at approximately the same time, however, their summed depolarization may be large enough to trigger an action potential. However, different neurons must fire at the same time for the target neuron to respond with an action potential.

An even more complicated case is that of a single neuron with two synapses, one excitatory and the other inhibitory. If the inhibitory synapse fires alone, it will cause the membrane to become slightly more negative and shift further from its threshold. If the inhibitory synapse fires at the same time as an excitatory synapse, their effects will cancel. Even if several excitatory synapses fire together in a way that would normally trigger an action potential, a single inhibitory synapse may prevent the target neuron from reaching threshold.

By summing a set of small positive and negative inputs, the neuronal membrane integrates information from many sources across time to determine whether an action potential will occur. This integration is the fundamental information-processing mechanism in all nervous systems, whether a loose network of neurons in a jellyfish or the 100 billion specialized neurons of the human brain.

The nervous system can also store the information it transmits and processes. The ability to store information adds another layer of complexity to neural processing of physiological information. Learning and memory are quite complex and are supported by equally complex anatomical and physiological specializations, but a simple case illustrates the basic mechanism by which a nervous system might store information.

Psychologist Donald Hebb argued that psychological processes were best understood in physiological terms. In 1949, he proposed that memories could be modeled as changes in assemblies of cells, specifically, as lasting changes in the relative strengths of synaptic connections. Hebb's idea was that experience—the information being stored—would permanently affect the relative strength of a synapse. This model is now called a *Hebbian synapse*, and the idea has dominated thinking about the cellular basis of memory since Hebb first proposed it. A number of different mechanisms have been proposed by which a Hebbian synapse could function. One mechanism has been especially well researched and seems to be common in vertebrate nervous systems.

The *NMDA receptor system* is an example of a Hebbian synaptic mechanism. One particularly important neurotransmitter in vertebrates is glutamate, which acts as the principal excitatory neurotransmitter in the vertebrate central nervous system. As is the case for many neurotransmitters, more than one kind of post-synaptic receptor responds to glutamate. These receptors are called the NMDA glutamate receptor and the AMPA glutamate receptor; they work in slightly different ways when they bind a molecule of glutamate.

Both NMDA receptors and AMPA receptors open ion channels that allow Na^+ to cross the membrane. However, NMDA receptors differ from AMPA receptors in two important ways:

- The channels opened by NMDA receptors also allow calcium (Ca^{++}) ions to enter the cell.

- NMDA receptors are blocked by another kind of ion, magnesium (Mg^{++}).

Because some Mg^{++} is always present, NMDA receptors do not normally respond strongly when stimulated by glutamate. However, if the postsynaptic membrane is already depolarized to some extent, Mg^{++} is released from the NMDA receptors, allowing them to open in response to glutamate.

The synaptic strength of a neuron with NMDA receptors may be able to change over time through the coincident activity of two sets of inputs. NMDA receptor channels will open only if the cell is already depolarized. When the receptors are activated, however, they allow Ca^{++} to enter the cell. Ca^{++} acts as a second messenger in many signal transduction pathways. If a cell with NMDA receptors is simultaneously stimulated by another excitatory input—such as a glutamate synapse with AMPA receptors—the influx of Ca^{++} could trigger long-term changes to the synaptic machinery of the cell, strengthening that synapse's response to the same level of stimulation. Put another way, Ca^{++} entering through NMDA receptors could switch the postsynaptic cell from a low-response state to a high-response state. This change would happen, however, only if the cell experienced a specific coincidence of excitatory inputs.

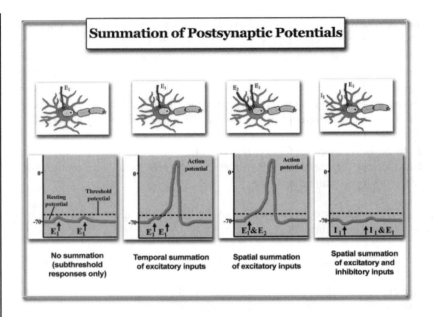

Summation of Postsynaptic Potentials

| No summation (subthreshold responses only) | Temporal summation of excitatory inputs | Spatial summation of excitatory inputs | Spatial summation of excitatory and inhibitory inputs |

The possibility of this kind of synaptic change is consistent with a cellular phenomenon called *long-term potentiation*. A neuron stimulated rapidly and repeatedly will normally develop a diminished response to stimulation. However, just the opposite happens with some cells in the brain—repeated and rapid stimulation of these cells increases their response to a given level of stimulation. The difference is that cells with this response have both AMPA and NMDA glutamate receptors. If these cells are stimulated at a low level, the glutamate released activates only the AMPA receptors. If the level of stimulation is high, however, the higher level of depolarization frees the NMDA receptors, allowing Ca^{++} to enter the cell. Ca^{++} triggers long-term changes in the neurons, making them more sensitive to synaptic input overall. As Hebb predicted, the "experience" of this kind of synapse causes a lasting change in its strength, providing the fundamental basis for the storage of information by neurons. As important as the NMDA receptor appears to be in information storage, other molecular, physiological, and anatomical mechanisms have been shown to be involved in information storage. ∎

Suggested Reading

Campbell & Reece, *Biology* (6th ed.), chapter 48.

Johnson, *Mind Wide Open: Your Brain and the Neuroscience of Everyday Life*.

Pinker, *How the Mind Works*.

Purves et al., *Life* (7th ed.), chapter 44.

Questions to Consider

1. Brains are often compared to computers. What are the strengths and weaknesses of this comparison?

2. Do you think that analyzing the molecular mechanisms of a Hebbian synapse will eventually allow us to fully understand learning and memory? Why or why not?

Sensory Function
Lecture 42

Sensory systems gather information from the environment through the activity of specialized cells called *sensory receptors* or *sensory receptor cells* that are specialized to detect particular kinds of physical stimuli and to convert those physical stimuli to physiological signals so that it can be transmitted to other parts of the organism.

This lecture begins by discussing the importance to homeostasis of monitoring an organism's external environment. We examine the sensory systems that carry out this function, delving as deep as the ion-channel mechanisms that underpin all the primary methods animals use to detect external stimuli. In addition, different types of sensory receptors divide stimuli into several modalities or qualities and can be further tuned to detect a narrow range of values within a modality. The lecture concludes by noting that much of what we as humans experience as being the outside world is, in fact, a creation produced by the brain from basic sensory stimuli.

To maintain homeostasis, organisms must not only monitor their internal environment, but must also monitor and respond to changes in the external environment. For example, moths fly at night, and much moth activity involves male moths flying around in search of receptive females. To enable males to find them in the dark, female moths release chemical signals called *pheromones*. Males have special receptors on their antennae that allow them to follow a pheromone trail upwind to a female.

At the same time, bats try to find moths and other insects to eat. To enable them to find insects in the dark, bats produce extremely high-pitched sounds called *echolocation signals*, and this sonar system guides them to their prey. Some species of moths have an "ear" tuned specifically to the pitch of bat echolocation signals. When they hear an approaching bat, these moths plummet to the earth, where they are safe from a bat attack. This nightly drama illustrates the importance of detecting and converting information from the external environment, which is as important to maintaining homeostasis as it is to moth survival.

Sensory systems detect and convert information from the external environment into physiological signals. A sensory system receives information from the environment through the activity of sensory receptor cells that are specialized to detect particular kinds of stimuli and transmit this information to other parts of the organism. Most sensory cells are modified neurons. Sensory receptors are often found with other cells in assemblies called *sensory organs*, which enhance the ability of sensory cells to collect information. The eye and ear are obvious examples of sensory organs. Sensory systems may also be specialized to detect information from the internal environment, as in the mammalian hypothalamus. Specialized internal sensory receptors detect information about the chemistry of blood, the position of joints and muscles, the status of the digestive system, and so forth.

On a conscious level, we are mostly aware of sensory systems detecting information about the external environment in the form of sight, sound, touch, taste, and smell. We also receive much information from the external environment about which we are unaware. Any given species of animal can detect an enormous range of information, and different kinds of animals may detect different kinds of information. Humans, for example, cannot sense moth pheromones or bat echolocation signals.

As diverse as sensory systems are, all share a few basic principles. Different forms of physical stimuli—light, heat, or chemicals, for example—are transformed by sensory systems into distinctly different qualities of sensation, which are called *perceptual modalities*. The division of sensation into different modalities was formally described by Aristotle, who proposed that there are five primary "sensory energies": sight, sound, touch, smell, and taste. In the 1830s, Johannes Müller proposed the law of specific sensory energies, which stated that different kinds of sensory nerves carry distinct sensory energies.

As Müller suggested, the modality of a sensation that results when a sensory nerve is activated is a property of the nerve itself, not the physical stimulus that activates it. For example, a sharp blow to the eye will "produce" a flash of light, because the eye's sensory neurons respond to extreme pressure, as well as light, but the brain interprets all activity of these neurons as being caused by light. Though Müller did not know the mechanism, we now know that sensory neurons respond to stimulation in only one way—by producing the same action potentials as other neurons. Because these action potentials are identical to those produced by other neurons, sensory modality is specified in two different ways.

First, the specificity of sensory modalities depends on anatomy. Sensory neurons, and the neurons they connect to, send their information only to areas of the nervous system that are specialized for receiving and processing that kind of sensory information. Neurons carrying visual information go to areas of the brain responsible for processing visual information, for example. Second, different kinds of sensory neurons respond best to only one kind of physical stimulus. The sensory cells in the eye associated with vision can be stimulated by extreme pressure but are exceptionally sensitive to light energy. The specific anatomy responsible for processing different modalities differs from species to species and, in complex brains, can be quite complex, making it difficult to draw generalities about the anatomical specification of sensory function.

Chemoreception is probably the most evolutionarily ancient form of sensory reception and is certainly the most ubiquitous.

The cellular and molecular mechanisms that determine sensory receptor response to physical stimuli are quite simple in essence. A sensory receptor must be able to convert a physical stimulus into a neural signal, which must involve a change in the receptor cell's membrane potential. This change, in turn, must be the result of the opening and closing of ion channels. A sensory receptor cell, then, must have a mechanism by which a stimulus can open or close gated ion channels. Converting a signal from one form to another is called *transduction* in general, or *sensory transduction*, in the case of receptor cells.

Despite the enormous diversity of animal sensory receptors, there are five basic mechanisms by which they transduce physical stimuli. *Chemoreceptors* detect molecules that bind selectively to membrane receptors, initiating a second-messenger cascade that causes ion channels to open or close. To a first approximation, chemoreception is no different from synaptic signaling or other types of molecular signaling between cells, except that the molecular signal may be of external origin. Chemoreceptors are involved in the sensation of taste and smell, and the detection of pheromones; chemical signals identify members of an animal social group; or mark a defended territory, among other functions. Chemoreception is probably the most evolutionarily ancient form of sensory reception and is certainly the most ubiquitous.

Chemoreceptor

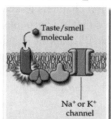

Photoreceptor

Mechanoreceptor Thermoreceptor Electroreceptor

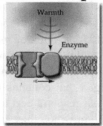

Mechanoreceptors detect mechanical forces that distort their cell membranes. They appear to have ion channels that are tightly bound to structural proteins so that, when the membrane is stretched, protein filaments literally pull the channel open. Mechanoreceptors are involved in our sensations of touch, body position, and hearing. For example, hair cells in the inner ear are bent by vibrations, which opens ion channels, causing these cells to depolarize and, thus, transducing sound into neural energy.

Photoreceptors have a pigment called rhodopsin that can absorb photons of light; when it does so, it changes shape, initiating a second-messenger cascade that causes ion channel proteins to change their shape. *Thermoreceptors* detect temperature; different kinds of receptors detect heat and cold using different molecular mechanisms that are not fully understood. In both cases, however, there appears to be a temperature-sensitive enzyme embedded in the cell membrane that opens and closes an associated ion channel.

Electroreception is even less well understood than thermoreception and more rare than any other mechanism. In this case, a change in the electric charge around the receptor cell membrane causes ion channels to change shape and open. A few organisms have electroreceptors that are particularly sensitive to weak electric fields; catfish, for example, have receptors sensitive enough to use the weak electric fields produced by other organisms to hunt their prey. Certain kinds of African and South American fish not only detect electric fields but also have specialized organs that generate changes in the electric field around them.

In any sensory modality, sensory systems may be tuned to a relatively narrow range. The way a receptor is tuned depends on the type of receptor it is. In chemoreception, specificity is inherent in the mechanism itself; different receptors selectively bind different kinds of molecules. For example, each of the four "basic tastes"—salty, sweet, sour, and bitter—corresponds to a different receptor. In mechanoreception, tuning is more generally a property of the sensory organ that contains the sensory cell. In hearing, different sensory cells in the ear respond best to different pitches, but this is a consequence of the structure in which they are embedded, not an intrinsic property of the cells themselves.

In photoreception, the composition of the light-detecting molecule determines tuning. Humans have three types of molecules that sense color; a mutation or deficiency of any one produces a condition known as colorblindness.

Differences in sensory modalities, and tuning within those modalities, represent only the most fundamental properties of a sensory stimulus. Sensory systems must be able to detect and process many more specific features of the external world to account for the richness of sensory experience. Much of this richness, however, comes not from sensory receptors themselves, but is the result of processing in the brain. ■

Suggested Reading

Campbell & Reece, *Biology* (6th ed.), chapter 49.

Freeman, *Biological Science*, chapter 43.

Purves et al., *Life* (7th ed.), chapter 45.

Questions to Consider

1. How can you account for the fact that people report "seeing stars" when they are hit on the back of the head?

2. From a *biologist's* point of view, do you think a tree falling in the forest makes a sound if no one is there to hear it?

How Muscles Work
Lecture 43

Obviously, the ability of an organism to change any number of similar physiological parameters is essential for it to be able to homeostatically regulate its internal environment. But one very, very effective way for an animal to improve its circumstances over all is simply to be able to move.

This lecture begins by describing the primary importance to homeostasis of an organism's ability to move itself. It examines the anatomy of muscles—movement effectors—from the whole organ level to the molecular level, and then describes the molecular basis for how muscle cells change their shape and in so doing enable animals to move. The lecture concludes by examining the control of muscle contraction, from the initial stimulus of a neuron to the movement of whole sections of tissue.

The ability of an organism to change any number of physiological parameters is essential for homeostatic regulation. One very effective way for an animal to improve its external circumstances is simply to move. For example, an ectothermic animal that cannot generate heat can nonetheless maintain its body temperature within a fairly narrow range simply by moving in and out of the sun. The ability to move is imperative for many other aspects of survival and reproduction, such as avoiding predators and finding mates. For this reason, the most important effectors an animal has are the ones that enable it to move—muscles.

Muscle movement is caused by changes in the shape of muscle cells. Muscle cells are specialized to change their shape—specifically, to shorten themselves in one dimension, a process called *contraction*. Different cells are specialized for different types of contraction and are responsible for movements as diverse as the undulation of jellyfish and the limb movements of insects.

Muscle cells are found wherever the contraction of whole tissues occurs in animals. In vertebrate animals, there are three major kinds of muscle tissue.

• *Smooth muscle* provides contractive forces for internal organs.

• *Cardiac muscle* is the specialized muscle type found in the heart.

• *Striated muscle* is used to move limbs, the trunk, the neck, and so forth.

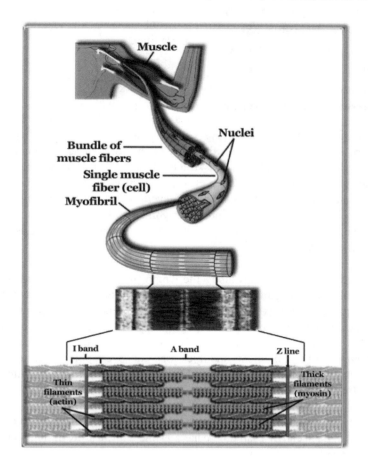

The contraction mechanism is the same in all types of muscle; for brevity, we will examine only striated muscle. A muscle is an organ composed of a hierarchical array of smaller units acting in parallel. The first level of organization is a set of muscle fibers that runs the entire length of the muscle. Each muscle fiber is a single, multinucleated cell that develops from the fusion of many embryonic cells along the length of the muscle. Each muscle fiber is, in turn, made up of a bundle of smaller units called *myofibrils*. A bundle of myofibrils runs the length of each muscle fiber.

Any single connection between a myosin and an actin is extremely weak, but in aggregate, all these connections generate considerable force.

Myofibrils have a repeating pattern of light and dark bands, as viewed under a microscope, with a narrow dark line separating each repeated set of bands. These are the striations that give striated muscle its name. The repeating pattern is called a *sarcomere*; the ends of the sarcomeres are marked by *Z-lines*, disk-shaped plates of a structural protein. The sarcomere is the basic functional unit of muscles. The myofibril is made up of bundles of even smaller fiber-like structures called *myofilaments*, which are long chains of proteins. There are two kinds of myofilaments: thin filaments, which are chains of the protein *actin*, and thick filaments, which are chains of the protein *myosin*.

The light and dark regions along the length of a single sarcomere are the result of different patterns of overlap between thin filaments and thick filaments. The relatively light bands on either end, just adjacent to the Z-lines, are called *I-bands* and represent regions with only thin filaments present. In the middle of each sarcomere is a broad darker region called the *A-band*, where thin filaments and thick filaments overlap. In the center of the A-band, another relatively light band called the *H-zone* is an area with only thick filaments present.

This banding pattern suggests a regular organization of thin and thick filaments. Each end of a sarcomere has a Z-line with an array of thin filaments attached to it and extending toward the center from either side. The middle of the sarcomere has an array of thick filaments extending from the middle to either end. The lighter regions on the ends of the sarcomere (the A-bands) and in the middle (the H-zone) appear lighter because there is no overlap between the two kinds of filaments. The A-band is darker because in it, the two kinds of filaments are interdigitated with each other.

The overlapping arrangement of thin and thick filaments is how the sarcomere and, hence, the whole muscle, contracts. In 1954, two pairs of researchers noticed that when a muscle cell contracts, the distance between the Z-lines shortens. More importantly, the I-band also shortens and the H-zone virtually disappears, but the length of the A-band does not change.

To explain this, these researchers proposed the *sliding-filament model* of contraction. By this model, neither the thin nor the thick filaments change length when the muscle contracts; instead, these two types of filaments move past each other. Changes in appearance of the light and dark bands of the sarcomere are consistent with the sliding-filament model. A relaxed muscle has a relatively large region at the ends of the sarcomeres where only thin filaments occur. As the muscle contracts, the thin filaments slide toward the center, pulling the Z-lines with them. As the sarcomere shortens, more and more of the thin filaments overlap with thick filament regions. The implications of the sliding-filament model are that some interaction between the thin and thick filaments must be responsible for moving them past each other, and that this interaction somehow generates the force to shorten the muscle cell.

The interaction between actin and myosin is the molecular mechanism behind muscle contraction. Myosin has a long tail region that weaves together with other myosin tails to form thick filaments. Myosin also has a head region that sticks out from the side of the thick filament. As with many other proteins, the shape of myosin changes depending on whether or not it is phosphorylated (that is, has a phosphate group attached to it). In a myosin that has been phosphorylated, the head region is bent like an outstretched arm. Phosphorylated myosin is in a high-energy configuration, while unphosphorylated myosin is in a low-energy configuration. A cyclic change between these configurations is the force behind muscle contraction.

As in other contexts, a molecule called adenosine triphosphate (ATP) donates the phosphate group in a phosphorylated myosin. ATP is a molecular "currency" used to store and transfer energy. ATP often donates its phosphate group to another molecule in a two-step process. First, the entire ATP molecule binds to the target molecule. Second, one of ATP's phosphate groups transfers to the target molecule. The target is now phosphorylated but also has the remainder of the ATP—now called adenosine diphosphate, or ADP—attached.

Only after a myosin has been phosphorylated and its head is bent forward can the head bind to a specific attachment site on an actin molecule in a thin filament. This attachment is called a *cross-bridge*. The formation of this cross-bridge triggers another configurational change in the myosin head, causing it to dephosphorylate. When the phosphate is lost (along with the ADP molecule), the myosin assumes its low-energy configuration. The myosin is still cross-linked to an actin, however, so the backward bending of the myosin head exerts a force on the actin filament, causing it to slide past by about 5–10 nanometers. The cross-bridge is only broken when another molecule of ATP binds to the myosin head, which restarts the cycle.

Any single connection between a myosin and an actin is extremely weak, but in aggregate, all these connections generate considerable force, which is further multiplied across the many myofibrils that make up each muscle fiber and the many muscle fibers that make up a whole muscle.

In general, skeletal muscle contracts when stimulated by a neuron. Like neurons, muscle cells have voltage-gated ion channels that respond to depolarization by causing a rapid change in membrane potential. The *neuromuscular junction* between a neuron and a muscle cell is a chemical synapse. Depolarization of the muscle cell, triggered by activity of the neuromuscular junction, must then somehow control the interaction between myosin and actin. Another set of proteins regulates the interaction between actin and myosin. Strands of *tropomyosin* block myosin's ability to link to actin, and the *troponin complex* controls the position of the tropomyosin. The configuration of the troponin complex, in turn, is controlled by Ca^{++} binding.

Calcium is stored in muscle cells in the *sarcoplasmic reticulum*, a specialized endoplasmic reticulum distributed around the myofibrils. Its many active Ca^{++} pumps remove Ca^{++} from the cytoplasm of the muscle cell and store it inside the sarcoplasmic reticulum. When an action potential depolarizes a muscle cell, Ca^{++} channels in the sarcoplasmic reticulum open, releasing stored Ca^{++} and causing the muscle cell to contract. When the muscle cell repolarizes, the Ca^{++} pumps remove Ca^{++} from the cytoplasm, storing it back in the sarcoplasmic reticulum. This causes the tropomyosin to block the actin binding sites, returning the muscle fiber to its resting condition. Muscles also require leverage, which in animals, is normally provided by a system of rigid structures called a *skeleton*. This relationship illustrates that no system in a complex organism can be understood without considering how that system fits together with all the other parts of the organism. ■

Suggested Reading

Campbell & Reece, *Biology* (6th ed.), chapter 49.

Freeman, *Biological Science*, chapter 43.

Purves et al., *Life* (7th ed.), chapter 47.

Vogel, *Prime Mover: A Natural History of Muscle.*

Questions to Consider

1. If muscle cells can only contract, then how do organisms move their limbs or other structures in more than one direction?

2. Calcium ions play two different and equally essential roles in making a muscle contract, one presynaptic and one postsynaptic. Can you explain these two roles of calcium?

The Innate Immune System
Lecture 44

Multicellular organisms face an even more difficult task in defending themselves, because they can be invaded not only by viruses but also by whole bacteria or fungal cells that enter their bodies intact, as well as a multitude of other single-celled and even multicellular parasites and disease-causing agents.

This lecture begins by noting the importance to survival of biological mechanisms that repair cellular damage and destroy invading organisms in the body. The necessary properties of such mechanisms, collectively called the *immune system*, are then discussed, and the lecture examines several barriers that attempt to prevent damage or intrusion altogether. The focus then shifts to the biological response to invaders or damage that cross these barriers. Of the two kinds of response, only the first (*non-specific* or *innate immune response*) is discussed, and the important mechanisms and active components of the innate immune system are examined.

To survive, organisms must maintain biological integrity in the face of invaders and other sources of injury that constantly assault them. The biological mechanisms that perform this function are collectively known as an immune system. Biological mechanisms that defend an organism from injury and infection must carry out several functions. First, they must be triggered by some stimulus produced upon injury or an attack by a pathogen (disease-causing agent). Second, there must be some mechanism or set of mechanisms that can counteract the injury or invasion.

Most multicellular organisms have defense mechanisms that meet these two requirements. In starfish, for example, damaged tissue sends out a signal indicating that damage has occurred; specialized cells drawn by this signal then engulf the invading material. This response is called *phagocytosis*, and the cells involved are called *phagocytes*. Phagocytosis is a critical part of human immune response as well.

Third, they must have the ability to distinguish between cells and molecules that normally occur in an organism's own body and foreign material, which allows defense mechanisms to respond more specifically to a potential threat. Non-specific defense mechanisms are important, but targeting foreign material instead of destroying everything in the area is more efficient. To recognize foreign material, a defense system simply needs to recognize some aspect of the molecular structure of the offending object or organism as foreign. Even animals as simple as sponges can discriminate "self" versus "non-self" in this way.

Two additional properties of defense mechanisms are characteristic of the very highly derived immune systems of vertebrate animals. The first of these properties is the ability to recognize different specific kinds of foreign material. Second, the vertebrate immune system can form a memory of previously encountered pathogens. These additional properties allow vertebrate immune systems to efficiently target and quickly counter particular kinds of threats with effective countermeasures. The fact that the human immune system has these properties has been understood for thousands of years. Using material from infected people to inoculate others against smallpox, for example, has been a common practice for centuries.

In 1796, the English physician Edward Jenner developed a safer approach to inoculation. Based on a hunch that similar agents were responsible for cowpox and smallpox, Jenner inoculated a boy with fluid taken from a cowpox sore and later inoculated the same boy with smallpox. The boy failed to develop smallpox, and Jenner's technique was quickly adopted worldwide. This type of inoculation is still called a *vaccination*, a term based on the Latin word for cow. These two properties are characteristics of the *specific immune response* or *acquired immunity* of vertebrates, in contrast to *non-specific defenses*, or *innate immunity*.

One of the primary defenses against pathogens is to keep them out of the body in the first place. One of the most important barrier mechanisms is the skin. The skin is the single largest organ of a typical vertebrate's body; in humans, it makes up fully 15% of adult weight. Skin is a complex, layered structure, and its outermost cells contain enormous amounts of the structural protein keratin, which makes them particularly resistant to structural damage.

These cells are continually replaced by new cells from layers underneath—they "throw themselves on the ramparts" to block pathogens. Skin is not only relatively impenetrable, but it is coated with extremely acidic secretions that inhibit the growth of many microorganisms. Sweat also contains an enzyme called *lysozyme* that digests bacterial cell walls.

In addition to skin, the digestive, respiratory, and urogenital tracts all open to the outside of the body, providing potential entry points for pathogens. The digestive tract is protected by saliva, which contains digestive enzymes, and by the fact that materials entering the mouth usually end up in the stomach, which contains very powerful digestive enzymes and hydrochloric acid.

The respiratory and urogenital tracts are protected by a thick coat of mucus, a secretion made mostly of a protein called *mucin*. Mucus is viscous and traps pathogens until they die of exposure to acids or digestive enzymes. The respiratory tract has a lining of cells with small, movable, hair-like structures called *cilia* that sweep mucus outside, where it can be expelled with the foreign material it has trapped.

In spite of adaptations that create a harsh environment for pathogens, many microorganisms, such as bacteria and fungi, do live on and in humans. These microorganisms are called *normal flora* and have their own adaptations, such as the ability to live in acidic environments, that allow them to exist in the harsh conditions of skin and mucus membranes. In most cases, our normal flora benefit us.

In spite of the many barriers that have evolved in animals, pathogens nonetheless often gain entry to the inside of an organism's body. Not only can some pathogens (Hepatitis A, for example) survive the harsh surface environment of an animal, but skin and other surfaces can be and often are physically damaged. A small cut is a potential source of entry to invading pathogens of all sorts. When pathogens do gain access to the body, they face what is sometimes called a second line of defense—a non-specific or innate immune response.

The primary defense against pathogens inside the body involves white blood cells that are attracted to a damaged area and begin to phagocytose bacteria and other kinds of material that are recognized as foreign. There are many types of white blood cells, but they are collectively called *leukocytes*. Leukocytes are not confined to the circulatory system proper (blood vessels and capillaries). They spend much of their time outside the circulatory system, patrolling interstitial fluid (the fluid found in the spaces between cells in tissues). These cells may move in and out of the circulatory system, but they most often return to the circulatory system via a separate set of collecting ducts called the *lymphatic system*.

Three kinds of leukocytes are especially important in innate immune response. When damage occurs, *neutrophils* are the first leukocytes to arrive. Neutrophils make up 60–70% of all leukocytes and constantly move throughout the tissues of the body. Damaged cells release chemical signals that attract them; once neutrophils arrive at a damaged or infected site, they begin to phagocytose

To recognize foreign material, a defense system simply needs to recognize some aspect of the molecular structure of the offending object or organism as foreign. Even animals as simple as sponges can discriminate "self" versus "non-self" in this way.

any foreign material. *Macrophages* are recruited more slowly to sites of damage or infection, both because they are less common and because they need to be induced, or switched, from an inactive to an active form. Macrophages are much larger and more effective at phagocytosis and live longer than neutrophils. *Natural killer cells* are not phagocytes; instead, they kill other cells by releasing proteins called *perforins* that form ring-like structures in the membranes of target cells, creating large holes and bursting the cells open. Natural killer cells play a special role in recognizing cells that have been infected by viruses or that have abnormalities that could become cancerous. All three of these types of cells are recruited by generic signals produced by pathogens or damaged cells and attack any material that differs from normal body cells.

In addition to leukocytes, a variety of proteins circulating in blood, lymph, and interstitial fluid also play an important role in non-specific immune function. The complement system includes about 20 proteins that act in concert to attack the cell walls of invading bacterial and fungal cells. As they become activated, some complement proteins also amplify the recruitment of other non-specific defenses, such as leukocytes.

Interferons constitute another set of proteins that plays an important role in innate immunity. These are secreted by cells that have become infected by a virus. Interferons act as signals to adjacent healthy cells to start producing compounds that interfere with viral replication. The recruitment of defensive leukocytes to damaged tissue and the activation of complement proteins are coordinated as part of a general physiological response called *inflammation*, as we saw in the case of histamine. The overall effect of inflammation is to increase blood flow, bringing proteins and leukocytes more quickly to the affected area.

In addition to local inflammation, more extensive infection may cause a systemic elevation in body temperature. This is called a *fever*, and it is also triggered by the inflammation response. When macrophages encounter damaged cells or invading microorganisms, they release molecular signals called *pyrogens*, which raise the set point of the hypothalamic thermostat to induce a fever. Fever is thought to be an adaptive response to infection, because it increases the rate of phagocytosis and the rate at which protein defenses can act and inhibits the growth of some kinds of pathogens. If non-specific immune responses are mobilized to too great an extent, they may harm normal, healthy cells and tissues as much as they help infected or damaged ones. ∎

Suggested Reading

Campbell & Reece, *Biology* (6th ed.), chapter 43.

Freeman, *Biological Science*, chapter 46.

Purves et al., *Life* (7th ed.), chapter 18.

1. How is an immune response a kind of homeostatic mechanism?

2. The ability to recognize similarities and differences in cell-surface molecules probably arose very early after life first appeared on Earth. What might have been the adaptive significance of this ability for the earliest single-celled organisms?

The Acquired Immune System
Lecture 45

There are two fundamental features that distinguish what we call the *specific immune response* or, equivalently, the *acquired immune response.* The first feature is the ability to recognize particular kinds of foreign material in a highly specific fashion. Hence, the name *specific immunity* is given to this. The second feature is the ability to acquire a long-term memory of exposure to these particular kinds of foreign materials.

T he lecture begins by discussing the acquired immune system response, in which previous exposure to a pathogen enables a fast and specific response if the same pathogen is detected again. The lecture then examines the process of clonal selection that creates the immune system's "memory" and discusses how the immune system keeps from attacking the individual's own cells. It then looks at the unique mechanism of genetic recombination responsible for creating the great diversity of antigen receptors necessary for the immune system to respond to the wide array of foreign materials it needs to recognize. The lecture concludes by examining the highly regulated way in which the acquired immune system is activated.

If a pathogen is resistant to non-specific defenses or multiplies too rapidly to be overcome, acquired immunity mechanisms will be activated. A set of leukocytes called *lymphocytes* is primarily responsible for the acquired immune response. There are two kinds of lymphocytes, *B cells* and *T cells*, and they are commonly found in the lymphatic system when they are not activated. In response to invasion by a pathogen or other foreign material in the bloodstream, lymph, or tissue fluids, B cells release copious amounts of proteins called *antibodies* that bind to the foreign material and help remove or destroy it.

There are several kinds of T cells, but two are particularly important in the specific immune response. *Helper T cells* play an essential role in initiating and coordinating the specific immune response; *cytotoxic T cells* kill cells of the host's own body that are infected by viruses or have abnormalities associated with cancer. Both B cells and T cells have receptor proteins on their cell surfaces that recognize foreign material. An *antigen* (short for "antibody generator") is any molecule that triggers an acquired immune response. Pathogens inevitably have surface molecules, such as glycoproteins, that will be recognized as antigens.

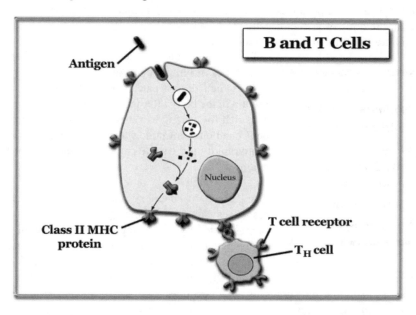

Any particular B cell or T cell has receptors that are specific to only a single antigen—but there are literally millions of different kinds of lymphocyte receptors. This raises two questions. Because antigen receptors are proteins, their ability to bind to specific antigens must depend on their structures, which in turn, must be reflected in their genes. How do so many receptor types arise from a relatively limited set of genes? If only one or a few lymphocytes in an organism's body will recognize a specific antigen, how do these few cells mount an effective response?

Clonal selection explains how a few cells can respond effectively to an intruder; it also accounts for the "memory" of the immune system. When a lymphocyte recognizes an antigen, it begins to divide rapidly, producing many daughter lymphocytes, all with the same antigen receptor type. This production of lymphocyte clones in response to an antigen is called *clonal selection*, because only a cell with the correct antigen receptor will be selected to produce clones.

Clonal selection produces two different kinds of cloned cells. *Effector cells* fight the antigen. Effector cells produced by B cells are called *plasma cells* and are the cells that secrete antibodies to attack the antigen. T cell effector cells are the cytotoxic T cells discussed earlier. Both types of lymphocytes also produce *memory cells*, which do not participate in the attack but remain in the body after the immune response has subsided for as long as several decades. Memory cells enable the immune system to respond much more rapidly if the same pathogen is encountered again.

Clonal selection explains how a few cells can respond effectively to an intruder; it also accounts for the "memory" of the immune system.

The effect of memory cells on subsequent responses to the same pathogen can be demonstrated by measuring antibody production in response to an immunological challenge. The concentration of antibodies in the blood of a person whose immune system is responding to a particular pathogen for the first time will gradually increase over a period of about a week or two, followed by a gradual reduction. If the individual is re-exposed to the pathogen, the concentration of antibodies will increase much faster and will reach much higher levels. Exposure to a different antigen will produce the exact same rate and level of antibody production as first-time exposure to the initial antigen. This difference in response to the second encounter with an antigen is called a *secondary immune response*. A person being vaccinated may be exposed to weakened or killed pathogens with some of the same antigens as the deadly form of the disease. The exposure triggers a primary immune response, which may be mild but still produces memory cells. These memory cells allow the immune system to respond rapidly to the more deadly form of the pathogen.

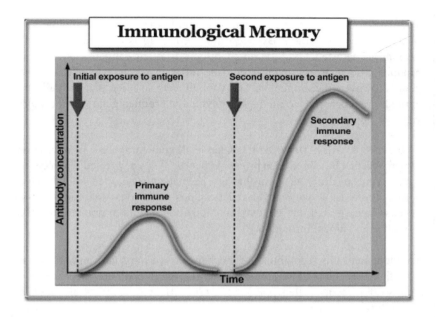

Immunological Memory

Initial exposure to antigen

Second exposure to antigen

Antibody concentration

Secondary immune response

Primary immune response

Time

The elimination of certain lymphocytes before the development of these cells is complete prevents the immune system from attacking the organism itself. The wide variety of antigen receptors makes it likely that lymphocytes will develop with receptors that recognize antigens on an individual's own healthy cells and tissues. Both B and T cells begin their development in the bone marrow. While they are developing, lymphocytes constantly encounter "self" cells and tissues. If a developing lymphocyte has receptors that bind to normal cell molecules, this binding triggers a cellular response that activates the young lymphocyte. Such a lymphocyte is not mature enough to mount an immunological response, but it will still activate certain signaling pathways. These pathways send signals to the young lymphocyte that cause it to self-destruct or to become permanently inactivated. By one estimate, as much as 90% of all developing lymphocytes are eliminated in this way.

The enormous diversity of antigen receptors is the result of a unique kind of genetic recombination. By one estimate, human B cells can potentially respond to between 1 million and 1 billion different antigens. One way of producing so many receptors would be for each receptor to have its own gene. However, the amount of DNA required is so large that virtually the entire human genome would then be devoted to producing antigen receptors, which is not the case.

In the 1960s, W. J. Dryer and J. Claude Bennett proposed an alternative hypothesis that has since been proven to be true. They suggested that receptor genes come in different parts that are permanently shuffled into different combinations as a lymphocyte cell develops. This idea was controversial because it suggested that genetic recombination occurs in non-sexual cells, as well as in gamete formation.

To understand this recombination mechanism, we must look in more detail at antigen receptors. The antigen receptors on B cells are members of a family of proteins called *immunoglobulins*. B cell receptors are actually antibodies with specialized regions that allow them to be embedded in the cell membrane. B cell receptors are composed of several distinct regions. The receptor itself comprises four different proteins—two identical short, light chains and two identical long, heavy chains. The light and heavy chains run in parallel, with the heavy chains bending away from each other in a Y shape. The light and heavy chains each have two regions. The *constant region* is exactly the same in every B cell receptor; the *variable region* differs among receptors. The variable regions of both light and heavy chains occur at the arms of the Y; they form the binding site of the receptor, which will be specific for only one particular antigen. T cell receptors are structurally different from B cell receptors but are also made of proteins with a constant region and a variable region.

In B cell receptors, four sets of genes contribute to each heavy chain. Three of these sets contribute part of the sequence that codes the variable region; the fourth set codes for the sequence of the constant region. When a stem cell in the bone marrow begins to differentiate into a mature B cell, its DNA is cut up and stitched together so that only one version of each of the three variable-region genes remains in the genome.

This is analogous to the way introns are cut out of transcribed RNA, but here, the cutting and pasting occurs in the DNA itself. Once this genetic rearrangement has occurred, the DNA of the cell is permanently altered and can now produce only one kind of heavy chain. The genes coding for the light chains of B cell receptors also undergo a similar genetic recombination; in the end, the number of possible receptors that can be produced by changing the variable regions of each light and heavy chain is extremely large. T cells undergo a similar type of recombination.

Acquired immune response is activated in a highly regulated series of steps. When B cells encounter an antigen, the effector cells they produce secrete antibodies into blood, lymph, and interstitial fluid. These antibodies envelope the pathogen, attaching wherever their antigen occurs. Antibodies bound to a pathogen make it easier to recognize and easier for other immune elements to attack.

When a T cell encounters a recognized antigen, it produces several kinds of cells. In addition to creating a hole in its membrane, a cytotoxic T cell sends signaling molecules to the target cell that cause it to self-destruct. Helper T cell clones not only contribute directly to defense but also activate acquired immune system response. When macrophages encounter foreign material, they engulf and digest it. They also combine fragments of the foreign material with MHC (major histocompatibility complex) proteins and present the foreign material on their own cell surfaces in combination with the MHC proteins.

When macrophages encounter T cells in the lymph nodes, the T cells are activated by the antigen-MHC complex. Once T cells are activated, helper T cells then turn on B cells, which produce effector and memory cells. The result is that when the receptors of B cells or T cells detect an antigen they recognize, they trigger a cascade of events that increases the destructive potential of the immune system and directs its attack on a highly specific target. ∎

Suggested Reading

Bazin, *The Eradication of Smallpox: Edward Jenner and the First and Only Eradication of a Human Infectious Disease.*

Campbell & Reece, *Biology* (6th ed.), chapter 43.

Freeman, *Biological Science*, chapter 46.

Pines, ed., *Exploring the Biomedical Revolution.*

Purves et al., *Life* (7th ed.), chapter 18.

Questions to Consider

1. Some pathogens have very high mutation rates. Why is it more difficult to develop vaccines for these pathogens?

2. Populations of indigenous peoples in the New World typically have been decimated by disease when they first encountered Europeans, even though the Europeans remained healthy. How does the phenomenon of acquired immunity help explain this fact?

Form and Function in Plants I

Lecture 46

There are a couple of reasons why we have been focusing on animals in this middle part of the course. The first reason, perhaps a selfish one, is that we ourselves are animals, and naturally we are interested in how we work when we are asking questions about form and function. A second reason is that some aspects of form and function in organisms are simply more elaborated in animals.

This lecture begins an examination of plant structure, development, and physiology, illustrating similarities and differences with analogous processes in animals. After introducing the general makeup of plants, we focus on angiosperms, a large and common group of plants that provides a useful illustration of basic plant structure. We then describe early plant development, which shares some surprising similarities with early animal development, and then discuss the emergence of the basic shoot-root axis of a plant. Finally, we examine the ABC model of flower development and learn how the complex structures of a flower develop from undifferentiated meristem tissue.

Before exploring how plants function, we must consider their particular structure. Plants are multicellular organisms; multicellularity evolved independently in plants and animals more than 1 billion years ago. Given this distant origin, it is not surprising that the structure of plants differs radically from the structure of animals. Plants, like animals, are eukaryotic organisms, however, and their cells differ from animal cells primarily in three ways. The first and most obvious difference is that, in addition to a lipid bilayer membrane, plant cells are also encased in a rigid cell wall made of cellulose (a very stable polysaccharide) embedded in a matrix of proteins and other kinds of polysaccharides.

The plant cell wall provides an even greater degree of protection for the cell than a cell membrane does, and it also lends structural rigidity to plant cells and tissues. For this reason, plants do not need skeletons to stand upright. One consequence of having a cell wall, however, is that individual plant cells cannot move in relation to other cells, which has important consequences for the way plants develop and otherwise respond to the environment.

The two other main differences between plant and animal cells involve two organelles found in plant cells that are not found in animal cells. *Chloroplasts* perform *photosynthesis*, the process by which energy from sunlight is captured and used to build organic molecules that store this energy. The *central vacuole* is derived from the endomembrane system and plays a number of different functional roles, including acting as a storage compartment and expanding rapidly by absorbing water.

Plants as a group are quite diverse in their structure. The most diverse and widespread group of land plants are those flowering plants called *angiosperms*. The structure of land plants reflects their existence at the interface of the ground and air environments; plant bodies are fundamentally divided into an above-ground shoot system and a below-ground root system.

Both shoots and roots are basically cylinders with concentric circles of different types of cells. Plant cells and tissues differentiate in different ways depending on whether they will become part of the shoot system or part of the root system. The root system of plants mostly consists of a main descending cylinder with other cylinders branching off it. The shoot system of a typical plant is essentially a main cylindrical stem extending upward, with smaller cylinders branching off it. The shoot system of plants also tends to include a large number of modified organs that take on divergent shapes—most notably leaves, which are specialized for light gathering, and flowers, which are the reproductive organs of angiosperms. Each part of a flowering plant is composed of three fundamental types of tissue:

- *Dermal tissue*, also called *epidermis*, is usually a single cell layer on the outside surface of the plant. Like animal skin, plant epidermis is especially durable. In some parts of the plant, dermal cells may also be specialized to take in or release materials.

- *Vascular tissue* runs along the center of the plant and includes two types of specialized tissues. *Xylem* is specialized to transport water along the length of the plant, mostly from the roots to the shoots; *phloem* transports sugars manufactured by photosynthesis from the leaves to the roots or other non-photosynthetic parts.

- *Ground tissue* makes up the rest of the plant and is essentially a tube of tissue running along the length of the plant, with vascular tissue on the inside and epidermis on the outside. Ground tissue performs a variety of functions but mostly serves as structural support and as a storage place for food or other compounds.

Compared to animal bodies, plants appear to have fewer specialized organs. Nonetheless, plant bodies do have specializations, with different cell types arranged in particular patterns relative to each other, which is the hallmark of multicellularity.

The development of a complex multicellular plant from the single cell of a fertilized zygote depends on three major processes: *cell division*, *cell differentiation*, and *morphogenesis*. These processes in plant development are largely similar to animal development, with two major differences. The first difference has to do with differentiation—fully developed plants have a significant number of relatively undifferentiated cells (*meristem tissues*) that can develop into many different kinds of cells. Meristem tissues usually occur at the tips of shoots and roots, as well as in a band running along the length of the plant. The second major difference involves morphogenesis—the cell walls of plant cells render them incapable of moving, meaning that morphogenesis in plant development must be limited largely to patterns of cell growth.

The shoot-root (or apical-basal) axis of a plant develops from an initial asymmetry in early development that is further reinforced by cell-to-cell signaling. The first division a plant zygote undergoes is asymmetric, producing one small daughter cell that will turn into the embryo and a larger cell that will form a nutritional support structure, called the *suspensor*. As the smaller daughter cell continues to divide, cells adjacent to the suspensor become root structures, while cells on the side opposite the suspensor become only shoot structures. The molecular mechanisms are still poorly understood, but it seems clear that, as in animals, cell-to-cell interactions between the embryo and the suspensor are responsible for this early specification. Once the shoot-root axis is established, the root apical meristem tissue at the suspensor end of the growing plant embryo is fated to produce only root system structures. The shoot apical meristem tissue at the opposite end is fated to produce only shoot system structures.

The three basic tissue types found in plants are also determined very early in embryogenesis, in the *globular stage*, when the embryo is a small ball of cells. Again, the mechanisms responsible are not well understood but must involve cell signals. At the globular stage, a plant embryo is a ball of cells; somehow, this ball turns into an elongated root system and a shoot system with specialized organs. This happens as plant cells are induced to grow in different planes in a precisely regulated fashion.

In plants, control of cell shape in development depends on controlling the cell wall. Chemical signals modify the structural integrity of the cell wall by loosening or tightening the connections among its elements. This control can also be exerted selectively on different sides of a single cell, allowing the plant to grow along a desired plane. The central vacuole plays an important role in morphogenesis by taking in water, which exerts pressure from the inside of the cell and pushes out the cell wall.

The first division a plant zygote undergoes is asymmetric, producing one small daughter cell that will turn into the embryo and a larger cell that will form a nutritional support structure, called the *suspensor*.

The ABC model accounts for the development of complex flower organs from a few master genes. Flowers in angiosperms are a collection of several kinds of organs that differentiate from a region of apical meristem. A basic flower is a concentric set of rings (called *whorls*) of these different organ types. The outermost ring is made of *sepals*—green, leaf-like structures that surround the unopened flower bud and spread out as the bud opens. The next ring is made of the flower's *petals*; next are the *stamens*, the male reproductive organs of plants, which produce pollen (male gametes). The innermost ring is made of the *carpels* (also called *pistils*), the female reproductive organs. The first insight into the development of these complex organs came from studying mutant plants with malformed flowers. Patterns of mutations suggested that each mutation was caused by a defect in one of three genes; it further suggested that the defective genes coded for transcription factors required for the development of each organ type. Thus, the genes involved must be genetic master switches.

The hypothesis that satisfied these observations has become known as the *ABC model of flower development*, which has three basic tenets. First, the model assumes that each of the three genes is expressed in two adjacent rings in the meristem that will give rise to a flower. The second feature is that this pattern of gene expression results in four different combinations of genes being expressed in four concentric rings. Finally, the model assumes that each of these four combinations will cause the rings in which they are expressed to develop into a different organ type.

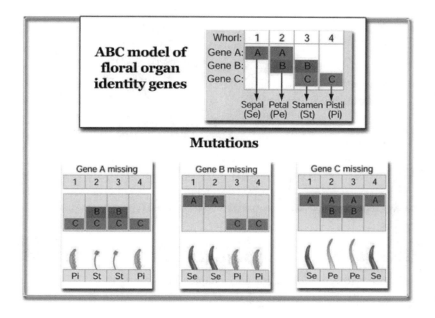

In the ABC model, combinations of the A, B, and C genes produce the different organ types. Furthermore, the model assumes that the protein produced by the A gene inhibits the production of C gene proteins and vice versa. The mutations predicted by the model from defective genes in different combinations corresponded exactly to experimental findings, which means that the highly ordered development of the different organ types needed to make a complex flower can be accounted for by the relatively simple, overlapping action of a very small number of master regulatory genes. ■

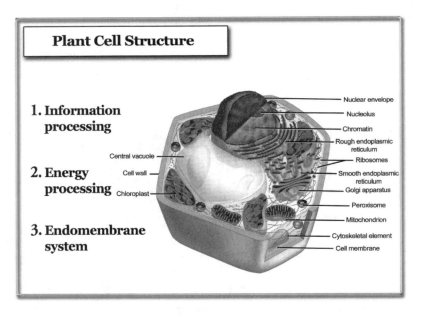

Plant Cell Structure

1. **Information processing**

2. **Energy processing**

3. **Endomembrane system**

Central vacuole
Cell wall
Chloroplast

Nuclear envelope
Nucleolus
Chromatin
Rough endoplasmic reticulum
Ribosomes
Smooth endoplasmic reticulum
Golgi apparatus
Peroxisome
Mitochondrion
Cytoskeletal element
Cell membrane

Suggested Reading

Campbell & Reece, *Biology* (6th ed.), chapter 35.

Freeman, *Biological Science*, chapter 20.2.

Raven, *Biology of Plants*.

1. Almost all animals have "mouths." What structure or structures of plants are functionally analogous to something like a "mouth"?

2. How does the genetic regulation of flower development contrast with genetic regulation of segmentation in fruit fly embryos?

Form and Function in Plants II
Lecture 47

Let's start by considering how plants manage their water supply. In a typical plant, water moves from the roots, where it is absorbed from the soil, upwards through the rest of the plant via the vascular xylem tissues. Much of the water taken in by the plant this way is eventually lost from the leaves through a process called transpiration.

In this lecture, we continue an examination of plant development and maintenance by looking at the role of transpiration in plant homeostasis, and by discussing the ways plants control this process. The rest of the lecture is devoted to a thorough treatment of oriented growth, or *tropism*, which plays a similar role in plant homeostasis as movement does in animal homeostasis. We conclude by noting that not all plant movement is slow; some plants move quickly in ways more characteristic of animals. In ways similar to homeostasis in animals, plants regulate their physiology, respond to stimuli, and otherwise coordinate and maintain their various parts in an adaptive fashion.

Plants control water balance in their tissues through *transpiration*. In a typical plant, water is absorbed from the soil through the roots and moves upward through the plant via the vascular xylem tissues. Much of this water is eventually lost through the leaves in a process called transpiration. An enormous amount of water moves through plants in this way. For example, on a single summer day, a maple tree 15 meters tall was estimated to lose 220 liters of water per hour to the atmosphere through transpiration. The tremendous amount of water plants use is, in part, a cost they pay for photosynthesis.

Plants have evolved many adaptations to conserve water by preventing water loss from their leaves. For example, the epidermal cells of leaves are typically covered with a layer of wax that minimizes water loss. In transpiration, most of the water is lost through specialized pores called *stomata* (the singular is stoma). These stomata can open and close, which allows the plant to control the amount of water it loses.

Plants' control of transpiration, however, is subject to a critical tradeoff. Plants need an adequate supply of carbon dioxide (CO_2) for photosynthesis, which they obtain from the air. If the stomata are open, a plant gains CO_2 but loses water; if the stomata are closed, it conserves water but gets little or no CO_2. Plants cannot simply turn off transpiration altogether; it is also used to transport nutrients to leaves and for evaporative cooling. This tradeoff shares much in common with animal homeostasis; both processes need feedback and control mechanisms that allow a favorable balance to be maintained.

Plants regulate their internal environment through sophisticated feedback and control mechanisms, just as multicellular animals do. Stomata are formed by a pair of elongated guard cells, which are shaped like kidney beans. These guard cells can change their shape, either widening the gap between two cells or narrowing it, thus opening or closing the stoma. Guard cells change their shape by taking in and releasing water. In addition, guard cell walls are not uniformly stiff. The guard cell wall adjacent to the opening of the stoma is much thicker than the surface that faces away from the opening. As a result, when guard cells take in water, they curve away from each other. The amount of water taken in by guard cells depends on the concentration of ions in the cell, specifically potassium (K^+). A high K^+ concentration in the cell will bring water in through osmosis. Most of the potassium and water that enter the cell are stored in the central vacuole.

Active K^+-specific ion channels are responsible for pumping K^+ into guard cells. Several kinds of signals, in turn, appear to regulate these ion channels. Light stimulates guard cells to take up K^+, because the plant requires CO_2 mostly during the day when light can drive photosynthesis. After dark, CO_2 is no longer needed, and closing the stomata reduces transpiration and saves water. Another signal that influences K^+ uptake is the concentration of CO_2 in open spaces inside the leaf. When CO_2 levels decrease, guard cells take up more K^+, become turgid, and open the stomata. Finally, the amount of K^+ in guard cells can also be controlled by a plant hormone called abscisic acid, which is produced in response to severe water deficiencies in cells on the inside of the leaf. Abscisic acid triggers the opening of ion channels that allow K^+ to leave the cell. As the concentrations of K^+ and water in the guard cells decrease, they become flaccid and the stomata close.

Although plants cannot move in the same way as animals, they can respond to the environment through oriented growth. Unlike in animals, plant growth tends to be open-ended. For example, a house plant near a window will bend in such a way that its leaves all face the window. If the same plant is rotated, it will straighten, then bend in the other direction so that its leaves face the window again. This adaptive behavior of plants is called *phototropism*. Phototropism raises two questions: First, how does the plant sense the direction the light is coming from, and second, what actually makes the plant bend?

In their 1881 book *The Power of Movement in Plants*, Charles Darwin and his son Francis detailed how they thought phototropism and other kinds of oriented movement in plants might work. The Darwins experimented on young oat seedlings, which show very strong phototropic response. They hypothesized that the tip of the growing oat shoot contained a tissue that detects light. When they cut off the tip of a shoot, it remained upright, even when strongly illuminated from one side. They found the same result when the tip was merely shielded from light instead of cut off.

Finally, the Darwins covered other parts of the shoot, which did not affect phototropic response. They concluded that only the tip was responsible for sensing light and proposed that it produced a chemical signal in response to light that was passed on to lower tissues, causing the growing shoot to bend toward light. The Darwins' hypothesis was tested several decades later by the Danish physiologist Peter Boysen-Jensen. Boysen-Jensen cut off and replaced the tips of growing oat shoots, separating them from the rest of the shoot by different materials. Shoots separated by gelatin, which passes chemical signals, exhibited phototropism, while those separated with mica, which blocks chemical signals, did not.

The question of how a diffusible chemical could cause an oriented response was addressed in another set of experiments by Dutch physiologist Frits Went in 1926. Went used gelatin blocks to collect the chemical secreted by oat shoot tips. When he placed these blocks on the centers of "decapitated" shoots, the shoots grew but without specific orientation. However, if Went placed such a block off center on a decapitated shoot, the shoot would both grow and bend away from the side in contact with the block. Went concluded that the chemical produced by the tip stimulated growth and that the effect of light on the tip must be to reduce the amount of this chemical on the side receiving light.

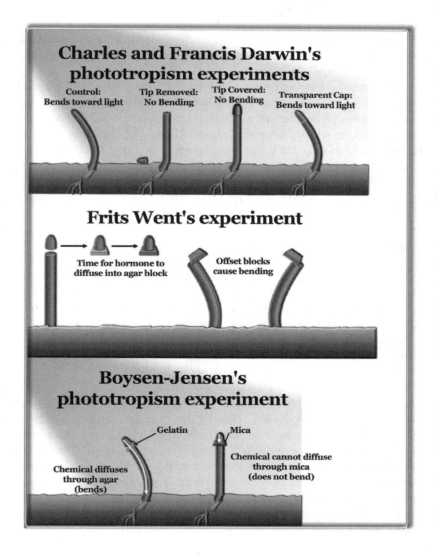

Charles and Francis Darwin's phototropism experiments

Control: Bends toward light

Tip Removed: No Bending

Tip Covered: No Bending

Transparent Cap: Bends toward light

Frits Went's experiment

Time for hormone to diffuse into agar block

Offset blocks cause bending

Boysen-Jensen's phototropism experiment

Gelatin

Mica

Chemical diffuses through agar (bends)

Chemical cannot diffuse through mica (does not bend)

Two alternative hypotheses were proposed to account for how light could produce such an asymmetric distribution of the growth-inducing chemical. Went himself proposed that the chemical was produced uniformly throughout the tip but that light caused it to migrate sideways, away from the light. The alternative hypothesis suggested that light either destroyed the chemical or prevented its production; thus, it would be found only on the shaded side of a growing tip.

These hypotheses were tested in a simple experiment performed by the plant physiologist Winslow Briggs. Briggs inserted a thin sheet of mica vertically through a shoot tip that had been cut off; the mica also extended through the gelatin block on which the tip was placed. The mica completely separated the two halves of a tip and the gelatin they sat on so that no chemical could pass from one side to the other.

Briggs then exposed the tip to a strong light from one side. If light destroyed or inhibited the production of the chemical signal, the illuminated half of the gelatin block would not contain any of the chemical signal, while the shaded half of the gelatin block would. Only the shaded half would be able to induce a phototropic response in a decapitated shoot. If, however, light had no effect on production or destruction of the chemical signal but, instead, caused its lateral movement, both halves of the block would contain it (because the mica prevented any movement from one side to the other) and both would be equally effective in causing a phototropic response when applied to a decapitated shoot. Briggs observed that an equal amount of the chemical signal remained on each side, demonstrating that light causes the lateral migration of the chemical signal, not its destruction.

The chemical responsible for phototropism is a plant hormone called *auxin* that is involved in many aspects of plant growth and development. The exact molecular basis of its action on plant cells is still the subject of research, but its major effect on plant cells is to cause them to elongate. The current hypothesis is that auxin activates ion channels that are specific for hydrogen ions, which changes the pH of the cell wall. This change in pH activates enzymes called *expansins*, which break down cellulose fibers in the cell wall, causing it to become more flexible. This weakening causes the cell to expand in one direction. The higher concentration of auxin on the shaded side of a growing shoot causes shaded cells to elongate more than cells on the sunny side. If a plant has the same number of cells on either side, but the cells on one side are longer, the shoot will bend toward the side with the shorter cells—which is the side facing the light.

Phototropism is just one example of how plants detect and respond to cues in the environment by changing their patterns of growth. Plants also exhibit similar kinds of tropisms in response to a number of other cues. For example, in a plant seedling on its side, the shoot will bend upward toward light, but the root will bend downward toward the ground. Such *gravitropism* is independent of light and appears to come from the movement of vesicles densely packed with starch inside the plant's cells.

Not all plant behaviors are slow, irreversible growth responses. Venus fly-traps and *Mimosa* leaves exhibit rapid changes in structure. In *Mimosa*, stimulation in one part of the plant is transmitted to other parts of the plant by changes in electrical potential, similar to action potentials in animal neurons.

For example, on a single summer day, a maple tree 15 meters tall was estimated to lose 220 liters of water per hour to the atmosphere through transpiration. The tremendous amount of water plants use is, in part, a cost they pay for photosynthesis. ■

Suggested Reading

Campbell & Reece, *Biology* (6th ed.), chapters 36 & 39.

Freeman, *Biological Science*, chapter 35.

Raven, *Biology of Plants*.

1. Some plants living in arid regions have evolved a way to incorporate CO_2 into an organic acid, using reactions that can occur at night, with this organic acid later supplying the carbon needed for photosynthesis. Can you explain how this mechanism helps the plant avoid desiccation?

2. Plants can detect information from the environment and respond adaptively to this information. Other than the obvious ability of animals to move longer distances, are plants and animals different in this regard? If so, how?

Behavior as an Adaptive Trait
Lecture 48

At the core of this discussion is going to be the relationship between a stimulus—a piece of information that an organism has available to it—and a response—the behavior that occurs as a result of receiving the information. The ideas of stimulus and response are not new to us. These ideas have appeared throughout our discussion of development and homeostasis. But today, we want to place these ideas more squarely in the context of thinking about how organisms behave.

Animals are most interesting in this respect because of their ability to move. Simple animals generally have simple responses to external stimuli, but even very complex organisms, such as birds, often respond in surprisingly simple ways to equally simple cues. Of course, animals can and do respond in complex ways to complex stimuli. The lecture concludes by examining why some behaviors are inflexible and others are not, and discusses the evolutionary factors that might help predict the level of flexibility an animal exhibits for a particular action.

As mobile organisms, animals can respond to external stimuli by movement. In the simplest case, animals move toward positive stimuli and away from negative stimuli. For example, a sow bug exposed to dry conditions becomes very active, moving about randomly. When it encounters an area with more moisture, its movement slows or ceases altogether. This kind of simple behavior is called a *kinesis*. A kinesis brings an animal closer to a preferred stimulus or farther from an undesirable one, without a specific orientation. In sow bugs, movement is triggered by an undesirable stimulus, dryness; decreased movement is triggered by a preferred stimulus, moisture.

As an example of a slightly more complex behavior, a planarian in a dish illuminated from one side will face the source of the light and move toward it. This kind of behavior is called a *taxis*; movement toward light is an example of *phototaxis*. A planarian has two light-sensing organs called *eyespots* located symmetrically on either side of its head. These eyespots do not resolve images, but they do detect the relative intensity of light. All a planarian has to do to orient to light is move until the intensity of light received by both eyespots is equal. Kinesis and taxis in animals, like tropism in plants, represent a simple kind of relationship between stimulus and response. The major difference is that taxis and kinesis involve movement through the action of muscles, whereas plant tropism involves movement through growth.

Though their physiology enables animals to respond in intricate ways to stimuli, they often behave as though they are making simple responses to surprisingly simple cues. The biologist G. Kingsley Noble studied the courtship behavior of the northern flicker, a bird found commonly across the United States, in the 1940s. The two sexes in this species look alike, except that the male has a prominent black mark on each side of his head, called a moustache. Noble found mated pairs of flickers—males and females that had paired up, were jointly defending a territory, had built a nest together, and so forth; he then captured the female and painted a moustache on her using removable black paint.

In sow bugs, movement is triggered by an undesirable stimulus, dryness; decreased movement is triggered by a preferred stimulus, moisture.

Noble observed that when such a female flew back to her nest, the male no longer recognized her—he treated her as though she were an intruding male and viciously attacked her. When Noble removed her moustache, she returned to the nest and was accepted by the male again as though nothing had happened. Though the male and the female had been intimately associated for weeks and were even raising young, the moustache appeared to be the single cue that flickers used to determine whether another individual was male or female. The painted moustache overrode all the myriad other cues that might have been used to recognize the other bird as a female, let alone as a mate.

Many kinds of animal behaviors are triggered by such simple cues, called *sign stimuli* or *releasers*. Sign stimuli are common; many aspects of animal behavior, including those involving mating and finding shelter, can be triggered by sign stimuli. The interesting feature of sign stimuli is that they demonstrate how animals often ignore much of the sensory information available to them and rely on a single cue to trigger behavior. Focusing on a single cue is more efficient and, thus, potentially more adaptive; the male flicker attacks potential rivals instead of his mate and usually needs only one piece of information to make the distinction. Complex animals, such as birds, certainly have the neural and motor capabilities to react in highly flexible and complex ways, but animal response is also sometimes much simpler than might be expected.

Behavioral biologist Konrad Lorenz performed experiments involving the nesting behavior of the greylag goose, a European species. These geese nest on the ground and their eggs are sometimes accidentally knocked out of the nest. When this happens, the female goose reaches over the edge of the nest and uses her beak to roll the egg back in. Lorenz was interested in the features the geese used to recognize their eggs, but in the course of this work, he noticed two important things about the way a female goose would retrieve a missing egg. First, the way the goose extended and retracted its neck and the pattern of side-to-side beak motions were virtually identical every time. Second, once the egg-retrieval behavior began, it continued to completion without adjustment, regardless of whether the goose still had the egg under its beak.

Many kinds of animal behaviors exhibit this same invariant, all-or-none character; Lorenz called these kinds of behaviors *fixed action patterns*. Fixed action patterns are another demonstration of how an animal's behavior often fails to make use of the enormous possible flexibility available to it. In the case of the geese, a fixed action pattern is presumably more adaptive, perhaps because it is more efficient or quicker than a more flexible response or allows the animal to look out for predators or otherwise monitor the environment.

The view of behavior as an adaptive trait implies that aspects of behavior that increase reproductive success can be selected for by natural selection. Sign stimuli and fixed action patterns can be viewed as adaptations in the same way as physiological processes or anatomical features might be; Darwin himself made the point that behaviors can evolve just like any other trait. However, the idea that adaptive behaviors can evolve as a consequence of natural selection requires us to assume that the expression of behavior is somehow under the influence of genes, because evolution works through gene frequency change in populations. The idea that the expression of behavior may have genetic underpinnings has often been considered controversial, especially in humans, but it is clear that behavior can be strongly influenced by genetics. The hybridization of different species of lovebirds is a classic example of how phenotypic differences in the behavior of the two species must be the result of genotypic differences. Since the lovebird experiment, many studies have demonstrated genetic determination of similarly complex behaviors.

Even the simplest behaviors, however, are influenced by many genes, and it is almost certainly a mistake to ascribe differences in complex behaviors to the action of a single gene. Reports in the popular press about the discovery of a gene that "controls" a complex behavioral trait are usually based on very small correlations between a particular allele or mutation and the expression of some behavior. It is often an over-interpretation to claim that a single particular gene "controls" or "determines" a complex behavior in any meaningful sense.

Although even complex animal behaviors can involve a remarkable *lack* of flexibility, animals exhibit an equally remarkable amount of flexibility in their behavior. Even in cases where a behavior seems genetically hard-wired, it can often be adjusted and fine-tuned. In the case of the lovebirds, hybrid offspring would eventually modify their behavior.

The ability of a response to a stimulus to be modified by prior experience is another hallmark of animal behavior. In the most general terms, this is what we commonly refer to as the ability to learn. Clearly, the ability to modify behavior as a result of experience and in response to various stimuli is often highly adaptive. The factor that determines whether a particular behavior will be flexible or inflexible is whether inflexibility or flexibility conveys a greater adaptive advantage.

For example, kangaroo rats respond to the very subtle sound of a rattlesnake moving through the air with a powerful backwards jump that, if successful, will propel them out of harm's way. Both the acoustic cues the rat responds to and the jump are highly stereotypic and inflexible. Furthermore, a kangaroo rat that has never encountered a rattlesnake before will show the same stereotypic escape response. In this case, it makes sense that the relationship between stimulus and response should be hard-wired. There simply may be no opportunity to learn the behavior, because it must be performed correctly the first time. Making any mistake is obviously costly; thus, flexibility conveys little advantage.

Just the opposite could be true if an animal benefits most by responding in different ways depending on the immediate circumstances or its prior experience. In fact, the kind of flexibility we observe in these contexts is often described in terms of "decisions" made by animals based on the information they have available. Whether an animal behavior is inflexible and highly determined or flexible and modifiable by experience will ultimately depend on which mode of operation is associated with greater reproductive success. Therefore, the degree to which behavior is learned and the learning process itself are adaptive traits.

Whether or not animals actually make decisions in the human sense of the word, examining their behavior illustrates an important point: The biological evolution of even the human mind must have been the product of selection acting on mechanisms that primarily maintain an internal environment. This may be a disquieting notion, but from the perspective of a biologist, it must be true to some extent. ■

Suggested Reading

Campbell & Reece, *Biology* (6th ed.), chapter 51.

Kruuk, *Niko's Nature: The Life of Niko Tinbergen and His Science of Animal Behaviour*.

Lorenz, *King Solomon's Ring*.

Purves et al., *Life* (7th ed.), chapter 52.

1. Mate recognition and predator avoidance behaviors often involve *releasers* and *fixed action patterns*. Can you think of other kinds of animal behaviors for which you would expect the response to stimuli to be simple and invariant and learning to be a disadvantage? What about the opposite?

2. The difference between *innate* and *learned* behavior is often described as a dichotomy. Why is this view an oversimplification?

Energy and Resources in Living Systems
Lecture 49

In the third and final section of this course, we are going to turn our attention to the theme of energy and resources. To introduce this theme and its importance, let me go back to a couple of specific examples we have discussed earlier.

This earlier material and the accompanying concepts set the stage for examining the third major theme of the course, "Energy and Resources." As with the earlier material, the discussion of this theme begins at the molecular level and progresses through the hierarchy of biological organization. As our discussion moves upward through this hierarchy, it will begin to address the field of ecology, which considers the effects of energy and resources on the scale of populations, communities of organisms, and the entire planet.

This course examines the subject of biology in three major sections, each with a unifying theme. The lectures explore each theme across the hierarchy of living systems, considering, first, the level of molecules and cells and progressing through higher levels of organization.

The first third of the course focused on the theme of Information and Evolution and began with the question of how living things could store and transmit information about their own structures in order to reproduce themselves. This information, of course, must have to do with the structure of proteins. It is stored in DNA in unique sequences of nucleotide bases that correspond to the unique sequences of amino acids that make up different kinds of proteins.

During mitosis, replicated DNA is divided into daughter cells in a way that ensures that both daughter cells get a complete complement of genetic information. We also examined how, in meiosis, the movements of homologous chromosomes can account for the way heritable traits are passed from parents to their offspring. This observation led us to a more formal look at the patterns of trait transmission known as Mendelian genetics, which in turn led to the conclusion that genetic variation is constantly introduced to the genetic makeup of organisms so that offspring will virtually never be the same as their parents.

The most profound consequence of this genetic variation is that it provides the substrate for evolution by natural selection, an idea first proposed by Charles Darwin in the 19th century, which has become the most important organizing idea in modern biology. In addition to natural selection, populations may change over time as a result of random genetic drift and other factors affecting the relative proportions of alleles in the gene pool of a population.

The Information and Evolution theme concluded by examining how evolutionary mechanisms might lead to speciation (the rise of new species), and then by asking how to organize this diversity using the tools of phylogenetic systematics. The genetic information found in every organism that exists today or has ever existed is the result of extensive modifications of the original genetic information found in the very first living organism on the planet.

The middle third of the course examined the second theme, Development and Homeostasis. Two general conditions are required for multicellular organisms to exist. First, a single cell with a single set of genes must be able to develop into a diverse set of cells, each with different characteristics, different functions, and different positions in a complex organism. This is the the fundamental problem of development. Second, multicellular organisms must have ways for their various parts to communicate in order to coordinate the activities of diverse parts with different functions and, in so doing, maintain a favorable and stable internal environment. This requirement leads to the concept of homeostasis and its many manifestations.

The discussion of Development and Homeostasis began at the molecular level of organization, considering, first, the problem of how different kinds of cells in the same organism can express different proteins at different times and in different places. The solution to this problem is the fact that not all genes in a cell's genome are expressed all the time. Examination of the mechanisms by which cells regulate gene expression revealed the critical role of proteins as transcription factors.

The course next turned to the question of how cells communicate to control and coordinate each other's activities. The binding of signal molecules outside the cell to membrane-bound protein receptors initiates a cascade of events inside the cell that activate or deactivate proteins, which in turn, affect the way the cell functions. We then examined how a single cell can develop into a complex organism. The basic processes of cell division, cell differentiation, and morphogenesis are responsible for the unfolding of a complex organism from a single cell.

In addition, different factors regulate these processes at different times in development. Proteins and mRNAs in a fertilized zygote largely control the earliest stages of development, with the developing individual's own genes playing a substantial role only at some later point, usually beginning with gastrulation. Signals from other cells play an essential role in determining a particular cell's fate in a developing organism, with diffusible positional signals being especially important in establishing the three-dimensional morphology of a complex organism.

Once development is complete, the complex structures and functions of multicellular organisms must be maintained, leading to the concept of homeostasis. Homeostasis requires the coordinated responses of effectors that counteract perturbations to a physiological system through negative feedback, returning the system to some optimal set point. To do this, organisms have evolved sophisticated systems for processing and transmitting physiological information.

Homeostasis, broadly considered, includes not only the ability to establish and maintain a stable internal environment but also the ability to maintain a favorable external environment and to defend the integrity of the organism against assaults from the outside world. In this context, we considered both how animals transduce information from the outside world into physiological information and how they react to the environment, usually through movement. This broad interpretation of homeostasis also led to a discussion of the immune system—the defense mechanisms animals have evolved to protect their internal environments from injury or attack by disease or parasites. The immune system is an impressive example of a highly coordinated and regulated homeostatic system. The middle third of the course ended by discussing behavior as an adaptation for maintaining an optimal environment.

The final section of the course will examine the theme of Energy and Resources. Transfer RNA (tRNA) provides an example to introduce the theme of Information and Evolution; with the help of the enzyme aminoacyl-tRNA synthetase, tRNAs must be bound to the correct amino acids for protein synthesis to occur. This molecular match-up represents the creation of order from disorder; however, it only occurs if energy is invested in the reaction. The energy in this case is donated by adenosine triphosphate (ATP), which acts like a molecular currency by storing and transferring energy in cellular functions. Energy is necessary for this process because the appropriate amino acid and tRNA molecule are very unlikely to form a chemical bond with each other spontaneously. The molecular mechanism responsible for muscle contraction provides another example of the importance of energy to create and maintain order. This process also requires ATP to function, with ATP donating energy to myosin in a way that is similar to, but slightly different from, its interaction with tRNA.

Signals from other cells play an essential role in determining a particular cell's fate in a developing organism, with diffusible positional signals being especially important in establishing the three-dimensional morphology of a complex organism.

In the most basic terms, the added energy in both cases imposes order on the system. Biological systems are generally characterized by a high degree of order, from molecules to ecosystems, which costs energy to create, maintain, and modify. Life requires energy, and if an organism runs out of energy, it dies. When an organism dies, it loses its orderliness—it decomposes.

Energy is critical for life and, thus, provides the organizing theme for the final third of the course. The examination of energy will begin as before on the molecular level by considering how energy is stored, processed, and produced by cells. This entails a close look at the biochemistry of cells and the role of energy in enabling this biochemistry to work. We will then look at ATP in more detail to gain a better understanding of how it can function as an energy currency in cellular processes. This will also include a more detailed examination of how enzymes work.

The importance of ATP as a common energy currency raises the question of where it comes from in the first place. This question will lead to a series of lectures on how ATP is produced by cells from the breakdown of other organic molecules through the processes of glycolysis, cellular respiration, and oxidation phosphorylation. Even then, it will be necessary to ask where the "fuel" used to produce ATP comes from—this question will lead to an examination of the process of photosynthesis, by which green plants, algae, and some kinds of bacteria capture energy from sunlight and convert this captured energy into sugars.

Once this is established, we will move up through the hierarchy of biological organization and look at the implications of energetics for living systems in general. We will also begin to consider resources, the other half of the theme of this section. In addition to energy to build molecules and tissues, living systems also need the raw materials from which they are built. These materials include such fundamental substances as carbon, water, and nitrogen, as well as other resources required for life.

The discussion of energy and resources at higher levels of biological organization—populations, communities, or ecosystems—raises the point that there is often too little of both. This limiting effect plays a major role in determining the nature of living systems at all levels of organization. This examination of energy and resources at higher levels of the hierarchy leads into the area of biology called ecology. Much of ecology has to do with how energy and resources are used by different kinds of organisms and how these patterns of use determine the abundance and distribution of species. This, in turn, leads to a consideration of the implications of energy and resource limitations for the biosphere—the entire planet. ■

Campbell & Reece, *Biology* (6th ed.), chapters 6 & 9.

Purves et al., *Life* (7th ed.), chapter 6.

Questions to Consider

1. The attachment of an amino acid to a tRNA molecule requires energy. Which other of the specific steps associated with the conversion of information in DNA into the structure of a protein do you think might require energy, and why?

2. Without a supply of energy, an organism will eventually die. What are some non-biological examples of systems that similarly depend on a continuous supply of energy to function, and how do they differ—if at all—from living systems?

How Energy is Harnessed by Cells
Lecture 50

How living systems use energy to create and maintain order can largely be understood as a matter of chemistry. Much of this chemistry is a matter of building polymers of biomolecules, those biomolecules we introduced early on in the course, including carbohydrates—those are sugars—nucleic acids such as DNA, proteins and lipids.

This lecture begins by examining the chemical basis by which organisms obtain energy, in the context of cellular *metabolism*, which refers to the entirety of all biochemical processes occurring in the cells of an organism. All metabolic reactions either produce or require energy. After discussing the nature of energy itself, the lecture examines the consequences of the energy imbalance created by reactions that require energy to build more complex molecules out of simpler ones. Living things overcome this imbalance by adding energy to their systems, and the lecture concludes by presenting an overview of the mechanism by which added energy is used to drive essential metabolic reactions.

The way living systems use energy to create and maintain order is largely a matter of chemistry. Much of this activity involves building polymers, such as carbohydrates, nucleic acids, proteins, and lipids. However, living systems also need to break down all kinds of biomolecules into smaller, less complex parts. A cell is essentially a miniature chemical plant that takes in raw materials, builds polymers, and breaks down other polymers for their raw materials and energy.

Metabolism is the term used for the sum total of all the biochemical processes in an organism's cells. A typical cell is capable of thousands of interconnected biochemical reactions. Some compounds are connected by biochemical pathways only to compounds that immediately precede or follow them in a particular sequence of reactions, but many compounds are connected to several others—even dozens of others—by branching and intersecting pathways. The metabolic pathways in a cell are not only complex, but more importantly, are all potentially interconnected. The product of each reaction is likely to be the substrate of another, and these products and substrates may themselves perform critical functions.

Metabolic reactions may be divided into two classes. Metabolic processes that break more complex compounds down into simpler ones are called *catabolic pathways*. Catabolic pathways are *exergonic*—they release energy. The most important catabolic pathways are those that break down sugars and make stored energy available in ATP. Taken together, this set of pathways is called *cellular respiration*.

Metabolic processes that assemble complex compounds from simpler ones are called *anabolic pathways* and are *endergonic*—they require energy. Anabolic pathways include those that synthesize proteins and nucleic acids. Much of what is important to understand about energy in living systems involves learning how energy that is released by catabolic pathways may be harnessed, stored, and transferred for use in anabolic pathways.

The study of metabolic processes begins with an understanding of the concept of *energy*. In physical terms, *energy* refers to the capacity to do work—that is, to move matter against an opposing force. Lifting an object, for example, requires work to move that matter against the opposing force of gravity. Energy can also refer to the ability to rearrange matter that resists movement. In terms of chemistry, energy is the ability to rearrange molecules by creating or breaking stable chemical bonds in molecules.

Energy comes in many forms—chemical, mechanical, electromagnetic—but all forms of energy can be considered to be one of two types.

- *Kinetic energy* is energy associated with movement or activity and performs work by altering the motion or properties of some piece of matter.

- *Potential energy* is stored energy; it can be stored in an object resisting a force, in chemical bonds, or in a concentration gradient, to mention a few ways.

Not all the energy in a system is available to do work. The energy that is available to do work in a system is called *free energy*; for simplicity, we will refer to the free energy in a system as its energy. The amount of energy in a system is related to how stable or unstable that system is—how likely it is to change spontaneously. Systems with much free energy tend to be relatively unstable and, thus, more likely to spontaneously change their state. Systems with relatively little free energy tend to be more stable and less likely to change spontaneously.

> **A ball at the top of a ramp is in a higher energy state than a ball at the bottom and it will tend to go to the bottom of the ramp spontaneously; if at the bottom, additional energy is required to get the ball to the top.**

In addition, high-energy systems are generally found in a more orderly state, whereas low-energy systems are more disordered, because energy is required to establish and maintain the orderly state of living things. The force of gravity on a ball provides an intuitive example of the relationship among energy, stability, and orderliness. A ball at the top of a ramp is in a higher energy state than a ball at the bottom and it will tend to go to the bottom of the ramp spontaneously; if at the bottom, additional energy is required to get the ball to the top.

A less intuitive example is that of concentration gradients across a membrane. A large concentration difference across a membrane is a high-energy state; the same concentration on both sides (that is, the lack of a difference in concentrations on either side of the membrane) is a low-energy state. Molecules will move spontaneously from the more concentrated side to the less concentrated side, but not vice versa.

Finally, a more complex molecule generally represents a higher energy and a less stable state than a simple molecule built from the same atoms. For example, the atoms that form a molecule of the sugar glucose can also be arranged to form several molecules of carbon dioxide and water. The glucose molecule is more complex than these simpler molecules and, thus, more orderly; it also has more energy stored in its chemical bonds. Glucose is more likely to spontaneously break down into water and carbon dioxide than water and carbon dioxide are to spontaneously form glucose.

The ways that energy changes over time in catabolic and anabolic reactions raises a fundamental question about energy in metabolism. Catabolic reactions run energetically "downhill"; that is, they start with high-energy reactants and end up with low-energy products. Therefore, we mioght expect catabolic reactions to occur spontaneously and release energy when they occur. By contrast, anabolic reactions run "uphill," transforming low-energy reactants into high-energy products. For this reason, we expect that anabolic reactions will not occur spontaneously and will require energy when they do occur.

This difference between catabolic and anabolic reactions raises the question of how reactions can go from a low-energy state to a high-energy state. Over time, systems tend to go from states of high energy to states of low energy, not the reverse; this is a manifestation of the Second Law of Thermodynamics, which predicts that disorder in any system will increase over time.

Because catabolic reactions run "downhill," they are consistent with the Second Law and should be able to proceed spontaneously. Anabolic reactions, on the other hand, appear to defy the Second Law. However, DNA replication, RNA transcription, and protein synthesis all involve anabolic reactions, making it clear that life simply could not exist without the ability for such reactions to occur. In fact, life itself is characterized by the fact that it appears to defy the Second Law.

Living organisms create and maintain an orderly state by adding energy to the system. Anabolic reactions require additional energy to run, which raises two questions: Where does this energy come from, and how do cells acquire it? In answer to the first question, catabolic reactions release energy, and in theory, a cell could obtain energy by running catabolic reactions. Cells in fact do something like this, although capturing the energy from catabolic reactions is a a complex process, as will become clear over the next several lectures.

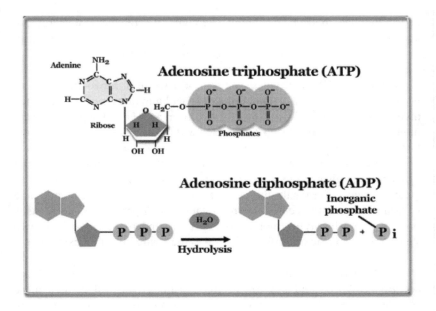

Assuming that cells can obtain energy from catabolic reactions, the answer to the second question is a process called *energy coupling* that living systems use to drive anabolic reactions "uphill." In energy coupling, the energy released by exergonic reactions (and usually stored in the form of ATP) is donated to anabolic reactions and used to drive them "uphill." ATP is related to the nucleotide adenine; it differs by having three phosphate groups attached to the ribose instead of just one. A phosphate group is a phosphorus atom bonded to four oxygen atoms, and the bonds between phosphate groups in the triphosphate "tail" of ATP store quite a bit of energy.

Furthermore, the high-energy bonds between phosphate groups are not completely stable. The bonds between the terminal phosphates can be broken, yielding a molecule of adenosine diphosphate (ADP) and an inorganic phosphate group ("inorganic" because it is no longer part of an organic molecule). The chemical reaction that turns a molecule of ATP into a molecule of ADP is called *hydrolysis*, because breaking the bond also requires a water molecule. The hydrolysis of ATP into a molecule of ADP and an inorganic phosphate is highly exergonic. It is the fact that energy can be stored in ATP in this way that allows living systems to use energy from catabolic reactions to drive anabolic reactions efficiently.

In most cases, ATP contributes energy to a reaction in a two-step process. For example, in the conversion of glutamic acid into glutamine, the first step involves the transfer of a phosphate group from an ATP to the glutamic acid molecule. This exergonic step donates some of the energy stored in ATP in the form of a high-energy phosphate group that is now attached to the glutamic acid, which is said to be phosphorylated. This phosphorylated intermediate is in a much higher energy state and, thus, less stable than unphosphorylated glutamic acid. As a result, the reaction of a phosphorylated glutamic acid with an ammonia molecule to form glutamine will proceed spontaneously. By coupling a highly exergonic reaction to an endergonic reaction in two steps in this way, the cell effectively makes the desired reaction exergonic.

Although energy coupling can drive endergonic reactions "uphill," it does not violate the Second Law of Thermodynamics. The cell gains a more complex, more orderly, higher-energy compound, but the energy stored in ATP has been lost. Fortunately, ATP is a renewable resource; ADP can be rephosphorylated into ATP, which leads to the important question of how ATP is produced. ■

Suggested Reading

Alberts et al., *Essential Cell Biology* (2nd ed.), chapter 3.

Campbell & Reece, *Biology* (6th ed.), chapter 6.

Purves et al., *Life* (7th ed.), chapter 6.

Questions to Consider

1. How is the cell like a miniature chemical plant? How is it *not* like a chemical plant?

2. Where is the energy in a molecule of ATP? What is the nature of this energy?

Enzymes—Making Chemistry Work in Cells
Lecture 51

Just figuring out how to make endergonic reactions run energetically uphill isn't enough. We also have to figure out how cells control these biochemical reactions—how they control both exergonic and endergonic reactions. Obviously, not every reaction that could run in a cell should run all the time. And, when reactions that should run do run, the cell needs to make sure that they run at appropriate speeds.

This lecture begins by reviewing the crucial nature of energy coupling, and then describes the *activation energy* of a reaction, which represents an initial "push" required to make even exergonic reactions run in many cases. The lecture then closely examines the role and function of enzymes, proteins that selectively lower the activation energy of specific reactions, allowing those reactions to run efficiently. The lecture concludes by exploring the general ways in which cells regulate enzyme function.

Energy coupling is critical to life, because the reactions that synthesize the complex biomolecules that make up living organisms largely are endergonic. Cells must also be able to regulate both exergonic and endergonic reactions. Furthermore, most biochemical reactions—even exergonic reactions—do not run spontaneously.

Most reactions, regardless of type, require some energy to run. For example, glucose is a complex molecule that contains more energy than a collection of simpler water and carbon dioxide molecules having exactly the same kinds of atoms in the same proportions. Its higher energy level also makes glucose less stable, so it seems reasonable that glucose should spontaneously break down into other molecules—but this is not usually the case. Many exergonic reactions do not run spontaneously; in cells, *most* exergonic reactions do not. Even exergonic reactions usually require the input of a small amount of energy to start breaking the chemical bonds of the high-energy substrate.

Chemical bonds are inherently stable. The bonds of even high-energy molecules must be destabilized slightly, by adding energy to the molecule, before they will begin to break. The energy that must be added for an exergonic reaction to run is referred to as the activation energy of the reaction. A simple graphical model of the change in energy over time in an exergonic reaction is a straight line with a negative slope leading from a high-energy reactant to a low-energy product. A more realistic graph for a typical exergonic reaction would instead be a curve that initially rises to a higher energy level, then falls toward the lower energy state of the product. The graph forms a "hill" that must be crossed to get from one state to the other; this hill represents the activation energy of the reaction.

In the case of the amino acid arginine, for example, an enzyme called carboxypeptidase A changes the half-life of arginine's peptide bond from seven years to half a second!

The existence of an activation energy for catabolic reactions to run is essential for life. If high-energy molecules, such as proteins, nucleic acids, carbohydrates, and fats, broke down at normal temperatures, organisms would spontaneously combust (or they would never be assembled in the first place). The complex molecules that make up living things can exist without spontaneously breaking down only because breaking them down requires an activation energy. As an aside, all exergonic reactions will eventually run spontaneously although at an extremely slow rate.

Chemists typically add activation energy in the form of heat to cause reactions to run, but living systems require a different approach. The temperatures needed to provide the activation energy of many biochemical reactions are sufficiently high that they would kill the cell. Even if high temperatures were not a problem for cells, this method does not allow selective control; that is, there is no way to significantly change the temperature of just one part of the cell.

An alternative way to cause reactions to run at a faster rate is to lower the amount of activation energy required. A *catalyst* is a substance that increases the rate of a chemical reaction by lowering its activation energy. Catalysts interact with the compounds involved in a chemical reaction, but are not themselves reactants; they are not transformed or consumed by the reaction. Non-biological catalysts are used by chemists to make reactions run faster. However, most non-biological catalysts are non-specific—they catalyze a very wide range of reactions. Catalysts in cellular metabolism must be much more selective.

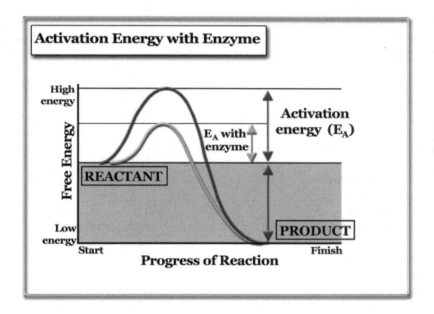

Enzymes are proteins that function as highly selective biological catalysts. An enzyme speeds the rate at which a reaction occurs by lowering the activation energy to a level in the range of the moderate temperatures of a living organism. Like any catalyst, an enzyme does not change the overall energetic relationship of a reaction; however, the effect they have on the rate of the reaction they catalyze can be astronomical, effectively turning a reaction on or off. In the case of the amino acid arginine, for example, an enzyme called carboxypeptidase A changes the half-life of arginine's peptide bond from seven years to half a second!

Unlike non-biological catalysts, each enzyme typically catalyzes only a single reaction. Enzymes have sites that bind to one or more of the reactants of the reaction they catalyze. A reactant that binds to an enzyme is called the *substrate* of that enzyme, and the place on the enzyme where the substrate binds is called the *active site*. The specificity with which an enzyme binds a particular substrate depends on the three-dimensional shape of the active site and the physical and chemical characteristics of the amino acids that make up the binding site. Only a narrow range of substrates, sometimes only one kind of molecule, fits the active site of an enzyme.

The way that enzymes interact with their substrates is often analogized to the physical relationship between a lock and a key. However, the physical structure of an enzyme is not necessarily rigid in the way an actual lock and key are. In many cases, the interaction of a substrate with an enzyme causes the active site of the enzyme to change shape, allowing the substrate to fit even more snugly into position. This more dynamic view of the physical interaction between an enzyme and its substrate is called the *induced-fit model*, because the substrate induces a tighter fit by causing the enzyme to change its shape slightly. This tighter fit brings the chemical groups associated with the active site even closer to help catalyze the reaction.

Once a substrate binds to the active site of an enzyme, the active site catalyzes the conversion of this substrate into the reaction's product, which drops off the enzyme. This same enzyme molecule will then interact with another substrate molecule, repeating the catalytic cycle. The turnaround time for an enzyme to act on a single substrate molecule is usually very fast; a typical enzyme may go through 1,000 substrate molecules a second, and some enzymes are much faster. Because of this and the fact that enzymes are not used up by the reactions they catalyze, a very small amount of a particular enzyme can have a major impact on the overall rate of a metabolic reaction.

Enzymes lower the activation energy of a reaction in a variety of ways. One of the simplest ways that enzymes catalyze reactions is by bringing two or more substrate molecules together in close proximity and in the proper orientation. Another common way for enzymes to catalyze reactions is by imposing additional molecular stresses on the substrate. As the substrate and active site bind together, the enzyme changes its shape, but the active site of the enzyme may affect the shape of the substrate, as well. This shape change puts more tension on the molecular bonds of the substrate, making them less stable and allowing them to be broken more easily. Finally, the amino acids at the active site of an enzyme may interact chemically with the substrate. This exchange also can destabilize the substrate molecule, allowing its chemical bonds to be broken more easily and, thus, allowing the desired reaction to run at a much faster rate.

The activity of enzymes may be regulated in several ways. One way in which cells can regulate enzyme activity is by expressing the genes for particular enzymes only when the metabolic reactions catalyzed by those enzymes should be active. The *lac* operon in prokaryotes is a good example of this method. Gene regulation, however, is a relatively slow way to regulate the activity of proteins. It is sometimes more adaptive to have proteins on hand that can be used immediately when needed.

There are two major ways other than gene regulation that cells use to control the activity of enzymes already present in the cell. To illustrate, consider the conversion of the amino acid threonine into the amino acid isoleucine. This conversion involves five steps, with each step catalyzed by a different enzyme; thus, there are four intermediate products in the metabolic pathway from threonine to isoleucine. In these kinds of metabolic pathways, one step often regulates the rest of the pathway.

One method of regulating enzyme activity is to separate enzymes and substrates into different compartments in the cell and only bring them together when the reaction should run. The disadvantage of this approach is that it requires mechanisms to transport substrates across cell membranes, which often takes extra energy and does not allow fine control of metabolic processes.

A second method of control, and the most important way in which cells regulate metabolic activity, involves *feedback inhibition*. Feedback inhibition occurs when a metabolic pathway is inhibited by its final product. For example, in the pathway that leads from threonine to isoleucine, isoleucine binds to the first enzyme in the chain. This binding is usually to a different site on the enzyme than the active site, and it changes the shape of the enzyme; this allosteric change renders the first enzyme in the pathway temporarily dysfunctional. As isoleucine accumulates, it slows down its own synthesis, preventing the cell from wasting chemical resources to synthesize more isoleucine than needed. The ways in which products interact with enzymes in metabolic pathways can be much more complex and subtle than in isoleucine. Nonetheless, feedback inhibition and other methods of enzyme control allow cells to fine-tune metabolic activities as their needs change. ■

Suggested Reading

Alberts et al., *Essential Cell Biology* (2nd ed.), chapter 3.

Campbell & Reece, *Biology* (6th ed.), chapter 6.

Purves et al., *Life* (7th ed.), chapter 6.

Tanford & Reynolds, *Nature's Robots: A History of Proteins.*

Questions to Consider

1. How are proteins that function as enzymes similar to proteins that function as transcription factors? How are they different?

2. Why might one suggest that an organism could spontaneously combust? What is the difficulty with this suggestion?

Cellular Currencies of Energy
Lecture 52

We will begin today with an overview of the energy needs of the cell, and a look at where this energy comes from and how it is stored in ATP and in a couple of other important energy-carrier molecules. This discussion will also lead us to consider a little more chemistry that we have to understand; specifically, how a reaction called an oxidation-reduction reaction works.

Enzymes often help couple ATP to such reactions, providing the energy they require; ATP is, in turn, produced through the processes of glycolysis and cellular respiration. The lecture examines the chemical nature of ATP that allows it to serve as an energy "currency" for cells, and then goes on to show how glucose stores energy, allowing it to act as a kind of cellular "fuel" for making more ATP. Finally, the lecture introduces the reactions that free this stored energy and describes the high level of control the cell exerts over these reactions—which are also controlled by enzymes.

Enzymes play a critical role in endergonic reactions by coupling energy from ATP. Enzymes catalyze exergonic reactions by lowering their activation energies, but this becomes a moot point for endergonic reactions that require energy to run. Nonetheless, enzymes play a critical role in mediating endergonic anabolic reactions as well. A key role of enzymes in endergonic reactions is to help couple energy donated by ATP to them. This energy coupling, in turn, often involves lowering the activation energy of the reaction that cleaves a phosphate group from an ATP molecule; the functional outcome of this event is to couple the energy stored in ATP to the reaction being powered. For this reason, these kinds of enzymes are called *coupling enzymes*.

The energy stored in ATP is used as well by cells in many ways other than the anabolic synthesis of complex organic compounds. ATP powers most other processes in the cell—anything that involves work and, therefore, requires energy. When ATP powers an anabolic reaction by phosphorylating one of the substrates, it is doing chemical work. In muscle movement, for example,

ATP provides a phosphate group that phosphorylates myosin; instead of driving a metabolic reaction, this phosphorylation changes the shape of the molecule. In this case, ATP is doing mechanical work.

ATP also provides the energy to power active ion channels and other proteins that transport substances across cell membranes. In these cases, ATP is performing what might be called transport work. Because of its many roles in powering cellular reactions and other processes, ATP is ubiquitous in living systems. By one estimate, a typical working muscle cell consumes 10 million molecules of ATP per second. By another estimate, it is thought that an average vertebrate animal consumes its body weight in ATP each day! Though it is difficult to know how truly accurate such estimates are, they nonetheless illustrate how much ATP is used by an individual organism.

ATP is generated through the processes of glycolysis and cellular respiration. After ATP donates a phosphate group to some reaction, the remaining molecule of ADP can be "recharged" into ATP by replacing the phosphate group. This process, however, requires energy. It seems reasonable to assume that catabolic reactions might provide the energy needed to make ATP from ADP through the action of coupling enzymes. This does happen, but not all catabolic reactions run in a way that allows cells to harvest the energy they release and store it in the form of ATP. Instead, most catabolic reactions give up the energy they release as heat, which is simply dissipated.

Only a small number of specialized reactions have evolved to capture the energy released by catabolic reactions and convert this energy into ATP. These reactions are associated with the metabolic processes of glycolysis and cellular respiration. These biochemical pathways are very similar across all organisms, suggesting that the fundamental mechanisms by which organisms extract and process energy must have evolved very early in the history of life.

The combined action of glycolysis and cellular respiration is the biological equivalent of burning organic compounds and can be represented by the following general equation: organic compound + oxygen → carbon dioxide (CO_2) + water (H_2O) + energy. Any organic compound, including carbohydrates, proteins, and nucleic acids, can be "burned" as fuel. The most common fuel is glucose, a relatively simple sugar.

Like most sugars, glucose is a chain of carbon atoms bonded to each other, with each carbon also bonded to hydrogen atoms and/or hydroxyl groups (an oxygen atom and a hydrogen atom bonded together). Glucose is a 6-carbon sugar, with the carbons usually occurring in the form of a ring. A glucose molecule is made of 6 carbon atoms, 12 hydrogen atoms, and 6 oxygen atoms; thus, its chemical formula is $C_6H_{12}O_6$. Using the general equation as the starting point, the chemical equation for the "burning" of glucose becomes: $C_6H_{12}O_6 + 6\ O_2 \rightarrow 6\ CO_2 + 6\ H_2O$ + energy.

The chemical energy in a molecule of glucose (or any other organic compound) is found in the chemical bonds of the carbon atoms and it is released through *oxidation-reduction reactions*. Many chemical reactions transfer one or more electrons from one of the reactants to another. These transfers are called *oxidation-reduction reactions* or *redox reactions*. In a redox reaction, the loss of electrons from an atom or compound is called *oxidation*, while the addition of electrons to a compound is called *reduction*. The exchange of electrons changes the original distribution of energy because some kinds of atoms "hold" their electrons more tightly than others. Atoms that hold electrons more tightly are said to be more electronegative.

Two kinds of atoms are especially important to consider in the breakdown of glucose—carbon and oxygen. Carbon is not very electronegative; it has a weaker pull on its electrons, which tend to occur at higher energy levels as a result. Oxygen is highly electronegative, and its electrons, therefore, tend to occur at lower energy levels. Oxygen electrons essentially hold less energy than carbon electrons. As a result, the bonds in a carbon-rich molecule, such as glucose, are full of energy because the carbon electrons exist at a higher energy state. If electrons are transferred from carbon atoms to oxygen atoms, energy will be released.

Not all redox reactions necessarily involve the complete transfer of electrons from one substance to another. For example, CO_2 is one of the products of combustion, and in it, some electrons have clearly stayed with the carbons. The oxygen in this molecule, however, draws the electrons closer to it, which has a similar effect to removing the electrons from the carbon. For this reason, the carbon in CO_2 is considered to be more oxidized than carbon in glucose. CO_2 is the most oxidized form of organic carbon and is the end product of the carbon found in glucose when it is completely "burned" in respiration. In general, organic molecules with an abundance of carbon-carbon and carbon-hydrogen bonds are excellent cellular fuels, because these bonds are the source of electrons that can be moved to lower energy states when attracted to oxygen.

Cellular fuels are oxidized in a step-wise process that controls the release of energy. Cells face a major problem when they oxidize glucose—oxidation can release energy in an uncontrolled fashion, making it very difficult to harness. Living systems solve this problem by gradually releasing the energy from glucose oxidation. When cells break down glucose to make ATP, they do so in a series of steps, each catalyzed by a different enzyme.

By one estimate, a typical working muscle cell consumes 10 million molecules of ATP per second. By another estimate, it is thought that an average vertebrate animal consumes its body weight in ATP each day!

An equally important aspect of step-wise oxidation is keeping oxygen out of the loop until the very end of the process. This is important because oxygen is so reactive that it is hard to control. Cells solve this problem by not passing electrons directly to oxygen but, instead, to organic compounds called *electron carriers* that are specialized to act as oxidizing agents.

The most important of these electron carriers is a compound called nicotinamide adenine dinucleotide (NAD). NAD exists in two forms: an oxidized form called NAD^+, which is positively charged, and a reduced form called NADH. (The "H" in NADH refers to an added hydrogen ion, which comes along when the molecule picks up two additional electrons.) NAD^+ functions as the electron acceptor in some of the steps of cellular respiration.

Oxidized form of Nicotinamide

"dehydrogenase"
Reduction
Oxidation

NAD +

NADH

NAD is chemically related to ATP and ADP; it includes an adenine base, a pentose sugar, and two phosphate groups, just like a molecule of ADP. At the end of the phosphate "tail," however, NAD has another pentose sugar and organic base, and this second base can pick up and release extra electrons. Just as ATP is responsible for the orderly transfer of energy in the cell, NAD is responsible for the orderly transfer of electrons in the cell. The electrons NAD captures are later used as sources of energy for the production of ATP. NAD traps electrons from glucose through the action of a class of enzymes called *dehydrogenases*, which remove hydrogen atoms from organic substrates. Dehydrogenases essentially remove two electrons and two protons (the equivalent of two hydrogen atoms) from the substrate and deliver two of these electrons and one proton to the NAD^+ molecule, releasing the other proton as a hydrogen ion.

Flavin adenine dinucleotide (FAD) is another compound that functions as an electron carrier. The oxidized form is called FAD, while the reduced form is called $FADH_2$. FAD and NAD^+ are functionally comparable—they are both able to capture electrons from other organic molecules with the help of dehydrogenases and donate these electrons to other biochemical reactions. The most important feature of NAD^+ and FAD is that electrons lose relatively little energy when they are transferred to NADH or $FADH_2$. These electron carriers are more electronegative than the compounds from which they capture electrons, but they are much less electronegative than oxygen.

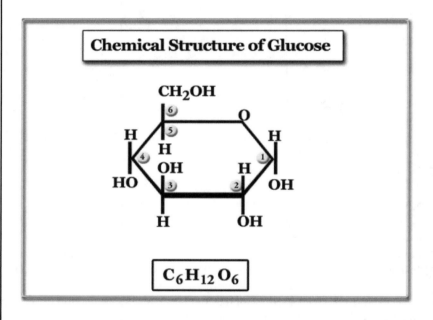

Chemical Structure of Glucose

$C_6H_{12}O_6$

NADH carries two electrons that represent a considerable amount of stored energy that might be harnessed by the cell. However, this stored energy is not in a form that is readily usable by the cell. The primary role of electron carriers is to shuttle high-energy electrons captured from the oxidation of glucose and other organic molecules to other cellular processes where their energy can be used to make ATP. ■

Suggested Reading

Alberts et al., *Essential Cell Biology* (2nd ed.), chapter 3.

Campbell & Reece, *Biology* (6th ed.), chapters 6 & 9.

Purves et al., *Life* (7th ed.), chapters 6 & 7.

Questions to Consider

1. How are "coupling enzymes" different from enzymes in general?

2. It is possible to light a sugar cube on fire. How is this different from burning a piece of paper? How is it different from the way cells metabolize sugars?

Making ATP—Glycolysis
Lecture 53

In today's lecture, we are going to build on this background and begin to look at those metabolic processes that have evolved to capture energy from the breakdown of organic molecules in a controlled fashion. We will focus our discussion on the breakdown of the sugar glucose, because, in fact, this is the most common organic fuel that is oxidized to produce cellular energy.

This lecture begins with an overview of the three energy-producing metabolic processes in the cell: *glycolysis*, the *Krebs cycle*, and the *electron transport chain*. After introducing each process, the lecture turns to an in-depth examination of glycolysis, including a discussion of the amount of energy it produces and the role played by the process of fermentation when oxygen is not present.

All anabolic and many catabolic reactions require energy in the form of ATP, which generally loses a phosphate to produce ADP in the process. Fortunately, ATP can be "recharged" by adding back a phosphate. The energy needed to produce more ATP in this way can be captured from catabolic reactions that break down organic molecules via controlled oxidation.

The complete breakdown, or oxidation, of glucose to release the energy stored in its chemical bonds involves three sets of metabolic processes: glycolysis, the Krebs cycle, and the electron transport chain. The Krebs cycle and the electron transport chain are collectively called cellular respiration, because they require oxygen.

Glycolysis is a catabolic pathway that breaks glucose into two 3-carbon pyruvates. Glycolysis includes 10 steps and, thus, 10 different enzymes, all of which occur in the cytoplasm of the cell. The breakdown of glucose into pyruvate is an exergonic process overall; some of the energy released is harvested by the cell in one of two forms. First, the cell produces two molecules of ATP for every glucose molecule through a process called substrate-level phosphorylation. Second, the cell also captures some energy in the form of electrons that reduce two molecules of the electron carrier molecule NAD+ to yield two molecules of NADH.

Although the cell obtains some of the energy stored in glucose in this way, there is still enormous energy stored in the pyruvate molecules which are the end product of glycolysis. The carbon in pyruvate is still in a highly reduced form, and even more energy can be extracted through further oxidation.

The *Krebs cycle* completely oxidizes the carbons in pyruvate and extracts the remaining energy. Most of the energy a cell harvests from glucose comes from the Krebs cycle. The Krebs cycle is named for German biochemist Sir Hans Krebs; like glycolysis, it is a multi-step metabolic pathway. The Krebs cycle has eight metabolic steps, each with a different enzyme, and is called a cycle because this pathway loops back on itself. Unlike glycolysis, the Krebs cycle occurs inside mitochondria (singular: mitochondrion), an organelle specialized for processing energy. For this reason, the cell must transport pyruvate from the cytoplasm to the inside of this organelle.

As the Krebs cycle completes the oxidation of pyruvate, it produces some ATP through substrate-level phosphorylation, in which coupling enzymes directly use the energy of an exergonic reaction to phosphorylate ADP, and also produces CO_2 as a waste product. The vast majority of energy that the cell captures from the Krebs cycle is in the form of electrons picked up by electron carrier molecules. In this case, these electrons are picked up both by NAD^+ (producing NADH) and FAD (producing $FADH_2$).

The energy captured in ATP is usable by the cell, but the energy captured in NADH and $FADH_2$ is not directly usable. Coupling enzymes can use the energy in the bonds between ATP phosphate groups to power other reactions, but the cell does not have a way to use electron energy directly to power most other reactions or processes.

The electron transport chain extracts the energy stored in the electrons captured by NADH and $FADH_2$ and uses this energy to produce more ATP. The electron transport chain involves a unique process called *oxidative phosphorylation* (in fact, these terms are sometimes used interchangeably). For now, it is necessary to bear in mind only that oxidative phosphorylation differs fundamentally from substrate-level phosphorylation. In oxidative phosphorylation, the cell captures energy from a redox reaction that donates electrons to an electron carrier. The electron carrier—NADH or $FADH_2$—carries these electrons to a different set of redox reactions that pass electrons from one compound to another, eventually donating them to an oxygen atom.

The way in which this chain of redox reactions actually results in the phosphorylation of ADP was a mystery long after the other processes of cellular respiration were fully understood. In brief, the redox reactions of the electron transport chain drive an active ion channel that pumps hydrogen ions (H^+) up a concentration gradient, then use this concentration gradient as a source of energy. By far, the vast majority of ATP produced during cellular respiration from the breakdown of glucose is produced by oxidative phosphorylation. Like the Krebs cycle, oxidative phosphorylation occurs inside mitochondria; the compounds of the electron transport chain itself are bound to an inner membrane of this organelle.

The Krebs cycle and electron transport chain function only if there is oxygen present to serve as the ultimate electron acceptor. The cells of most organisms perform cellular respiration in the presence of oxygen and, thus, continue through glycolysis into the Krebs cycle and oxidative phosphorylation. This is called *aerobic respiration*.

Some organisms, however, break down glucose only in an environment that lacks oxygen. Furthermore, cells that normally perform aerobic respiration sometimes find themselves temporarily lacking oxygen. In these cases, the cells can perform glycolysis only. Extracting energy from glucose in the absence of oxygen is called *anaerobic respiration*. Anaerobic respiration recovers much less energy from glucose—only two molecules of ATP from each molecule of glucose. It also requires the elimination of the end product of glycolysis in some other way, which is called *fermentation*. Aerobic respiration is far more efficient, but it can take place only if oxygen is present.

Glycolysis breaks down glucose into two molecules of pyruvate. Glycolysis starts with a molecule of glucose and splits it into two 3-carbon pyruvate molecules. Pyruvate is a more oxidized carbon compound than glucose, because its carbons are more associated with oxygen than hydrogen. Splitting glucose and partially oxidizing the carbons in pyruvate releases some of the stored energy, which is captured in the form of two ATP molecules and two NADH molecules.

There are 10 reactions involved in the glycolytic pathway, each catalyzed by a different enzyme. One way to examine glycolysis would be to look at each reaction, the enzyme that catalyzes it, and the product of each reaction in the sequence. Fortunately, we can understand the key issues without going into this level of detail. If the reactions of glycolysis are represented on a graph of energy versus time, each exergonic reaction in the pathway will cause a step down to a lower energy value, while each endergonic reaction will cause an upward step. Obviously, glucose, at the very beginning of the pathway, will be at a higher energy level than the product at the very end, pyruvate—thus, glycolysis is exergonic overall.

The cells of most organisms perform cellular respiration in the presence of oxygen and, thus, continue through glycolysis into the Krebs cycle and oxidative phosphorylation.

However, the graph would also show that, of the 10 steps between glucose and pyruvate, the first five are endergonic. The energy needed to drive these reactions is donated by two molecules of ATP, yielding a doubly phosphorylated 6-carbon sugar. The cell needs to invest some energy in the first several reactions of glycolysis because, by phosphorylating the 6-carbon sugar, glucose's molecular structure can be rearranged to make it easier to split the molecule and oxidize it in a controlled fashion. These first five upward steps may be referred to as the *energy-investment phase* of glycolysis.

Once energy has been invested in glucose and its molecular structure rearranged, the enzyme aldolase splits the 6-carbon molecule in half, creating two 3-carbon sugars called glyceraldehyde-3-phosphate (G3P). G3P is the energetic high point of the reactions of glycolysis and is also an important compound in photosynthesis, as we will see later.

The five steps of glycolysis following the production of G3P are mostly exergonic; they may be referred to as the *energy-harvesting* or *energy-yielding phase*. The first step of the energy-harvesting phase is a highly exergonic reaction that releases enough energy to reduce a molecule of NAD$^+$ into NADH and adds yet another phosphate group to each 3-carbon molecule, which the molecule will eventually give up to make ATP.

The second step of the energy-harvesting phase also is highly exergonic and is where some ATP is finally produced through substrate-level phosphorylation. This happens twice for each molecule of glucose that enters glycolysis, producing two ATP molecules. The next two reactions rearrange the molecule, preparing it for the final exergonic reaction, which yields more ATP by substrate-level phosphorylation. The end result is a pair of 3-carbon pyruvate molecules.

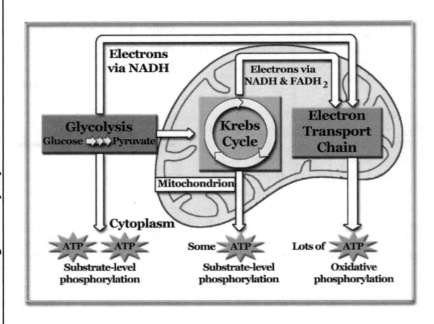

From one molecule of glucose and the investment of two ATP molecules, the cell obtains four molecules of ATP, giving a net yield of two ATP molecules for each molecule of glucose, which represents only about 3% of the extractable energy in glucose. The cell also harvests some energy in the form of NADH, but this energy is not directly usable.

The production of NADH during glycolysis presents another problem. The cell needs NAD^+ to accept electrons during the first energy-harvesting reaction; however, the supply of NAD^+ is limited. For glycolysis to proceed, the cell must allow NADH to give up its electrons somehow, producing more NAD^+. If the cell is performing aerobic respiration, NADH ultimately will give up its electrons to the electron transport chain, which will produce ATP through oxidative phosphorylation. This not only produces large amounts of ATP, but it also recycles NAD^+.

In anaerobic respiration, however, some other mechanism must recycle NADH. This mechanism, called *fermentation*, refers to a set of reactions that transfer electrons from NADH to pyruvate or a derivative. There are two main types of fermentation. In alcohol fermentation, pyruvate is converted to ethanol, as in brewing and wine making. In this case, yeast performs fermentation; many bacteria also use alcohol fermentation under anaerobic conditions.

In lactic acid fermentation, pyruvate is reduced to lactate, as in yogurt and cheese production. In addition, during hard exercise, muscles may be breaking down sugar by glycolysis so quickly that NADH cannot be oxidized fast enough, and they will begin anaerobic respiration. Accumulation of lactate causes muscle soreness, though the lactate is eventually converted back to pyruvate. ∎

Questions to Consider

1. Why does one molecule of glucose contain more stored energy than six molecules of carbon dioxide, even though they include the same number of carbon atoms?

2. The cell must "spend" two molecules of ATP for every four ATPs it obtains from the glycolysis of one glucose molecule. Why?

Making ATP—Cellular Respiration
Lecture 54

In today's lecture, we are going to continue our discussion of cellular respiration by looking at the processes that cells use to extract this energy from pyruvate, enabling them to produce actually what are huge amounts of ATP—the ATP that organisms need to power themselves.

The lecture begins by reviewing the fact that glycolysis extracts relatively little of the energy available in glucose. The complete harvest of this energy involves several additional processes, starting with the conversion of pyruvate to acetyl-CoA and continuing through the Krebs cycle and the electron transport chain. After discussing these processes, their energy outputs, and their waste products, the lecture concludes by noting that electrons, the carriers of most of the energy in glucose, must be further converted through the process of oxidative phosphorylation before the cell can make use of the energy they store.

The reactions of glycolysis make available only a tiny fraction—about 3%—of the chemical energy stored in a molecule of glucose. If oxygen is available to a cell, the pyruvate produced by glycolysis may be oxidized further by the reactions of the Krebs cycle, which produces carbon dioxide (CO_2) as an end product, the most oxidized form of carbon. The Krebs cycle thus completes the oxidation of the glucose molecule.

The cell begins to harvest pyruvate's energy by partially oxidizing it to form another molecule called acetyl-Coenzyme A (acetyl-CoA). This first step yields quite a bit of energy and cleaves off one of the three carbons found in pyruvate. Acetyl-CoA then enters the Krebs cycle, which ultimately yields two more molecules of CO_2 and extracts much more energy. The conversion of pyruvate to acetyl-CoA is catalyzed by a very large multienzyme complex called the *pyruvate dehydrogenase complex*. This complex is composed of about 60 separate protein subunits.

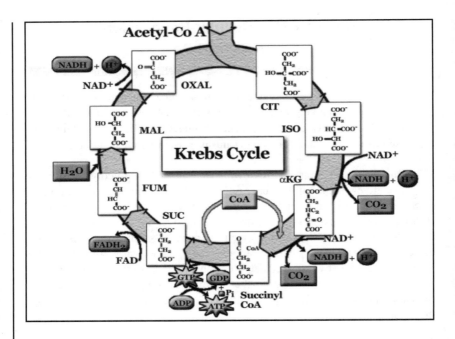

The pyruvate dehydrogenase complex splits the 3-carbon pyruvate into a 1-carbon unit, which will be lost as a molecule of CO_2, and another 2-carbon unit. This 2-carbon molecule is generically called an acetyl group, and it is this acetyl group that will enter the Krebs cycle. The 2-carbon acetyl group does not enter the Krebs cycle on its own, however; the pyruvate dehydrogenase complex also adds a Coenzyme A molecule to the acetyl group, creating a molecule of acetyl-CoA.

The bond formed between Coenzyme A and the 2-carbon acetyl group is a very high-energy bond, much like the high-energy bonds found between phosphate groups in ATP, and stores a great deal of energy in acetyl-CoA. This added energy will drive the first reaction of the Krebs cycle. The change in energy level in the conversion of pyruvate to acetyl-CoA is almost as great a drop as the change in energy level across the entire process of glycolysis. Some of this energy is captured by reducing a molecule of NAD^+ to produce NADH; much of it is used to form the bond between the acetyl group and

Coenzyme A. By producing acetyl-CoA from pyruvate, the cell has captured more energy in the form of NADH, completely oxidized one carbon atom, and reinvested some energy in the 2-carbon molecule that will be further oxidized in the Krebs cycle by the addition of Coenzyme A.

The 2-carbon molecule of acetyl-CoA produced by the cell can then enter the Krebs cycle, which extracts as much of the energy in the carbon bonds as possible. The Krebs cycle is referred to as a *cycle* because its intermediate compounds—the compounds between each enzymatically catalyzed reaction—regenerate themselves in a cyclic fashion. Glycolysis, for example, begins with the substrate glucose, and ends with the product pyruvate. In a similar way, most metabolic pathways start with a particular substrate and end with a particular product or set of products.

In the Krebs cycle, however, none of the eight intermediate compounds is ever really used up; the final product serves again as a substrate for the first reaction.

In the Krebs cycle, however, none of the eight intermediate compounds is ever really used up; the final product serves again as a substrate for the first reaction. Hans Krebs's realization that these reactions occurred in a cycle was primary to his understanding of how this process works, eventually earning him a Nobel Prize.

The two carbons in acetyl-CoA enter the Krebs cycle in its "first" step, where acetyl-CoA combines with a 4-carbon compound called oxaloacetate to form a 6-carbon compound called citrate. The energy used to drive this endergonic reaction is provided by breaking the high-energy bond of Coenzyme A. Once Coenzyme A cleaves off, it will combine with another acetyl group to form another molecule of acetyl-CoA.

Once citrate has been formed, the remaining reactions of the Krebs cycle oxidize this molecule in a step-wise fashion. In two different steps, a carbon is lost in the form of a molecule of CO_2. Thus, by the end of the cycle, what was a 6-carbon molecule is a 4-carbon molecule again—specifically, oxaloacetate. This oxaloacetate combines with another molecule of acetyl-

CoA, and the cycle starts again. From the point of view of energy levels, the entire Krebs cycle process runs energetically "downhill." Once citrate is formed, the remaining reactions are all either exergonic or essentially energetically neutral. Of course, oxidation of the carbons in the intermediate compounds releases energy, some of which is captured by the cell. For each molecule of acetyl-CoA that goes into the cell, three molecules of NAD^+ are reduced to NADH and one molecule of FAD is reduced to form $FADH_2$. In addition, one molecule of ATP is produced in one of the steps by substrate-level phosphorylation of guanine triphosphate (GTP), a related molecule.

The two carbon atoms lost in the Krebs cycle are released in the form of CO_2 and, thus, are in their most oxidized state. CO_2 is essentially a waste product of the Krebs cycle. Including the initial formation of acetyl-CoA, each "round" of the Krebs cycle oxidizes one 3-carbon pyruvate, yielding three molecules of CO_2. The 4-carbon oxaloacetate molecule is also a relatively low-energy compound, but it moves back up to a high-energy state when it combines with another molecule of acetyl-CoA to form another molecule of citrate. The added energy comes from both the high-energy CoA bond and the reduced and, therefore, high-energy bonds in the two carbons of the acetyl group itself.

The Krebs cycle yields energy in several different forms, not all of which can be used directly by the cell. The complete oxidation of one molecule of glucose—by glycolysis, the oxidation of pyruvate to acetyl-CoA, and the Krebs cycle—directly produces six molecules of ATP, but the cell had to invest two molecules of ATP, so the net gain is only four molecules of ATP. The energy stored in four molecules of ATP still represents only a small fraction of the total free energy in the glucose molecule.

However, the cell also captures energy in the form of electrons picked up by NADH and $FADH_2$. Each oxidized molecule of glucose produces two molecules of NADH during glycolysis, two molecules of NADH during the oxidation of pyruvate to acetyl-CoA, and six molecules of NADH and two molecules of $FADH_2$ during the Krebs cycle. These 12 electron-carrier molecules represent the vast majority of the energy extracted from the glucose molecule. Unfortunately, whereas the energy stored in the phosphate bonds of ATP is readily usable by the cell, the energy stored in these captured electrons is not. The cell must somehow take the energy stored in electron-carrier molecules and convert it into the usable form of ATP.

The electron transport chain is a series of linked redox reactions that releases the energy in NADH and $FADH_2$ in a step-wise fashion. In eukaryotic cells, the molecules associated with the electron transport chain are physically embedded in an internal membrane of the mitochondria. In prokaryotes, which lack mitochondria and other internal compartments, the molecules of the electron transport chain are embedded in the cell membrane itself. One reason this physical arrangement is important is that, by being embedded in a cell membrane, the molecules of the electron transport chain can be held tightly in close physical proximity to each other, facilitating their ability to pass electrons between each other.

Most of the components of the electron transport chain are proteins that are specialized for accepting and passing on electrons in redox reactions. Each compound in the chain is slightly more electronegative than the previous one; thus, an electron that has entered the chain will be pulled energetically "downward" from molecule to molecule, losing some of its energy at each step. NADH and $FADH_2$ interact with the least electronegative molecules in the electron transport chain, passing their electrons to these molecules. These electrons then move down the chain through successive redox reactions. At the end of the electron transport chain, an electron is passed on to an oxygen atom, where it reaches its lowest energy state.

Oxygen is an ideal final resting place for electrons in the electron transport chain for several reasons. First, oxygen is extremely electronegative. In fact, oxygen can be thought of as "sucking" electrons through the electron transport chain to itself. Second, oxygen is abundant in most places where life occurs; theoretically, there is no need to worry about running out of oxygen. Third, when oxygen receives electrons, it quickly combines with hydrogen ions to produce water; this is where the water comes from in our equation for "burning" glucose. Water is relatively easy to handle as a final waste product of cellular respiration.

As in the breakdown of glucose in glycolysis and the Krebs cycle, gradually handing electrons down to oxygen via the electron transport chain releases their energy in a controlled fashion. At the end of the electron transport chain, the cell has completely oxidized the electrons it captured from the respiration of glucose, and NAD^+ and FAD can pick up more electrons. This recycling is an important outcome of electron transport; if NADH and $FADH_2$ cannot unload their electrons, cellular respiration quickly comes to a halt.

The complete oxidation of glucose eventually yields energy that can be used to do work in the form of ATP. For every electron carrier molecule that passes its electrons to the electron transport chain, the cell produces approximately three molecules of ATP through the process of oxidative phosphorylation, the details of which will be the focus of the next lecture. ■

Suggested Reading

Alberts et al., *Essential Cell Biology* (2nd ed.), chapter 4.

Campbell & Reece, *Biology* (6th ed.), chapter 9.

Freeman, *Biological Science*, chapter 6.

Purves et al., *Life* (7th ed.), chapter 7.

Questions to Consider

1. What do the reactions of the Krebs cycle and those of glycolysis have in common? How are they fundamentally different?

2. Most of the chemical energy stored in the carbons of glucose is extracted by the Krebs cycle, but the cell gains little usable energy from these reactions themselves. Why?

Making ATP—The Chemiosmotic Theory
Lecture 55

How the process of oxidative phosphorylation works will be the subject of today's lecture. As I told you last time, oxidative phosphorylation turns out to be where the real energy payoff of cellular respiration occurs. It is through this process that the cell converts most of the energy it obtains by metabolically burning glucose into the useful form of ATP.

This lecture begins by reviewing the puzzle concerning how the electron transport chain is involved in ATP production, and then outlines a radical theory—chemiosmosis—that was proposed to explain it, a theory which was eventually shown to be true. The lecture explores the nature and function of mitochondria and cell membranes, both of which are essential to the production of ATP through chemiosmosis, before discussing the mechanism of oxidative phosphorylation in detail. In conclusion, the lecture notes that metabolic pathways can "burn" a much wider range of fuels than simply glucose and that, though it is relatively inefficient, glycolysis has historically and does currently power much of life on Earth.

For many years after glycolysis, the Krebs cycle, and the electron transport chain were well understood, scientists struggled to understand how the electron transport chain was coupled to ATP production. The basic mechanism of substrate-level phosphorylation was well understood. Substrate-level phosphorylation generally involves an enzyme that couples energy from an exergonic reaction directly to the phosphorylation of ADP to produce ATP. This is how ATP is produced by some of the reactions in glycolysis and the Krebs cycle.

Biologists could not find a similar coupling enzyme in the electron transport chain, but most assumed one must exist, because they thought such an enzyme was the only possible mechanism of coupling the energy released from a redox reaction or any catabolic reaction. There is no such enzyme, however. Instead, the process of *oxidative phosphorylation* links electron transport to the production of ATP in a completely novel way. The chemiosmotic theory provides the mechanism behind oxidative phosphorylation of ADP to produce ATP.

In 1961, British biochemist Peter Mitchell made a radical proposal; he suggested that the energy released by the electron transport chain's redox reactions was not directly coupled to ATP synthesis. Instead, he proposed that the chemical energy released by these redox reactions was used to pump hydrogen ions across a membrane against their concentration gradient.

This type of active pumping builds a strong concentration gradient, which represents stored energy that could be used to phosphorylate ADP into ATP. Mitchell's hypothesis came to be known as the *chemiosmotic theory of ATP production*, because it suggested that ATP production was driven by a diffusion force similar to osmosis. For many years, Mitchell's ideas were rejected; eventually, however, biochemists began to verify several key predictions of the chemiosmotic theory, and Mitchell was awarded the Nobel Prize in 1978.

Understanding the chemiosmotic theory requires taking a closer look at the structure and function of the mitochondrion, a specialized energy-processing organelle. Glycolysis, the Krebs cycle, and electron transport occur in different parts of the cell, and their locations are important to their functions. Glycolysis is thought to be the oldest biochemical pathway associated with energy processing; thus, it is not surprising that its enzymes, substrates, and products are found throughout the cytoplasm, in no particular spatial relationship to each other.

By contrast, the compounds associated with the Krebs cycle and the electron transport chain are isolated in a specialized compartment, an organelle called the mitochondrion. For this reason, pyruvate produced in glycolysis has to enter the mitochondrion before it can be further oxidized by the Krebs cycle. Like all organelles, mitochondria are enclosed by lipid bilayer membranes, but a mitochondrion has two membranes instead of one. A smooth outer membrane defines the exterior of the organelle, but an inner membrane folds back and forth inside the mitochondrion, creating a set of inpocketings called *cristae* that extend into the organelle's center.

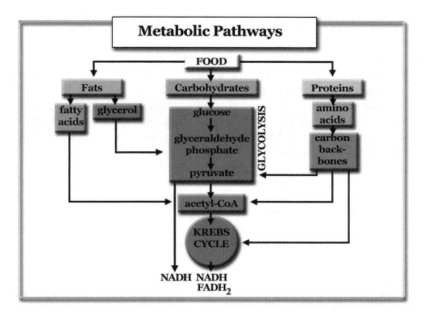

Metabolic Pathways

Because mitochondria have two membranes, they have two distinct inner compartments. One compartment is formed by the space between the outer and inner membranes and is called the *intermembrane space*. The second compartment, which is the inside of the inner membrane, is called the *matrix*. The enzymes, substrates, and products of the Krebs cycle are located inside the matrix. The compounds associated with the electron transport chain, however, are physically embedded in the inner membrane.

Understanding the structure and function of biological membranes is fundamental to understanding the chemiosmotic theory. The basic structure of the cell membrane is a dual layer of lipid molecules called *phospholipids*. A phospholipid has a phosphate group at its head end, from which extends long carbon-chain tails typical of a kind of lipid called a fatty acid.

Phospholipids arrange themselves in a neat two-layer row with heads, which are attracted to water, facing out and the fatty acid tails, which are repelled by water, facing in. The chemical properties of a phospholipid bilayer make it difficult for many kinds of molecules to cross the membrane. In particular, molecules that carry an electric charge, such as ions, cannot easily cross cell membranes.

Charged ions can cross lipid bilayers, however, by traversing transmembrane ion channels. If an ion channel is passive, ions will run down their concentration gradient. If an ion channel is active, the ion might be pushed up its concentration gradient, but only if some energy is invested. Like any form of stored energy, the energy stored in a concentration gradient across a membrane can be used to do work.

The basic mechanisms of chemiosmosis and oxidative phosphorylation have been elucidated, though many of the details remain unknown. Mitchell's chemiosmotic theory proposed that hydrogen ions are actively pumped from the matrix into the intermembrane space, creating a very high concentration of hydrogen ions in the intermembrane space relative to the matrix.

Though much work has been done on the chemiosmotic theory since Mitchell first proposed it, details of how this pumping of hydrogen ions takes place are still being worked out. What is clear is that the molecules of the electron transport chain are grouped into several complexes with other proteins not directly involved in redox reactions. For some of these complexes, the energy released by redox reactions pumps hydrogen ions from the matrix side of the membrane to the intermembrane side.

A key experiment demonstrated directly that the concentration gradient across the mitochondrial inner membrane drives ATP synthesis. Mitochondria that had been removed from cells changed the rate at which they produced ATP depending on experimental manipulations of the concentration gradient; in particular, the rate of ATP production increased when the concentration of hydrogen ions in the intermembrane space increased and vice versa.

The mechanism that connects the concentration gradient to ATP production involves a protein called ATP synthase, which resembles a lollipop with the stick inserted in the inner membrane and the candy head sticking out into the matrix. ATP synthase is a large complex of different protein subunits grouped together into three main parts: one set of subunits forms a tube called the rotor that extends through the membrane, a second set forms the knob (the head of the lollipop), and a third set forms the rod that connects the rotor to the knob. ATP synthase appears to act as an ion channel that is selective for hydrogen ions. Because the rotor extends through the inner membrane, hydrogen ions will pass through it from the intermembrane space, where their concentration is high, into the matrix, where their concentration is lower.

This movement of hydrogen ions through the rotor appears to make both the rotor and the rod spin. It appears that this spinning motion somehow transfers energy that catalyzes the formation of a bond between ADP and an inorganic phosphate group, generating a new molecule of ATP. Chemiosmosis and ATP synthase generate ATP in a way analogous to the way a water wheel might be driven by stored energy. It takes energy to pump water uphill, but some of that energy is then stored in the position of the water. This stored energy can be converted into the kinetic energy of rushing water, which can turn a water wheel. The generation of ATP through chemiosmosis and ATP synthase is called oxidative phosphorylation because it is ultimately powered by the oxidation of electrons that enter the electron transport chain.

Few organisms consume only glucose; instead, organisms obtain most of their energy from the breakdown of other organic compounds, including complex carbohydrates, proteins, and fats.

Few organisms consume only glucose; instead, organisms obtain most of their energy from the breakdown of other organic compounds, including complex carbohydrates, proteins, and fats. Because glycolysis and the Krebs cycle connect to many other metabolic pathways in the cell, cellular respiration can accept a wide range of carbohydrates for catabolism. Proteins can also be used for fuel but must first be broken down to their constituent amino acids. Fats feed into the metabolic pathway in the middle of glycolysis or break down to acetyl-CoA.

The energy-processing mechanisms of the cell are quite efficient. It is difficult to compute exactly, but by a rough estimate, 34 molecules of ATP are produced by oxidative phosphorylation for every molecule of glucose. Added together with the 4 molecules of ATP produced by substrate-level phosphorylation, the total energy yield is about 38 molecules of ATP for every oxidized glucose molecule.

Aerobic respiration recovers about 40% of the energy in glucose, making it about 10 times more efficient than glycolysis and more efficient than a typical modern automobile engine, which is only about 25% efficient.

Compared to aerobic respiration, the 3% efficiency of glycolysis seems quite inefficient, but it is enough for life to sustain itself. Much of the history of life on Earth was written by organisms that could perform glycolysis only, and many of the most successful organisms existing today are anaerobic and, thus, can achieve only this 3% efficiency. Nonetheless, it was only after the pathways of the Krebs cycle and oxidative phosphorylation arose that life could become larger, multicellular, and much more complex, because living things could access the energy they needed to build and sustain increased complexity. ■

Suggested Reading

Campbell & Reece, *Biology* (6th ed.), chapter 9.

Freeman, *Biological Science*, chapter 6.

Prebble & Weber, *Wandering in the Gardens of the Mind: Peter Mitchell and the Making of Glynn*.

Purves et al., *Life* (7th ed.), chapter 7.

Questions to Consider

1. How does the function of a mitochondrion depend on its structure?

2. Both substrate-level phosphorylation and oxidative phosphorylation use energy obtained from the oxidation of glucose to produce ATP. What is the fundamental difference between these two processes with respect to how they obtain this energy?

Capturing Energy from Sunlight
Lecture 56

You know, sometimes when I give a lecture I really get tired out. It takes a lot of energy to give a good lecture, and I really use a lot of ATP in the process. In fact, it takes a lot of energy just to live. Remember, I told you that a vertebrate animal such as myself might consume its body weight in ATP every day. In my case, that's over 180 pounds of ATP that I am using up.

L et's begin by emphasizing that living things require a continuous supply of fuel to generate ATP, and by pointing out that many organisms can only obtain this fuel by eating other organisms. Some kinds of organisms, however, generate fuel directly by converting the energy of sunlight into high-energy organic compounds through the process of photosynthesis. After providing an overview of how photosynthesis works, the lecture explores in more detail the properties of light and the components of the cell that support this process.

Cells can only generate ATP indefinitely if they have the organic fuel to power the process. In order to keep generating ATP, many organisms have to eat, because food supplies the organic compounds that fuel cellular respiration and oxidative phosphorylation. If this were not necessary, life would violate the Second Law of Thermodynamics. The only way a system can maintain an orderly, high-energy state is to add energy from the outside.

Any number of organic compounds beside glucose can serve as a source of energy, because the biochemical pathways of cellular respiration stand at the crossroads of the highly interrelated pathways of metabolism. Fat, protein, and complex carbohydrates can all be processed and fed into pathways of cellular respiration to generate ATP.

The only way humans, for example, can acquire organic compounds is by eating something else made of organic compounds—some other living thing or something that was alive. Many other organisms have this same requirement; such organisms are called *heterotrophs* ("other feeders").

Not all organisms are heterotrophs, however; some kinds of organisms are *autotrophs* ("self feeders"), which generate their own food. Heterotrophs obtain organic compounds by eating autotrophs or other heterotrophs that have eaten autotrophs. As long as autotrophs manufacture new organic compounds, heterotrophs will not run out of food. Autotrophs do not defy the Second Law of Thermodynamics, however; they can make high-energy organic compounds only by using some non-organic source of energy to power the anabolic reactions necessary to build these compounds. Most autotrophs, such as green plants and algae, use energy captured from sunlight to synthesize high-energy organic substances; for this reason, these organisms are called *photoautotrophs*.

The only way humans, for example, can acquire organic compounds is by eating something else made of organic compounds—some other living thing or something that was alive.

The Sun is the ultimate source of energy on Earth. All of the energy used by living things ultimately comes from the Sun, with the exception of a few types of prokaryotes that live in extreme environments, such as deep-sea thermal vents, and that can extract energy by breaking down inorganic compounds. Energy produced by the Sun reaches Earth in the form of sunlight, a small proportion of which is captured by autotrophs that use it to synthesize organic compounds. The organic compounds manufactured this way represent the total amount of energy available to all of the living organisms on the planet. In the short run, heterotrophs might eat whatever organic material is around, but in the long run, we will run out of food if autotrophs do not produce more organic material.

The flow of energy from the Sun is one-way: Energy from the Sun is taken up by autotrophs, spread to heterotrophs that eat those autotrophs, and eventually lost from living systems and dissipated back out into space. The Sun uses its nuclear fuel at a fairly steady rate and will run out of fuel in about 5 billion years, depending on how the estimate is calculated. When this happens, life will no longer be able to exist on Earth.

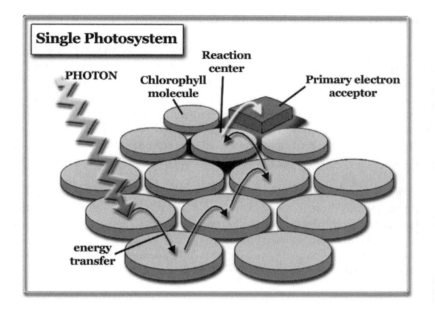

Single Photosystem

PHOTON

Chlorophyll molecule

Reaction center

Primary electron acceptor

energy transfer

Photosynthesis is the process by which autotrophs convert the energy in sunlight into energy-rich organic compounds. The chemical equation that describes the oxidation of glucose is:

$$C_6H_{12}O_6 + 6\ O_2 \rightarrow 6\ CO_2 + 6\ H_2O + \text{energy}$$

The chemical equation that summarizes the process of photosynthesis is:

$$6\ CO_2 + 6\ H_2O + \text{energy} \rightarrow C_6H_{12}O_6 + 6\ O_2$$

It is immediately apparent that, in theory at least, photosynthesis is the reverse of the process of cellular respiration. In photosynthesis, cells use carbon dioxide and water to build glucose, and the highly oxidized carbon in CO_2 is reduced; that is, the electrons associated with these carbon atoms are allowed to occur at a higher energy level.

One obvious difference between cellular respiration and photosynthesis is that cellular respiration releases energy, whereas photosynthesis proceeds energetically uphill and, therefore, needs to have energy added. However, in terms of the basic chemical relationships involved, running the biochemical reactions of photosynthesis has the same effect, again in theory, as running the reactions of cellular respiration backwards. Of course, photosynthesis is not simply cellular respiration reversed; instead, getting from CO_2 and water to a molecule of glucose via photosynthesis involves biochemical reactions that are quite different from those of cellular respiration, and the two sets of metabolic pathways barely intersect with each other.

Photosynthesis involves two distinct processes. First, the cell must somehow capture energy from sunlight. This part of the process is referred to as the *light reactions* of photosynthesis. Second, the energy captured from sunlight is used to build glucose using the carbon in CO_2. This part of the process is called the *Calvin cycle*, or sometimes the *dark reactions*, because they do not directly require light to run.

Photosynthesis occurs in organelles called *chloroplasts*. As in cellular respiration, some aspects of photosynthesis depend on where its reactions take place. The organelle where photosynthesis occurs is called a chloroplast. Chloroplasts have some similarities to mitochondria, as well as substantial differences. Because all eukaryotic cells use mitochondria to perform cellular respiration, both plant and animal cells have mitochondria; chloroplasts are found only in plant cells.

Like mitochondria, chloroplasts have a complex internal organization, with different compartments separated by membranes. Chloroplasts have both outer and inner membranes, but the inner membrane of a chloroplast is relatively smooth. The space between the outer and inner membranes is called the *intermembrane space*, and the space inside the inner membrane is called the *stroma*.

In addition to these outer and inner membranes, chloroplasts also have a third membrane system called the *thylakoid membrane*. The thylakoid membrane forms compartments called *thylakoids* that often occur in neatly layered stacks called *grana* (singular = *granum*). The thylakoids in a chloroplast are interconnected, and the space inside them—the thylakoid space—is important for photosynthesis, similar to the way in which the intermembrane space of mitochondria is important for cellular respiration. The light and dark reactions of photosynthesis take place in different parts of the chloroplast—the light reactions in the thylakoid membranes, and the dark reactions in the stroma.

Light has several properties that are important for understanding how photosynthesis works. Light is a form of energy called *electromagnetic radiation*. We see electromagnetic radiation of different wavelengths as different colors. In fact, we can see only a small range of wavelengths, and we call this range of electromagnetic radiation *visible light*. Electromagnetic radiation can be modeled as waves, but it can also be modeled as particles, because the energy in electromagnetic radiation occurs in discrete, discontinuous packets called *photons*.

When a photon encounters matter, one of three things will happen: The photon will reflect off the matter, be transmitted through the matter, or be absorbed by the matter. When a photon is absorbed by matter, it transfers its energy to that matter. To perform photosynthesis, a cell must acquire energy from sunlight. Doing so is not as simple as absorbing photons, however, because once a molecule absorbs energy from a photon, it will likely lose that energy as heat. Photosynthesis must be able to capture energy from photons in such a way as to hold onto it.

Chlorophyll is a molecule that is specialized for capturing light in a way that allows the energy to be preserved and used in photosynthesis. Chlorophyll is a kind of pigment with a head region called a porphyrin ring, which includes a magnesium atom in the center, and a tail that is a long chain of carbon atoms with hydrogen atoms attached to them. Chlorophyll molecules are embedded in the thylakoid membranes of chloroplasts.

When a photon of light hits a molecule of chlorophyll, it excites the electrons in that molecule to a higher energy state. In chlorophyll, as in other molecules, the electrons return to their resting energy level, releasing the absorbed energy as heat and light of a longer wavelength, in a process called *fluorescence.* A single chlorophyll molecule thus is not very useful, but a group of chlorophylls organized as a photosystem can harvest light energy very effectively.

A *photosystem* is a set of a few hundred pigment molecules clustered tightly together in the thylakoid membranes of chloroplasts. Along with molecules of chlorophyll, other kinds of pigments, generally referred to as accessory pigments, are also associated with photosystems. These accessory pigments are specialized to absorb photons having different wavelengths (different energy levels) than the wavelengths best absorbed by chlorophyll. By doing so, accessory pigments increase the efficiency of the photosystem. The pigments in a photosystem are so tightly packed together that when any of them absorbs a photon, it may pass the photon on to adjacent pigment molecules instead of fluorescing it. Each time one of these pigment molecules absorbs the photon being passed around, its electrons are elevated to a higher energy state.

The energy in the photon eventually reaches a region of the photosystem called the *reaction center*, which contains a molecule called a *primary electron acceptor*. When a photon reaches a chlorophyll molecule adjacent to the primary electron acceptor, the excited electron may be transferred from the chlorophyll to the electron acceptor through a redox reaction.

Once the energy from photons causes an electron to be captured by an electron acceptor molecule in a photosystem, that energy is now captured and stored in a more lasting fashion. However, the energy in an electron captured this way cannot be used directly by the cell and must be converted into a more usable form. ∎

Suggested Reading

Campbell & Reece, *Biology* (6th ed.), chapter 10.

Freeman, *Biological Science*, chapter 7.

Purves et al., *Life* (7th ed.), chapter 8.

1. In what way do living organisms appear to defy the Second Law of Thermodynamics?

2. If the substrates of photosynthesis are the waste products of cellular respiration and vice versa, why doesn't photosynthesis simply proceed as the reactions of cellular respiration run in reverse?

The Reactions of Photosynthesis
Lecture 57

In today's lecture, we are going to continue our discussion of photosynthesis, the process by which green plants and other photosynthetic organisms make sugar out of sunlight.

We begin with the question of where added mass comes from when a plant grows. The answer to this question, obtained from an experiment done more than 300 years ago, leads us to consider how photosynthesis must capture energy from sunlight in a form that can be used to power the manufacture of organic compounds. After exploring the light reactions of photosynthesis, which perform this function, we discuss the Calvin cycle which uses this stored energy to build complex organic compounds for long-term energy storage.

An experiment performed in the first half of the 17th century by Belgian doctor Jean Baptiste van Helmont revealed that growing plants do not obtain their added mass from soil. Van Helmont planted a small tree in a pot of soil after carefully weighing both the tree and the soil. After 5 years, van Helmont found that the tree had gained an enormous amount of mass—about 75 kilograms—but the soil in the container had lost only about 50 or 60 grams. Van Helmont concluded that the added mass could not come entirely from the soil and, therefore, must come from somewhere else. He incorrectly concluded, however, that the added mass must have come from water. Like any living organism, a tree is made of carbon-based compounds; water, however, does not include carbon.

It is common knowledge today that trees get the carbon they use to build organic compounds from carbon dioxide (CO_2) in the air. Ultimately, all of the carbon found in all living systems on Earth is taken up originally as CO_2 by photosynthetic organisms. CO_2 however, is the lowest-energy form of carbon. Therefore, photosynthetic organisms must not only acquire carbon from the atmosphere, but must also incorporate it into high-energy carbon compounds. Highly organized assemblages of chlorophyll molecules capture energy from photons by transferring an excited electron to a primary electron acceptor. This transfer is a redox reaction: The chlorophyll molecule that loses its electron becomes oxidized, while the primary electron acceptor molecule becomes reduced.

The light reactions of photosynthesis convert captured light energy into a form that can be used by the plant to build reduced carbon compounds. Chloroplasts convert energy stored in electrons in a way that is similar to how mitochondria handle electrons captured during cellular respiration. Immediately after the primary electron acceptor picks up an extra electron, it transfers this electron to an electron transport chain embedded in the membrane of the chloroplast's thylakoids. The electron transport chain of the thylakoid membrane includes similar kinds of molecules as the electron transport chain of cellular respiration. The specific molecules are not necessarily the same, but the electron transport chains in the thylakoid membrane and the inner membrane of a mitochondrion are functionally equivalent.

Electrons passed to the thylakoid electron transport chain have their energy level stepped down gradually through a series of redox reactions, and the energy released is used to pump hydrogen ions against their concentration gradient. In the chloroplast, hydrogen ions are pumped from the stroma into the space inside thylakoids.

Energy stored in the concentration gradient of hydrogen ions is used to drive the production of ATP through the action of ATP synthase, as is the case for oxidative phosphorylation in mitochondria. Because the ultimate source of energy to drive this process is sunlight, ATP production through chemiosmosis and ATP synthase in chloroplasts is called *photophosphorylation*. In cellular respiration, electrons captured from the breakdown of glucose molecules are eventually passed to oxygen. In chloroplasts, the two possible fates for electrons captured from chlorophyll are called *cyclic electron transport* and *non-cyclic electron transport*.

The difference between cyclic electron transport and non-cyclic electron transport is whether the electron involved is recycled back to the photosystem. In cyclic electron transport, an electron captured from a chlorophyll molecule in a photosystem is eventually passed back to chlorophyll itself. Electrons are temporarily boosted out of the photosystem by the energy absorbed from photons. In non-cyclic electron transport, an electron captured from a chlorophyll molecule is eventually passed to another electron carrier molecule called nicotinamide adenine dinucleotide phosphate ($NADP^+$). $NAPD^+$ is very similar chemically to NAD and, like NAD^+, can accept electrons in a reaction catalyzed by dehydrogenase, yielding reduced NADPH. In non-cyclic electron transport, the cell not only gains ATP from electron transport and photophosphorylation, but it also captures a large amount of energy in the form of a reduced electron carrier molecule.

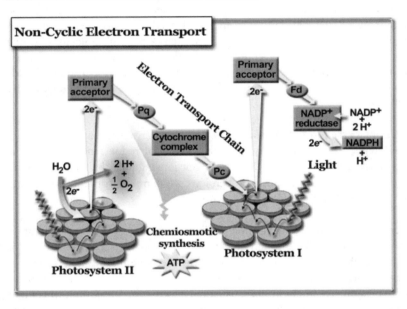

Non-cyclic electron transport involves two different kinds of photosystems, both embedded in the thylakoid membrane, called *Photosystem I* and *Photosystem II*. They differ in the nature of the primary electron acceptor at the reaction center. Non-cyclic electron transport illustrates the key features of the light reactions. The process begins when the electron in a chlorophyll molecule is excited by a photon and eventually transferred to the primary acceptor in a redox reaction. In non-cyclic electron transport, the electron is captured initially in Photosystem II. This captured electron is passed to an electron transport chain, where it is stepped down in energy through a series of redox reactions, creating a concentration gradient of hydrogen ions across the thylakoid membrane.

In non-cyclic electron transport, electrons captured from Photosystem II are passed to chlorophyll molecules in Photosystem I. The result is that chlorophyll molecules in Photosystem II lack electrons and, thus, become strong oxidizing agents. In cyclic electron transport, these "holes" would be filled by electrons returning from the electron transport chain, but in non-cyclic electron transport, these electrons are passed on to Photosystem I.

The electron that will fill this "hole" in Photosystem II comes from water, which splits into two hydrogen ions and one oxygen atom. As in cellular respiration, where oxygen was a necessary reactant, water is a necessary reactant in the light reactions, contributing electrons to build glucose and producing oxygen as a waste product.

Meanwhile, Photosystem I has absorbed light energy and will pass excited electrons to its primary electron acceptor, leaving "holes" in Photosystem I that must be filled by electrons coming from Photosystem II. Excited electrons picked up by the primary electron acceptor of Photosystem I are passed on to $NADP^+$, reducing it to NADPH. At this point, an electron has been removed entirely from the photosystems and passed on to an electron carrier for use elsewhere.

The light reactions of photosynthesis convert captured light energy into a form that can be used by the plant to build reduced carbon compounds.

The ultimate source of this electron is water; thus, the movement of electrons in non-cyclic electron transport follows a path from water to NADPH. For every two electrons that follow this path, the cell has gained a small amount of ATP from photophosphorylation and one molecule of NADPH.

Compared to non-cyclic electron flow, cyclic electron flow is like a short circuit for electrons that transferred to the primary electron acceptor in Photosystem I. Instead of being transferred by a redox reaction to NADPH, electrons captured from chlorophyll molecules in Photosystem I cycle back to chlorophyll; thus, cyclic electron flow produces no NADPH or O_2. Cyclic electron flow does produce some ATP, however, because excited electrons return to the chlorophyll of Photosystem I via the electron transport chain. Cyclic electron flow probably represents the first mechanism that evolved to capture energy from sunlight about two billion years ago. On its own, cyclic electron flow does not produce much ATP, but the ATP it does produce is essentially free. However, cyclic electron flow does not capture energy in reduced energy carrier molecules like NADPH.

ATP is the common energy currency of cells, but it does not have a very long "shelf life." Organic compounds provide a much more convenient and stable way to store energy. The evolution of two kinds of photosystems and non-cyclic electron flow between them enabled photosynthetic organisms to store energy in stable high-energy organic compounds.

The Calvin cycle uses the energy in ATP and NADPH to synthesize carbohydrates. The Calvin cycle, like the Krebs cycle, is a cyclic metabolic pathway, with the final product also being the first reactant in the series. Carbon is incorporated into one of the intermediates in the cycle, becomes reduced, and leaves the cycle as a high-energy organic compound. Although its biochemical steps are completely different, the Calvin cycle accomplishes the reverse of the Krebs cycle: Three molecules of CO_2 enter the Calvin cycle, and then, with some energy, a reduced 3-carbon sugar is produced. In the Krebs cycle, reduced carbons enter and oxidized carbons leave, with a gain of energy; in the Calvin cycle, oxidized carbons enter and reduced carbons leave, with energy needing to be added. Though we often refer to photosynthesis as responsible for producing glucose, the Calvin cycle does not directly yield glucose but, rather, the 3-carbon sugar glyceraldehyde-3-phosphate (G3P). The Calvin cycle can be divided into three phases:

In the carbon fixation phase, a new carbon atom enters the cycle as a molecule of CO_2, which combines with a 5-carbon compound called ribulose bisphosphate (RuBP). This phase is catalyzed by the enzyme "RUBISCO", and the 6-carbon sugar it produces immediately splits into two 3-carbon molecules.

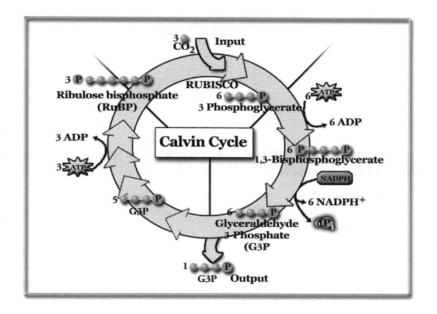

In the reduction phase, these 3-carbon molecules are reduced to form higher-energy molecules by the addition of electrons from NADP and phosphates from ATP. The most reduced form is G3P, which leaves the cycle.

In the regeneration phase, some G3P is rearranged to produce more RuBP. For every six molecules of G3P produced, one molecule leaves the cycle and the other five are rearranged to form three molecules of RuBP.

At the end of the Calvin cycle, three low-energy carbons from CO_2 have been reduced and incorporated into high-energy G3P. A plant may use G3P either directly as an energy source to produce more ATP, or as the starting point for pathways that build more complex compounds. It is difficult to compute directly, but it appears to cost a chloroplast more energy to synthesize one glucose molecule than a mitochondrion releases by disassembling it. Fortunately, as long as the Sun keeps shining, there is a limitless supply of energy for photosynthetic organisms to produce organic compounds. ■

Calvin, *Following the Trail of Light: A Scientific Odyssey*.

Campbell & Reece, *Biology* (6th ed.), chapter 10.

Freeman, *Biological Science*, chapters 7 and 33.2.

Purves et al., *Life* (7th ed.), chapter 8.

Questions to Consider

1. After photosynthetic organisms appeared in evolutionary history, it eventually became impossible for life to arise spontaneously from non-living matter. Why?

2. All organisms are made primarily of carbon-based organic compounds. How do plants and animals differ in where this carbon comes from?

Resources and Life Histories
Lecture 58

I want to begin this lecture by introducing you to a friend of mine. This friend is Elvis, the bacterium. The reason that I want to introduce you to my friend Elvis, this bacterial cell, is because Elvis is really, really good at doing something. Specifically, what Elvis is good at doing is reproducing.

This lecture begins by noting that many organisms have the capacity for the kind of explosive population growth normally associated with bacteria. This unchecked growth does not often occur, however, because the energy and other resources necessary for organisms to survive and reproduce are limited in most populations. Because the resources available to individuals are limiting, organisms optimize their lifetime reproductive success by making tradeoffs at various points of their lifetimes between devoting resources to reproduction and devoting resources to their own growth and maintenance. These life history tradeoffs, in turn, are reflected in many of the adaptations that characterize different species.

All organisms have the potential for explosive population growth, but this growth typically is limited by available resources. When a bacterium reproduces, for example, it simply divides, creating two daughter cells for each parent cell. If nothing hinders a bacterium's reproduction, the results would be quite remarkable. If the bacterium could divide once every 20 minutes—a realistic value—and this single bacterium and all its progeny divided unimpeded for 36 hours, at the end of that time, the bacterium and all its progeny would be so numerous that they would cover the entire surface of the Earth in a layer about a foot deep. In a month, the descendents of the first bacterium would weigh more than the visible universe and would be expanding outward at the speed of light.

Darwin recognized from Malthus that all organisms have this growth potential; Darwin wrote, "There is no exception to the rule that every organic being naturally increases at so high a rate that, if not destroyed, the Earth would soon be covered by the progeny of a single pair." This potential for excess reproduction was a key element of Darwin's theory of natural selection.

In general, however, organisms do not exhibit this kind of growth for sustained periods because they simply do not have sufficient resources to do so. Our exploration of energy and resources in living systems at higher levels of biological organization will center on the issue of how these resources are limiting and how limitations influence the organization of living systems, from the adaptations of individual organisms to the organization of entire ecosystems.

All work done in biological systems is powered by the energy stored in ATP, but other resources can be just as essential to life. Energy flows into living systems from sunlight and is transformed into high-energy organic compounds by photosynthesis, which uses as raw materials CO_2 and H_2O. In addition to glucose, photosynthesis also produces O_2 as a waste product.

All organisms have the potential for explosive population growth, but this growth typically is limited by available resources.

The carbon fixed by photosynthesis has one of two fates. First, the organic compounds produced by carbon fixation may be fed into the processes of cellular respiration and "burned" as organic fuel to produce ATP. About 90% of the G3P produced by photosynthesis has this fate. Second, organic carbon fixed in photosynthesis may be used as the starting point in the manufacture of other biomolecules and, thus, becomes the material organisms are made of. About 10% of the carbon is used this way. The organic material that makes up a plant or any other organism is referred to as *biomass*.

It seems intuitive that what limits the growth of living systems is the amount of CO_2, H_2O, and sunlight available. However, organic molecules also incorporate a number of other important elements. Nitrogen is found in the amino acids that make up proteins. Phosphorus is used in nucleic acids, ATP, and other molecules. Sulfur is found in two important amino acids, cysteine and methionine. Many other elements, such as magnesium, occur in smaller amounts in living things, but are nonetheless essential for the proper functioning of biomolecules. Other elements, such as potassium, may not be incorporated directly into organic molecules but are still essential to life. All of these other elements are important resources that can cycle in and out of living systems just as carbon does. Living systems need these other resources just as much as they need sunlight, carbon dioxide, and water.

Even after considering essential and potentially limiting mineral nutrients, we are still defining *resources* in simplified terms. Any number of other factors may be resources that limit the ability of a particular organism to survive, grow, and reproduce. Regardless of the resource, in general, there often is not enough to go around. As a consequence, it matters where an organism lives, which other organisms live around it, and how these organisms interact with each other.

In the most general terms, *ecology* is the name used for the interactions of organisms with each other and with their environments. Any examination of the implications of energy and resources at levels of biological organization above the cell becomes an exploration of of the science of ecology.

Individuals with the highest Darwinian fitness are those that leave the most offspring in a population in a given environment, but organisms do not necessarily devote all their resources to producing offspring. It seems obvious that adaptations should evolve that increase an organism's ability to gain resources and convert those resources into offspring. However, some of the resources an organism acquires must be used for that organism's growth. Other resources must be used for maintenance—including not only physiological maintenance, but also acquiring food, finding shelter, and the like. Regardless of the resources an organism can acquire, it is important to consider how it allocates those resources.

The way an organism allocates resources differs among different kinds of organisms and usually changes across different stages of an organism's lifespan. An organism's pattern of resource utilization across its lifespan is called the organism's *life history*, which may be divided into stages. For example, consider the life histories of four very different organisms—a tree, a marmot (a kind of large ground squirrel), a salmon, and a moth. Some organisms, such as the tree, are always gathering energy and resources. Many organisms, such as moths and marmots, acquire resources only during part of their life histories.

All life histories have one or more stages of growth. In a marmot or a moth, the growth stage is confined to an early period of life. Many organisms, however, devote resources to growth for an extended period, as in a salmon, or continue to devote resources to growth throughout their entire lives, as in the case of a tree. Throughout most life histories, some resources must always be devoted to maintenance. Some organisms will go through periods, such as hibernation, in which all they do is a form of maintenance. Finally and most important, all life histories include a phase during which resources are devoted to reproduction. In the moth or the salmon, reproduction occurs only once, at the very end of the life history. In a tree or a marmot, reproduction can occur at repeated intervals after the organism has reached maturity.

Life histories can vary dramatically among organisms; furthermore, variations among species reflect the action of natural selection, with each life history presumably maximizing reproductive output across an individual's lifetime. Darwinian fitness must be measured in terms of the total reproductive success of an organism over its lifetime, and there are different ways to maximize this fitness by allocating resources over an organism's life history.

The fact that an organism must divide up the total amount of resources available to it among different needs in its life history leads to life-history tradeoffs. A life history strategy that would yield the greatest overall reproductive output might include beginning reproduction at an early age, producing many offspring at each instance of reproduction, and having many reproductive events. Because any organism faces resource limitations, however, changes that improve fitness by means of one life-history trait often reduce fitness by means of another. The most important of these tradeoffs involves when and how much energy is devoted to reproduction, which is illustrated by two different patterns of variation in life histories among different bird species.

Life History Table

Key:
- ▬▬▬ Growth
- ▬▬▬ Maintenance
- ▬▬▬ Reproduction
- ▬▬▬ Obtaining Resources

Tree

Marmot

Salmon

Moth

The first pattern is a tradeoff between the resources invested in reproduction and the long-term survival of birds. Bird species with high annual fecundity (production of offspring) tend to live for shorter periods of time and vice versa. In other words, there is a life-history tradeoff between how much an organism invests in reproduction and how long it lives. Reproduction typically requires a significant investment in resources, which are, therefore, not available for such needs as long-term maintenance.

This is called a *tradeoff* because the two extremes represent two different ways of maximizing reproductive success. The life-history patterns of different organisms can represent an evolutionary compromise of conflicting demands on the resources available to that organism. An important point is that neither extreme of a tradeoff performs "better" from an evolutionary point of view; the two extremes simply represent two different ways of maximizing reproductive success.

The second pattern has to do with when a bird species first begins to reproduce. In general, species that begin to reproduce at an earlier age have shorter lifespans. The sooner an organism starts devoting significant amounts of resources to reproduction, the sooner those resources are denied to maintenance, lowering the average probability of survival. On the other hand, the sooner an organism starts reproducing, the sooner its own offspring will grow up and themselves start reproducing.

Many adaptations of organisms—including patterns of growth and reproduction, aspects of physiology and anatomy, and aspects of behavior—reflect life-history tradeoffs. The nature of these tradeoffs, in turn, is ultimately determined by the energy and resources available to an organism. ■

Suggested Reading

Campbell & Reece, *Biology* (6th ed.), chapter 52.

Smith & Smith, *Elements of Ecology* (5th ed.), chapter 12.

Sterns, *The Evolution of Life Histories*.

Questions to Consider

1. Can you explain how the idea of limiting resources fits into Darwin's theory of evolution by natural selection?

2. Some species provide a significant amount of parental care to their young, whereas other species provide little or nothing to offspring after they are born. All other things being equal, which species would you expect to have a longer life span on average?

The Structure of Populations
Lecture 59

Today we are going to begin a series of lectures in which we look at how the availability of energy and resources affects the size and structure of populations of organisms, groups of organisms of the same kind. That is, we are going to be moving our discussion of the significance of energy and resources from the level of the individual to the level of a group of individuals—a population.

Our discussion of "energy and resources" moves here to the level of populations of organisms, first by redefining what we mean by *population* in an ecological context and outlining the important characteristics of a population from an ecological perspective. In addition to providing information on the current state of a population, these characteristics can be used to predict how the population will change over time in response to various external and internal factors. Modeling and gathering data on population changes also makes it easier to compare patterns across different species, or across different populations within a single species.

Examining the significance of "energy and resources" at levels of biological organization above the cells or the individual organism requires redefining the concept of *population* and understanding how populations are characterized. In the context of our earlier discussion of biological information, we defined a population as a group of organisms that can transfer genetic information among themselves. In ecology, a population may be defined as a group of individuals of one species that simultaneously occupy a particular area.

At any given moment, any single individual organism occupies only one spot, is of one particular age, and has done a certain amount of reproduction. A population is made up of many individual organisms, each of which may differ in these life-history traits.

The sum of the life-history traits of the individuals in a population determines the *structure* of that population, which depends on and illustrates how the population distributes and uses resources. More important, describing a population's structure is the first step toward predicting how that population may change over time. Three main characteristics describe a population's structure: the density, spacing, and age distribution of its individuals.

A population's *density* refers to the number of individuals per unit area or unit volume. Density is a key attribute because many of the factors that regulate changes in population size depend on it. Measuring the density of a particular species living in a square kilometer might seem as simple as capturing all the individuals, counting them, and dividing the number of individuals by the area. The difficulty with this approach is that the species in question likely occupies only some subset of the space; for example, a species of bird may occupy space around hedgerows at the edges of a field, but not the entire space of the field.

Another problem with measuring density is that it is not always clear what should be counted. In a population of birds, for example, it may seem obvious to count the total number of individuals; in other cases, this is not so obvious. Measuring the population density of a plant may not be as accurate as measuring the total biomass, which may more accurately reflect patterns of availability or resource use.

Spacing, or *population dispersion*, measures how individuals in a population are distributed with respect to each other within the space they occupy. Individuals in a population are typically dispersed in one of three patterns. If organisms are *randomly dispersed*, the position of each individual in a population is independent of any other individual. If *uniformly dispersed*, individuals are spaced at approximately even intervals in the available space. In animals, uniform dispersion usually results from behavioral interactions. In plants, uniform dispersion often results from individuals intruding on each other.

By far the most common type of dispersion is when individuals clump together. *Clumped dispersion* patterns can arise from a number of factors, including soil types or the availability of critical minerals in plants and social behaviors in animals that create benefits, such as improved ability to find a mate. Patterns of dispersion in a population provide information on the effective density of a population, what resources are important for an organism, and how that organism interacts with other organisms of the same species or other species.

The final characteristic of a population to consider here is its *age distribution*, the proportions of individuals that fall into different age classes. In some species, individuals are born, reproduce, and die in a single season, and generations of individuals never overlap. In many cases, though, generations overlap in time. Age distributions can be a critical factor in determining how the population will change over time.

The age distribution of a population may be represented as an *age pyramid*. The individuals in a particular age class are represented by a horizontal bar, with the width of these bars representing the number of individuals in each age category.

At any given moment, any single individual organism occupies only one spot, is of one particular age, and has done a certain amount of reproduction. A population is made up of many individual organisms, each of which may differ in these life-history traits.

In an industrialized European country, such as Sweden, the bars that make up the age pyramid may be all more or less uniform in width. This pattern is characteristic of a population with high survival among adults and a steady birth rate that matches the death rate. A developing country, such as Mexico, may have very wide bars at the bottom of the graph, with bar width decreasing rapidly up the pyramid. This shape is characteristic of a growing population with a disproportionate number of younger individuals.

The United States has a relatively uniform pattern of age distribution, but also a noticeable bulge among middle-aged individuals that reflects the Baby Boom, an enormous increase in the birth rate in the United States between about 1947 and 1964. Humans less than 15 years old or more than 45 years old rarely reproduce. In the United States, individuals in the Baby Boom generation largely reproduced a decade or two ago, leading to an echo that was seen in a second increase of individuals in the youngest age classes. A developing country might have a large proportion of individuals in reproductive age classes and younger, indicating rapid population growth overall. If an age pyramid showed a predominance of individuals in post-reproductive age classes, simply considering the total number of individuals in this population would give a misleading picture of how it would change in the future.

The characteristics of a population can be used to model population dynamics—the way a population changes over time. The structure of a population is not usually static but fluctuates over time. These fluctuations are sometimes slow and subtle, but they can include extreme "crashes" in size followed by rapid population growth that approaches a maximal rate of increase. Predicting whether a population will remain stable or will fluctuate, and how it will fluctuate if it does, is important for at least two reasons. First, understanding the factors that influence population structure over time reveals how biological systems are affected by the energy and other resources available to them. Second, as the resources of the planet are increasingly stressed and modified, predicting how populations of organisms will respond to those changes allows us to understand how human activities influence changes in the biosphere.

The simple knowledge of when individuals are born and die provides a considerable amount of information about how a population will change over time. Individuals in a population come and go, but a population will change its size depending on the relative balance between inputs to and outputs from the population.

The knowledge that births and deaths occur in a predictable fashion on average has been understood and used in human societies since Roman times; the statistical study of population characteristics is called *demography*. Births, deaths, immigration, and emigration are particularly important demographic events or parameters, because they determine the number of individuals in a population at a given time.

The rates at which demographic events occur in a population depend on a number of factors. Extrinsic factors include those that affect the availability of resources, but also any other aspect of the environment that influences how likely individuals are to be born or to die. Intrinsic factors involve the life-history characteristics of the species in question; some species invest much in reproduction every year, some species start reproducing early in their lifespans, and so on.

Demographic information about a population is often represented in the form of a *life table*. The rows represent different age groups, while the columns include information about the numbers of individuals in each age group, their survival, and their reproductive rate (fecundity).

A life table is usually constructed to show the fate of a cohort of individuals that are all born at the same time and followed throughout their lifetimes. In the first row, the number of individuals will be the total number of individuals in the cohort. In the next row, the number of individuals will be lower because some individuals have died. At the same time, the reproductive rate will increase as individuals become old enough to reproduce.

Each successive row will represent fewer and fewer individuals, and patterns of survival will shift as individuals progress through different ages. In the last row, no individuals would be left, and the life table would be a complete picture of the demographic changes in a typical population. Such a complete life table can be used to predict how perturbations to the population might affect its future structure.

Another common way to look at the demography of a population is in the form of a graph showing survivorship—the number of individuals still alive in a cohort. These graphs form *survivorship curves*, which are snapshots of age-dependent survival and can be used to compare different species or different populations of the same species.

Survivorship curves are often compared to three idealized patterns. In individuals that tend to live out their entire lifespan after they are born, survival rate is high throughout the lifespan and plummets in older individuals, producing a convex Type I curve. Type I curves are typical of humans and other large mammals that produce few young but care extensively for them. At the opposite extreme, a Type III curve drops sharply at the left of the graph, reflecting very high death rates among young, and flattens out as the death rate of the few individuals who survive to maturity

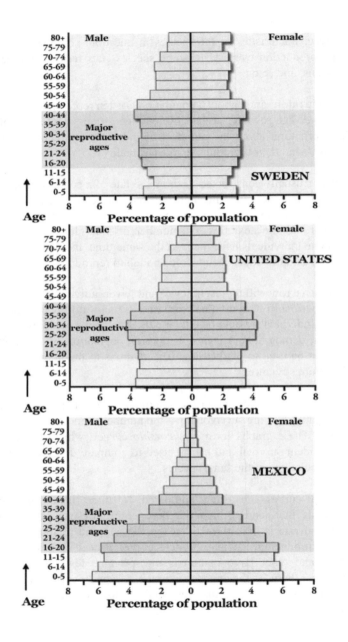

declines. Type III curves are common among organisms, such as many species of fish for example, that produce many offspring but provide them with little care. Finally, an intermediate Type II curve reflects cases where the death rate remains relatively constant across the life history of a species. This pattern is characteristic of many species of small birds, once they have survived to make it out of the nest. Many species exhibit survivorship curves that are more complex than these ideal curves, but most survivorship curves based on empirical data do generally show Type I, II, or III patterns at different times in their life histories. ■

Suggested Reading

Campbell & Reece, *Biology* (6th ed.), chapter 52.

Freeman, *Biological Science*, chapter 48.

Kingsland, *Modeling Nature: Episodes in the History of Population Ecology* (2nd ed.).

Purves et al., *Life* (7th ed.), chapter 54.

Smith & Smith, *Elements of Ecology* (5th ed.), chapter 10.

Questions to Consider

1. Human populations have exhibited an increasingly clumped distribution over the history of our species. What might be some reasons for this trend in terms of resource distribution and use?

2. What kind of information obtained from life tables could be useful for managing a fishery? What kind of information from survivorship curves could be useful?

Population Growth
Lecture 60

> Remember, I told you that if a single bacterium was left to its own devices and given unlimited resources, it would multiply so fast that within 36 hours its progeny would cover the entire surface of the Earth to a depth of a foot; and in a month, it would fill the entire visible universe, and so forth.

Of course, the key assumption here was that individuals in this bacterial population, all the descendants of the original bacterium, had no restrictions on their ability to gain access to energy and resources. We begin by examining the reasons behind the obvious fact that populations cannot experience unlimited growth for an indefinite period of time. We begin with a simple model of exponential growth and then develop a more complex model that takes births and deaths into account, and can be modified to further account for differing growth rates and the limit a population's environment imposes on population size. The logistic growth predicted by this model corresponds more closely to actual population growth than a simple exponential model.

Unrestricted growth of a population of bacteria provides an example of exponential growth. A bacterium given unlimited food would multiply so fast that, within one month, its progeny would weigh more than the visible universe and would be expanding outward at the speed of light. Of course, this assumes that none of the descendents of the original bacterium had restrictions on the ability to gain access to energy and resources. This assumption is usually unrealistic (though it is sometimes met for a short period of time under certain conditions), but this kind of population growth provides a good starting point for understanding population growth in general.

As a physical model, assume that the thickness of a piece of paper represents the size of a population; a typical piece of paper is about .0025 inches thick. Population growth can be represented by folding the paper. After one fold, the thickness doubles to .005 inches. With every generation—that is, every fold—the paper thickness doubles. If the original sheet of paper was folded 50 times, it would be 44 million miles thick—almost half the distance from the Earth to the Sun! The point of this example is to illustrate that in each successive generation, the number of individuals added for each individual in the population remains constant, but because the total number of individuals is increasing, the total number of new individuals accelerates dramatically.

The growth of actual populations of organisms is more complex than this simple paper folding model suggests. One deficiency is that this model assumes that each individual simply adds one new individual to the population in each generation. Another major problem is that the model assumes that no individuals die. Recognizing these shortcomings allows a more complete model of how populations grow when resources are not limited. This model still assumes that populations can grow indefinitely without running low on resources, which is usually not the case, but it provides a more realistic way of including births and deaths.

A general mathematical model that describes how the size of a population will change over time can begin with the equation $N_1 = N_0 + B - D + I - E$. N is the size of the population in individuals; N_0 is the size of the starting generation, while N_1 is the size of the next generation, which includes births, deaths, and other additions and subtractions. B is the number of individuals added to the population by births at each generation, and D is the number of individuals lost from the population by death. I is the number of individuals that immigrate into the population, and E is the number of individuals that emigrate out of the population with each generation.

When a population's density begins to approach the carrying capacity of an environment, this can have a profound effect on population growth rate. If individuals cannot obtain sufficient resources to reproduce, per capita birth rates will drop.

In words, the equation states that the size of the population at one generation will be equal to the size of that population at some previous point in time, plus all the individuals that have been added by births and immigration, minus all the individuals that have been subtracted through deaths and emigration. The equation can be simplified by considering only births and deaths, giving $N_1 = N_0 + B - D$. Real populations may be significantly influenced by immigration and emigration, but these factors can be ignored without changing the sense of a general model.

It is often more useful to know not the absolute size of a population but, instead, the rate of change in population size over some period of time, because the significance of the absolute size of a population of organisms may be hard to interpret in many cases. The growth equation can be rewritten in terms of a rate of change: $\Delta N/\Delta t = B - D$. In this equation, ΔN is the change in population size occurring over Δt, a given time interval. Δt may equal a generation or a fixed unit of time, such as a year. In words, this equation states that the change in population size per unit time is equal to the number of births occurring during that time minus the number of deaths.

It is often difficult to know the absolute numbers of births or deaths in a population. Instead of using absolute values, however, we can use the average rate of births and deaths per individual (per capita), which can be obtained from life tables.

This approach allows further simplification of the equation to $\Delta N/\Delta t = bN - dN$, where b is the per capita birth rate and d is the per capita death rate, and N is the current population size. In words, this equation states that the change in population size per unit time is equal to the birth rate of the average individual times the number of individuals, minus the death rate of the average individual times the number of individuals.

To make this equation truly useful, it can be rearranged to read $\Delta N/\Delta t = (b - d)N$. This form of the equation points out that what matters is the difference between the per capita birth and death rates. This difference is called r, the per capita growth rate; thus, the equation becomes $\Delta N/\Delta t = rN$. In calculus notation (which simply means that the time interval becomes infinitely small), this is $dN/dt = rN$. In words, this equation states that the change in the population size per unit time equals the per capita growth rate times the population's size.

This equation provides a simple way to determine the future size of a population in terms of just two parameters: the present size of the population (N) and the per capita growth rate (r). Looking at the possible values of r provides most of the desired information about change over time.

- If $r > 0$, the population will increase in size over time.

- If $r = 0$, the population size will stay constant.

- If $r < 0$, the population will decrease in size.

A population living under ideal conditions will maximize the difference between its birth and death rates. This maximum growth rate is called the *intrinsic rate of increase* (r_{max}). Population increase under these conditions is $dN/dt = r_{max}N$.

This pattern of growth is called *exponential growth*, because a plot of population growth produces a J-shaped curve characteristic of an exponential function. Although the per capita rate of increase (r) remains constant, the curve gets steeper over time, because the number of individuals (N) is constantly increasing.

If r is only a little larger than zero, exponential increase will take more time to start an obvious upward trajectory. As r becomes more positive, the slope of the growth curve becomes steeper much sooner. Whether it happens quickly or not, any population in exponential growth will eventually exhibit a very steep growth curve. Bacteria, for example, have a relatively high r_{max}, while humans have a relatively much lower r_{max}. A pair of humans would need about 4,000 years to fill the visible universe with their offspring if undergoing exponential growth, as opposed to one month for a bacterium.

Most populations clearly do not undergo exponential growth; they simply do not have the resources to do so. However, some populations do experience periods of exponential growth, such as when a population becomes established in a new environment or when a population that has been drastically reduced by catastrophe is rebounding from that event.

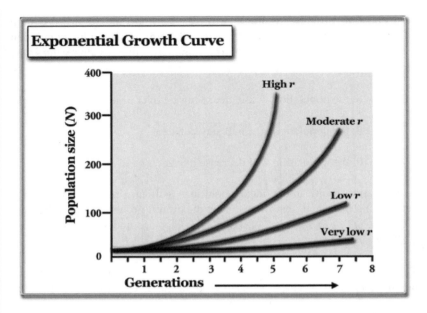

Exponential Growth Curve

Most natural populations do not experience exponential growth, at least not for long. For most populations, as the size of the population increases, the observed per capita growth rate of that population tends to decrease. For this reason, we expect the overall rate of increase of the size of the population as a whole to slow down. The size of a population and its growth rate are connected because resources are finite; there is ultimately some limit to the number of individuals that can occupy a habitat. This limit is called the *carrying capacity* and is given the symbol *K*. While r_{max} is a property of a species, K is a property of the environment.

When a population's density begins to approach the carrying capacity of an environment, this can have a profound effect on population growth rate. If individuals cannot obtain sufficient resources to reproduce, per capita birth rates will drop; if individuals cannot obtain sufficient resources to maintain themselves, per capita death rates will rise. In either case, r will decrease and population growth will slow.

The previous model of population growth can be modified to incorporate the effects of approaching a carrying capacity. This model, called the *logistic growth model*, incorporates the effects of population density on population growth, essentially allowing r to vary from r_{max} when the density is far below K to effectively 0 when K is reached. The resulting equation is:

$$dN/dt = r_{max}N[(K - N)/K].$$

By multiplying r_{max} by $(K - N)/K$, the effective value of r decreases as N increases. As N approaches K, the new term approaches 0 and population growth diminishes. If N is much smaller than K (the current population size is much lower than the carrying capacity), the term approaches 1 and population growth is close to what would be predicted by r_{max}.

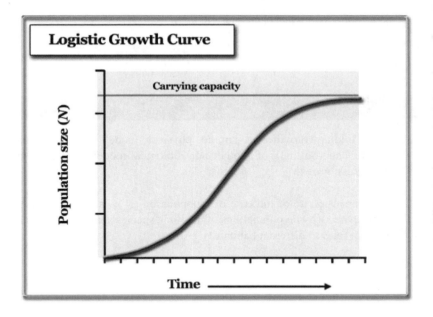

A graph of population size over time for a population undergoing logistic growth produces an S-shaped curve. When N is much less than K, growth is almost exponential. As the population grows, N approaches K and the rate of population growth begins to decline. The highest rate of population growth occurs at intermediate population sizes.

Both the exponential growth model and the logistic growth model predict the growth of populations over time, though the logistic growth model predicts more accurately the growth of actual populations in which the environment imposes an upper limit on the number of individuals that can survive. ■

Suggested Reading

Campbell & Reece, *Biology* (6th ed.), chapter 52.

Freeman, *Biological Science*, chapter 48.

Purves et al., *Life* (7th ed.), chapter 54.

Smith & Smith, *Elements of Ecology* (5th ed.), chapter 10.

Questions to Consider

1. Paper folding provides a simple physical model of exponential growth. Can you think of another non-biological model or example of exponential growth?

2. If the intrinsic rate of increase of a population (r_{max}) is a property of a species, then why do populations of the same species sometimes grow at different rates in different habitats?

What Limits Population Growth?
Lecture 61

What about logistic growth? Do natural populations actually follow the S-shaped curve we described last time that is predicted by the logistic growth model? This is the question that we left off with last time, and this is where we are going to pick up our discussion of population dynamics today.

We begin by examining how the growth of real populations sometimes fits and sometimes diverges from the predictions of the logistic growth model. The lecture then turns to the question of what mechanisms regulate the size of real populations. In general, the factors that limit population growth can be grouped into one of two categories, depending on whether they are related to the density of the population or not. The lecture concludes by noting that the growth and ultimate size of populations in the wild often are determined by both types of factors acting in concert.

The logistic growth model predicts the growth of some real populations, but not all. For example, the growth of a population of a single-celled pond organism called *Paramecium* can closely match the S-shaped curve predicted by the logistic growth model. Logistic growth can also be observed in wild populations of organisms, as in the case of a population of fur seals on St. Paul's Island off the Alaska coast recovering from over-hunting. Not all populations closely follow a logistic growth curve, however, even under controlled laboratory conditions. For example, population growth in *Daphnia*, another common pond organism, often deviates from logistic growth by initially overshooting the predicted carrying capacity, then decreasing to less than the carrying capacity, finally reaching the carrying capacity and stabilizing there. This pattern of population growth can be observed in populations of many different kinds of organisms.

Given that the logistic model does not predict this pattern of growth, it must include assumptions that are not met by all populations. For example, the logistic model assumes that the potential negative effects of the population size approaching the carrying capacity have an instantaneous effect on population growth. In fact, there is often a delay in the response of the growth rate of a population that has approached or exceeded the carrying capacity.

The growth of real populations often diverges from logistic growth. The logistic model predicts that a population will maintain a relatively stable population size once it reaches its carrying capacity. Even if a population overshoots its carrying capacity, the model predicts that the population size should remain at the carrying capacity once it is reached. This often does not occur in natural populations; instead, many populations fluctuate in size and never appear to stabilize at a particular carrying capacity. These population fluctuations can be quite dramatic, as much as an order of magnitude in size in the example of Darwin's finches.

On the other hand, some natural populations do remain remarkably stable once they reach their carrying capacity, and even populations that fluctuate often do so within some regular range of minimum and maximum population sizes. These observations lead to the question of what actually regulates the size of a population. The mechanisms that affect the growth and size of populations may be grouped into two general categories.

- *Density-dependent factors* intensify as the population size increases and diminish as the population size decreases.

- *Density-independent factors* influence a population's size in the same way regardless of that population's density.

Density-dependent population regulation occurs in a variety of ways. The logistic model of population growth is really a model of density-dependent population regulation. As a population approaches its carrying capacity, the increasing number of individuals in the population divides the available resources ever more finely. As the resources available per individual decrease, the per capita birth rate decreases and the per capita death rate increases. If resources available per individual decrease enough, the growth rate may become negative, as more individuals die than are born.

This response of population growth to population density is an example of negative feedback, analogous to negative feedback in homeostasis. The main difference here is that the mechanisms responsible for this negative feedback effect have not evolved to regulate populations; instead, they arise as a consequence of a linkage between population density and factors that influence birth and death rates.

In addition to the availability of resources, a number of other factors can link population density to population growth rate. There may be competition for less obvious resources, such as nesting sites, suitable substrates for rooting, and so on. Predators may also be attracted more to areas where their prey is more dense. In addition, diseases may be more readily transmitted and, thus, cause more mortality in more dense populations, and waste products can build up disproportionately in a crowded population and have a negative effect on population size.

The effect on population size of density-independent regulating factors is often unpredictable and catastrophic.

It is fairly easy to demonstrate density-dependent effects in natural populations and sometimes possible to identify which factors are specifically responsible. For example, in song sparrows, the number of males that fail to obtain breeding territory increases as the total number of males increases; similarly, as the number of breeding females in the population increases, the average number of offspring produced per female decreases. Finally, the probability that a young bird will survive its first winter decreases as the population size increases.

In the case of the *Eurosta* fly, larvae feed on the goldenrod tissues all summer long, form pupae, and spend the winter inside their galls before emerging in spring as adults. *Eurosta* larvae and pupae inside galls are attacked by several predators, including wasps, beetles, and birds. Experiments show that such predation, not resource limitation, appears to be the primary density-dependent factor responsible for maintaining *Eurosta* populations at relatively constant sizes.

The effect on population size of density-independent regulating factors is often unpredictable and catastrophic. Density-independent factors are often related to weather (or climate) and other disturbances of the habitat. For example, the first freeze of the fall has a major effect on survivorship in many insect populations. This effect is density-independent because the percentage of the insects killed by the frost is unrelated to the number of insects in the population—all that matters is when the first frost occurs and how cold it gets. Some species of migratory birds can also be adversely affected in a density-independent way by an early snow or ice storm that occurs before the birds have migrated south for the winter.

Most factors that affect population size in a density-independent manner are related to unpredictable environmental events—often the weather, but also droughts, fires, or floods. These events occur irregularly, but they can have a profound effect on the birth and death rates of a population. For example, Australian *Thrips* are a kind of insect that feeds on pollen, leaves, and flower tissues; they often feed on roses and other cultivated flowers. The number of flowers available for *Thrips* to feed on corresponds to the season, with more flowers in the summer and fewer flowers in the winter, although there are always some flowers and *Thrips* remain reproductively active all year long.

During the Australian winter, cooler temperatures slow the development of *Thrips*, and many do not get old enough to reproduce before the flower they are on dies and falls to the ground, killing the *Thrips* living on it. This is one form of density-independent regulation that prevents the populations of *Thrips* from reaching a carrying capacity, because the resource they live on (the flower) does not stay alive long enough for much population growth in cool weather. With the onset of spring, the weather warms up and the *Thrips* increase their population size to very high levels, because they can mature more rapidly in the warmer weather and reproduce before the flowers they live on die.

Population growth appears to be exponential during this period and remains unchecked until the onset of summer, when heat and dryness cause an increase in mortality and the population crashes back down to a very low density. This crash also occurs well before density-dependent factors have come into play—that is, before the *Thrips* have approached their carrying capacity. Thus, two density-independent factors, both associated with climate, ultimately determine the population size and dynamics of these *Thrips* populations.

In many populations, both density-dependent factors and density-independent factors act together to determine dynamic changes in the size and structure of the population. Populations may remain near their carrying capacity, regulated by density-dependent factors, but suffer periodic fluctuations superimposed on them by density-independent factors. The logistic growth model, as well as the general fact that resources are limited, suggests that all populations must be affected by density-dependent effects resulting from negative feedback of factors affecting birth and death rates. At the same time, it is hard to imagine any population that is not potentially affected by extreme fluctuations in climate or other environmental factors with a density-independent effect on population size. Identifying cases where density-dependent and density-independent effects on population size can be isolated, however, provides insight into how resources do—or do not—help explain the abundance and distribution of populations of organisms. ■

Suggested Reading

Campbell & Reece, *Biology* (6ᵗʰ ed.), chapter 52.

Kingsland, *Modeling Nature: Episodes in the History of Population Ecology* (2ⁿᵈ ed.).

Purves et al., *Life* (7ᵗʰ ed.), chapter 54.

Smith & Smith, *Elements of Ecology* (5ᵗʰ ed.), chapter 11.

Questions to Consider

1. How is density-dependent regulation of population size similar to homeostatic control of a physiological parameter? How is it different?

2. Are populations that are regulated by density-dependent factors more or less stable than populations regulated by density-*independent* factors? Why do you think so?

Costs and Benefits of Behavior
Lecture 62

You might think that the female should always make more eggs, right? Then she will have more offspring. But it turns out that small eggs will hatch into small offspring. And, those small offspring, because they are small, will be less likely to survive. So the tradeoff here really is a tradeoff between producing a few high-quality offspring, or many low-quality offspring.

This lecture begins by reviewing how organisms flexibly allocate resources in changing circumstances. Behavioral ecologists study the evolutionary significance of patterns of resource allocation by focusing on the costs and benefits of different behaviors and examining the tradeoffs organisms make between these costs and benefits. Every behavior has costs and benefits that may affect the fitness of the individual performing it. One kind of behavior of particular significance in this regard is social behavior, which conveys unique advantages and disadvantages that depend on an organism's interactions with other members of its species.

Organisms may allocate the resources available to them in different ways to maximize their reproductive success. Life histories vary among different species, but individuals in a population of the same species also allocate resources differently. For example, female side-blotched lizards vary greatly in the number of eggs they produce in a single reproductive event. Some females lay as few as two eggs, while other females lay up to nine eggs.

The life history tradeoff here is that females that lay fewer eggs lay larger eggs, while females that lay more eggs lay smaller eggs. A female has a certain amount of resources for a single reproductive event but can allocate them in different ways. It might seem obvious that a female should always make more eggs; however, small eggs hatch smaller offspring, which are less likely to survive. The tradeoff, then, is between producing a few high-quality offspring or many low-quality offspring.

As with the lizards, individuals in a population can flexibly change aspects of their behavior to maximize both available resources and their own reproductive success. The field of biology that integrates the behavior of organisms with its ecological and evolutionary consequences in populations is called *behavioral ecology*.

Any behavior an organism can perform has both costs and benefits. An organism has limited resources to devote to the different kinds of behaviors it can perform, and spending these resources represents a cost. A particular behavior may be costly, but this cost may be offset by some benefit that accrues as a consequence of the behavior. A behavior's costs, however, can be more complex or subtle than simply expending the energy or other resource needed to perform it. Behavioral ecologists separate the costs of behavior into three broad categories.

- *Energetic costs* refer to the amount of energy (and other resources) expended to perform a behavior.

- *Risk costs* refer to the increased chance of being injured or killed while performing a behavior.

- *Opportunity costs* refer to the opportunities to accrue other benefits that an organism forfeits when it performs a particular behavior.

The territorial behavior of song sparrows illustrates these different kinds of costs. As in many species of birds and animals in general, male song sparrows defend territories from which they exclude other males. A territory is a valuable resource because it provides the resources needed to build a nest and raise offspring. To defend a territory, a male song sparrow will patrol its perimeter, stopping to sing periodically; the male's song serves as an aggressive "keep out" signal to other males. If the male sees another male intruding on his territory, he will try to chase the intruder out; if the intruder does not leave, the territorial male might attack him, resulting in a serious fight in which the birds peck at each other with their beaks. Territorial defense clearly has an energetic cost; it takes energy for the male to patrol his territory, sing, and chase other birds. This energy is unavailable for other uses, such as maintenance or the performance of other kinds of behaviors.

There also is a risk cost associated with territorial defense, which comes from the fact that a male may become injured if it fights with another male. If an individual is injured, its likelihood of dying is greatly increased—it might even be killed in combat. Finally, there are opportunity costs associated with territorial behavior, as the male cannot court or mate with females, search for food, or perform other beneficial behaviors when he is defending his territory.

The lecture began by predicting that an animal should perform a particular behavior if the benefits of doing so outweigh the costs. Behavioral ecologists measure benefits in evolutionary terms; specifically, benefits ultimately involve increasing the survival or the reproductive success of an individual or both. Understanding the costs and benefits of a behavior provides insight into how an individual responds flexibly to its circumstances. As the costs or benefits associated with some behavior shift—because different resources become available or the demography of the population changes, for example—different behavioral strategies might become more or less adaptive.

Even with a general understanding of the costs and benefits of behavior, measuring these costs and benefits can be extremely difficult. For example, it is theoretically possible to measure the amount of energy expended on a behavior by measuring oxygen consumption or CO_2 production—but how would this be done for a bird defending its territory in the field? Behavioral ecologists must often infer which costs and benefits are important and how animals assess them.

For example, a species of Hawaiian bird called a honeycreeper feeds on nectar from flowers and defends territories that include nectar-producing flowers. The benefit to a honeycreeper of holding a territory might be measured in the amount of nectar it can obtain from the flowers in the territory. Individuals should then only defend territories that contain a sufficient number of flowers to provide the food required to at least offset the cost of defense.

If the distribution of flowers is too sparse to provide the necessary food, the birds should cease being territorial. Furthermore, birds should cease being territorial if the distribution of flowers is too dense, because there is no point in defending territories if equal access allows all individuals to obtain the resources they need. In other words, there should be two flower-density thresholds that predict whether or not birds in a population will actually defend territories.

This is, in fact, the pattern observed; honeycreepers stop defending territories if the number of flowers available is less than a minimum or more than a maximum. Individuals defend territories only in an intermediate range of flower densities, a range in which the benefit obtained from exclusive access to the nectar available in an area is greater than the energetic cost of defending that area.

As a second example, birds that are *brood parasites*, such as the brown-headed cowbird, neither build their own nests nor raise their own offspring. Eggs in a bird's nest are normally laid by the female that built the nest, but brood parasites lay their eggs in the nests of other species.

In North America, female brown-headed cowbirds lay their eggs in the nests of many kinds of small birds, most of which are too small to remove a cowbird egg with their beaks. A bird whose nest has been parasitized has two options: It can abandon its nest and build a new one, or it can continue to incubate its nest and raise both its own young and the young cowbird.

Abandoning the nest entails the cost of having to build a new nest and to lay a new set of eggs. Continuing to incubate the cowbird egg also entails a cost: Fewer of the host's own offspring survive than in unparasitized nests, because young cowbirds take food that would have been eaten by the host's young. In a study of a parasitized species called the prothonotary warbler, whether or not a bird abandoned a parasitized nest depended on the territory in which she nested. Prothonotary warblers build their nests in cavities in trees or stumps, and the number of suitable cavities for building a nest differs in different areas.

A female is more likely to continue to incubate her eggs after her nest has been parasitized if there few other good nesting sites on her territory than if there are many alternative nesting sites. This observation does not specifically measure the costs and benefits of abandoning a nest but allows the inference that the costs of abandonment are usually lower than the costs of continuing to incubate; this is true, however, only if other good nesting sites are available. This type of understanding of relative costs and benefits provides insight into what costs and benefits are relevant to a species.

Perhaps the most important feature of an organism's environment to which it must respond is other organisms, especially individuals of the same species. In some species, associations between individuals may consist of simply the joining of eggs and sperm. Gametes may be broadcast into the environment and come together through mechanisms over which the organism has little or no direct control. However, individuals of many species associate for longer periods of time during reproduction or beyond. These associations often revolve around behaviors that provide care for offspring, improving the reproductive success (and, thus, fitness) of the parents by increasing the probability of survival and reproduction by their young.

As with the lizards, individuals in a population can flexibly change aspects of their behavior to maximize both available resources and their own reproductive success.

In general, interactions among individuals of the same species are called *social behavior*, which we expect to occur when it results in a higher rate of survival and more offspring than is possible for solitary individuals. Social behavior may improve foraging success or expand the kinds of food that can be obtained; packs of African wild dogs, for example, can capture prey too large for any one dog to subdue alone. Social behavior may also reduce predation, as in flocks of birds, where the nature of a flock makes it difficult for predators to attack a single individual.

Improved foraging and predator protection are the most generally applicable benefits of group living, although other benefits may occur, such as increased ability to defend a group territory, improved care for offspring through communal feeding, or even a greater ability to save energy by sharing body warmth. Group living has associated costs; an almost universal cost is higher exposure to disease and parasites. Other potential costs include the fact that groups may be more conspicuous than individuals, increasing the possibility of detection by predators, as well as increased competition for resources, such as nesting sites and mates. Another problem of living in a group is that it increases the possibility that some other individual will copulate with one's mate—*extra-pair copulation* and the resulting loss of reproductive success is a potentially major cost of group living. ∎

Suggested Reading

Alcock, *The Triumph of Sociobiology.*

Campbell & Reece, *Biology* (6th ed.), chapter 51.

Krebs & Davies, *An Introduction to Behavioural Ecology* (3rd ed.).

Purves et al., *Life* (7th ed.), chapter 53.

Questions to Consider

1. Much of the theory used in behavioral ecology is derived from the field of economics. Why do you think this is so?

2. If cliff swallows and other colonial species suffer greater disease transmission when living in larger groups, why don't these animals always nest in small colonies or by themselves?

Altruism and Mate Selection
Lecture 63

In today's lecture we are going to continue our discussion of behavioral ecology by considering the costs and benefits not just of associating with other individuals in a group, but more specifically the consequences of interacting with particular individuals in the population.

We begin by categorizing kinds of social interactions in terms of which of the individuals in an interaction benefits and which incurs a cost. One type of interaction, an altruistic interaction in which the individual performing a behavior incurs a cost in order to benefit another, is particularly difficult to explain in terms of natural selection. An expanded definition of fitness that includes the reproductive success of genetically related individuals provides an explanation. The lecture then turns to the problem of mate choice, perhaps the most important kind of social interaction for any individual, and explores the qualities on which mate choice is often based, the way individuals choose, and traits that have evolved to increase the chances of being chosen.

Social interactions among individuals in a group can be categorized by whether they result in a benefit or a cost to each of the two individuals in the interaction. Four categories of social interaction can be defined this way.

- A behavioral interaction that benefits both the performer and recipient of the behavior is a *cooperative act*.

- An interaction that benefits the performer but costs the recipient is a *selfish act*.

- An interaction that costs the performer something but benefits the recipient is an *altruistic act*.

- Finally, an interaction that costs both the performer and the recipient is a *spiteful act*.

In general, it is easy to imagine how natural selection can lead to the evolution of both cooperative and selfish behaviors. If a social interaction confers an overall benefit to the performer, it seems reasonable that individuals in a population will perform it, regardless of whether the recipient benefits or suffers—what is important is that the performer benefits on average. True spiteful behavior is not typically observed—animals do not appear to act in a way that incurs cost for both themselves and for the recipient. However, behaviors in social groups that appear to incur some cost to performer while benefiting the recipient are common. At face value, altruistic behaviors make no sense from an evolutionary perspective, because they appear to carry only costs without conferring any benefits on the performer.

Social interactions among individuals in a group can be categorized by whether they result in a benefit or a cost to each of the two individuals in the interaction.

Two examples of altruistic behavior illustrate this apparent conundrum. Belding's ground squirrels are similar to chipmunks; however, unlike chipmunks, they live in colonies in open areas that are vulnerable to many kinds of predators, including hawks and coyotes. Like many social animals, these ground squirrels have a particular signal called an *alarm call* they give in response to seeing a predator. When a predator approaches the colony, the first individual to spot the predator often gives an alarm call, alerting other individuals who then retreat into their burrows. There is an obvious and demonstrated cost to giving the alarm call—the caller calls attention to itself and takes time to give the call and, thus, is more likely to be taken by the predator. That the recipients of this behavior benefit from it is equally apparent.

In a second example, a species of African bird called the white-fronted bee-eater lives in large colonies of many nesting pairs. Most male-female pairs receive assistance in raising their young from non-breeding adults, both males and females, called *helpers*. Helpers gather food, defend the nest hole, and watch for predators. Helpers are adult birds and, thus, physiologically capable of reproducing on their own, but they forego their own reproduction—an obvious cost to themselves—to help the reproductive efforts of other birds, an obvious benefit to others. This raises the question of how this behavior could evolve, if the animal performing the behavior foregoes its own reproduction.

The answer to both puzzles comes from understanding the genetic relatedness between the performer and recipient of an altruistic act. Specifically, altruistic behaviors may evolve when performers and recipients are closely related, because an individual can enhance its reproductive success either directly, by producing offspring of its own, or indirectly, by promoting the survival and reproduction of close relatives.

Reproductive success is normally considered in terms of the production of offspring, but what is truly important is the transmission of alleles from one generation to the next. By helping a close relative reproduce, an individual promotes transmission of many of the alleles it possesses, because close relatives share many alleles.

The extent to which any two related individuals in a population share alleles is called the *coefficient of relatedness*. For example, as is typical of diploid organisms, each human shares an average of 50% of her alleles with her parents and about 50% of the same alleles with each brother or sister. The coefficient of relatedness with these individuals, therefore, is 0.5.

An individual may increase its genetic representation in the next generation not only by producing offspring of its own but also by helping close relatives produce offspring. The total, or *inclusive*, fitness of an individual includes both its own production of offspring and the effect it has on the production of offspring by relatives. Kin selection is the mechanism by which individuals increase their inclusive fitness by aiding the survival and reproduction of closely related individuals.

An individual may perform an act detrimental to its own reproduction but that enhances the reproduction of a close relative because, from a genetic point of view, the increased reproductive success of a close relative represents a kind of benefit. When the benefits of increasing the reproductive success of relatives exceed the costs of decreasing the altruist's own reproductive success, the altruist's inclusive fitness is enhanced and the behavior may evolve.

In Belding's ground squirrels, young males tend to settle at some distance from where they were born; by contrast, young females tend to settle much closer to the site of their birth. As a consequence, females are likely to live near close relatives, while males are likely to live with unrelated individuals. The prediction is that female ground squirrels should be more likely to give alarm calls than males, because only females would benefit close kin in doing so. This is precisely what is observed—alarm calls are usually given by females, and males hardly call at all. An even stronger proof is the observation that a female ground squirrel becomes less likely to give an alarm call as the number of closely related kin in her area decreases. If all of a female's close relatives die, she virtually ceases to give alarm calls.

In the case of bee-eater helpers, helpers most often help their own parents or siblings. Sometimes, however, bee-eaters will help more distantly related individuals, and the probability that a helper will help another individual is directly related to the coefficient of relatedness between the two. If a helper has a choice of two nests to assist, it will almost always pick the nest whose young will be most closely related to it. Bee-eater helpers become helpers in the first place because their breeding opportunities are limited by available resources. Many birds cannot breed, so the next best thing is to help a related bird and gain increased inclusive fitness.

Interactions with potential mates are another critically important aspect of an animal's social behavior. Choosing a mate may be one of the most significant interactions between individuals in a population, because the choice of a mate can have a profound influence on an individual's reproductive success. There is often an asymmetry in the way females and males approach mate choice. Males usually initiate courtship and often fight each other for opportunities to mate; females, on the other hand, typically choose among competing males. The reason for this asymmetry has been ascribed to the fact that females often have a higher cost of reproduction.

Types of Social Acts

	Act benefits recipient	Act costs recipient
Act benefits performer	Cooperative	Selfish
Act costs performer	Altruistic	Spiteful

In some cases, the higher price of reproduction may simply reflect the fact that female gametes tend to be larger and more costly to make than male gametes; in other cases, physiological or behavioral costs are much more significant. In mammals, for example, females nourish growing embryos in their bodies for a considerable time after fertilization, essentially paying the entire metabolic cost of early development.

Females are often—but not always—the "choosier" sex. The ability to choose a mate conveys two general benefits: the advantage of choosing a mate with superior genes and the advantage of choosing a mate that will directly provide better resources. The question of how a female identifies a superior mate has long been the subject of debate, but it appears to depend on the fact that males display traits that reliably signal something about their quality to females.

In the African bird called the long-tailed widowbird, the tail feathers of the males are disproportionately long, an example of a very common pattern in which the "chosen" sex of a species displays elaborate ornaments or performs elaborate courtship behaviors, both of which are called *sexually selected traits*.

Charles Darwin introduced the idea of sexual selection to account for the evolution of traits that appear to have no function other than to increase mating success. He suggested that such traits would evolve if they increased an individual's likelihood of obtaining mates by making bearers better able to compete for or more attractive to potential mates. Swedish behavioral ecologist Malte Andersson demonstrated that the long tails of widowbird males are attractive to females by capturing a group of males and manipulating their tail lengths. Females showed a strong mating preference for males with longer tails—the longer the better.

The probable reason that females base their decision on the length of a tail—or any other exaggerated sexually selected trait—is that the ability of an individual male to express a sexually selected trait reflects that male's overall vitality and vigor and, thus, provides an accurate indicator of a male's overall quality. This hypothesis works only if the ability of a male to produce a sexually selected trait depends in some way on his quality. In widowbirds, it suggests that only males with sufficient resources can devote enough of those resources to producing a longer tail. Several experiments have demonstrated that the ability of a male to produce an exaggerated ornamental trait does, in fact, correlate with aspects of its health.

Behavioral ecology focuses on the "choices" individuals make to maximize their ability to obtain resources, live longer, and reproduce more. However, the fact that animals appear to make "choices" does not mean that they are "thinking" about those choices in any common sense of the word, simply that selection has acted to enable the animal to respond adaptively to different conditions. ■

Suggested Reading

Campbell & Reece, *Biology* (6th ed.), chapter 51.

Dawkins, *The Selfish Gene* (2nd ed.).

Freeman, *Biological Science*, chapter 47.3.

Krebs & Davies, *An Introduction to Behavioural Ecology* (3rd ed.).

Purves et al., *Life* (7th ed.), chapter 53.

Questions to Consider

1. Do you think inclusive fitness and kin selection are necessary to explain altruistic behavior in humans? Why or why not?

2. Animals may or may not "think" in the sense of having mental states similar to our own. From the perspective of behavioral ecology, what does it mean to say an animal makes a "decision" if it does not "think" about that decision?

Ecological Interactions Among Species
Lecture 64

As we will see, the most important interactions among species in a community also have to do with resources, either because two species share a similar set of resources, or because one species uses another species as a resource.

This lecture begins by expanding the discussion of energy and resources to consider multiple species living in a single environment. As with social interactions among species, interspecies interactions can be categorized by which species benefits and which suffers as a result. The interaction between predators and their prey (or parasites and their host) is thought to be one of the most important in nature for influencing the structure of biological communities, and the remainder of the lecture is devoted to examples of predator-prey interactions and the principles that can be derived from them.

To this point in our discussion of energy and resources, we have considered only a single species at a time. The discussion of factors affecting the size and growth of populations assumed that a population of one species would be unaffected by populations of other species in the same area. Similarly, the discussion of how individuals in a population interact assumed that the only individuals that mattered were individuals of the same species. In other words, the assumption to this point has been that species sharing the same space do not interact in any way that affects each other's density, distribution, or behavior. More often than not, however, this assumption is not true, and the distribution, abundance, and behavior of a species depend not only on resources critical to that species but also on the distribution and abundance of species with which they co-occur. This lecture will begin to consider energy and resources in living systems at the level of *communities*, which are assemblages of species that live in the same area and can interact. The study of biological communities is called *community ecology*.

The interactions among species in a community can influence its abundance and distribution of each in a variety of ways. Different kinds of interactions can be grouped into a few major types according to whether they have a positive or negative effect, or no discernable effect at all, on one or the other of the interacting species. The type of interaction in which two species each have a harmful influence on the other is called *competition* and occurs most commonly when two species use the same limiting resources. In the logistic model of population growth, members of the same species compete for resources; competition between species is conceptually similar to intra-specific competition except that individuals of different species compete for similar resources.

Another possible interaction between species occurs when individuals of one species benefit from their interaction with another species, while the individuals of the second species are harmed. This type of interaction usually occurs when one species uses the other species as food; that is, one species is a predator or a parasite of the other species. This kind of interaction is called a *predator-prey interaction* or *host-parasite interaction*.

Termites can digest cellulose—which is why they can eat wood—but not by themselves. Instead, bacteria living in their guts break cellulose down into smaller molecules that termites can digest.

Competition and predator-prey interactions are particularly important kinds of ecological interactions, but there are other kinds of interactions between individuals of different species. Members of both species might benefit from interacting, for example; these species are called *mutualists*, and their interaction is called *mutualism*.

Mutualistic interactions are very common in nature. For example, cellulose is potentially a tremendous source of fuel, but most animals cannot digest it. Termites can digest cellulose—which is why they can eat wood—but not by themselves. Instead, bacteria living in their guts break cellulose down into smaller molecules that termites can digest. Both the termites and the bacteria benefit from an increased food supply, and neither can live without the other.

Types of Ecological Interactions

	BENEFIT (+)	HARM (-)	NO EFFECT (0)
BENEFIT (+)	Mutualism	Predator-prey Host-parasite	Commensalism
HARM (-)	Predator-prey Host-parasite	Competition	Amensalism
NO EFFECT (0)	Commensalism	Amensalism	----------

In rarer interactions, members of one species may benefit from the presence of another species, while the other species is simply unaffected. This kind of interaction is called *commensalism*, which is difficult to identify, because it is hard to prove that there is absolutely no cost or benefit to one of the species in the interaction. An interaction often cited as true commensalism occurs between cattle egrets—a kind of bird—and grazing cattle. The egrets most often forage near grazing cattle, because the cattle flush out insects and other small animals as they move, which the egrets then eat. The cattle almost certainly gain nothing from this interaction, but neither do they lose anything; the egrets, however, clearly benefit from the interaction.

Finally, it is possible for two species to interact so that one species is harmed while the other species is unaffected. This interaction is called *amensalism* and is thought to be rare; in fact, some biologists question whether any real cases of amensalism have ever been documented, because of the difficulty of demonstrating conclusively that there is no effect at all on one species. One possible example of amensalism involves large mammals that congregate around drinking holes. These animals trample the ground around the hole, severely damaging the plants that would ordinarily grow at the water's edge. The mammals benefit from their access to water but not from the damage they do to the plants; the plants, of course, are harmed by the interaction. These kinds of ecological interactions provide a framework for thinking about how different species living in a community may interact with each other and, thus, influence each other's population size and structure.

Predator-prey interactions, and their consequences for the structure of communities, have long been a major focus of ecological research. When a predator captures and eats a prey individual, it reduces the size of the prey population. The resources the predator obtains in this way will contribute to increasing the size of the predator population. For this reason, it seems likely that as the predator population increases, the prey population should decrease correspondingly. This has to be true to some extent, but it cannot continue forever.

Consider a hypothetical case with only two species in an environment, one a predator and the other its prey. An individual predator must find a certain number of prey individuals per unit of time to satisfy its resource needs; if the population of prey is large enough that predators on average can find enough prey, the predator population size will increase. However, an increased number of predators will cause the prey population to decrease as they are eaten at an ever-increasing rate. At some point, predators will have increased and prey decreased to a point at which the predators can no longer find sufficient prey to survive and reproduce. At this point, the predator population will decrease.

As the predator population decreases, predation will also decrease, decreasing the per capita death rate of the prey. As a result, the prey population may start to increase again at a future point in time. Once the prey population increases to a certain point, there may again be sufficient prey for the predators to increase their numbers. This kind of interaction between predators and prey logically would lead to a cyclic pattern of increase and decrease, with changes in size of the predator population lagging behind corresponding changes in the prey population. These predator-prey cycles have, in fact, been observed in both the laboratory and the wild.

Two examples illustrate predator-prey cycles. Moose on Isle Royale in Lake Superior lived free from any predators since at least the beginning of the 20th century. In 1949, however, a particularly cold winter froze the lake enough to allow a few wolves to cross the ice to the island. The population sizes of both the moose and wolves began to be monitored regularly in 1958. After the introduction of wolves to Isle Royale, the population sizes of the two species began to oscillate. As the moose population increased, so did the wolf population, but once the wolf population grew very large, there was a subsequent decrease in the moose population.

The decrease in the moose population was followed by a corresponding decrease in the wolf population and, finally, as the wolf population decreased, the moose population started to rise. This pattern of oscillation in the moose and wolf populations on Isle Royale represents a very long predator-prey cycle. This cycle may have ended, however; the appearance of a viral wolf disease in the 1980s caused the wolf population to crash to a very low level from which it has not recovered.

The second case is perhaps the most well-known example of a predator-prey cycle, involving populations of snowshoe hare and lynx in Canada. The data for this example come from records extending over almost a century of the pelts obtained by fur trappers working for the Hudson Bay Company. Estimates of the sizes of the snowshoe hare and lynx populations reveal strong cyclic fluctuations in the population size of both species on a 9- to 11-year cycle, with the predator population lagging behind the prey population. This pattern seems to fit the predator-prey oscillation model perfectly, but there is an important qualification—the cause of the population cycle in this case is subject to other interpretations.

Populations of hares in areas without lynx also show similar cyclic fluctuations in population size; thus, an increasing predator population may not be the only factor that limits the growth of the hare population or may not be a factor at all. The hare population may crash on a 9- to 11-year cycle as a result of other density-dependent effects, such as deterioration in the hare's food supply caused by overgrazing. This idea was tested experimentally by adding food, excluding predators, and improving the quality of food in hare populations. A combination of adding food and excluding predators had the most dramatic effect and illustrates that more than one factor affects hare population cycles.

Accounting for the abundance and distribution of one species usually requires considering how that species interacts with other species that occupy the same space. Predator-prey interactions may be characterized by oscillations in the population size of both predator and prey, but it can be difficult to infer the specific processes responsible for this pattern. ∎

Suggested Reading

Campbell & Reece, *Biology* (6th ed.), chapter 53.

Freeman, *Biological Science*, chapter 49.

Peterson, Rolf O., *The Wolves of Isle Royale: A Broken Balance.*

Smith & Smith, *Elements of Ecology* (5th ed.), chapters 13 and 15.

Questions to Consider

1. How might you describe the ecological interaction between humans and animals kept as pets? What about between humans and farm animals?

2. Herbivory occurs when an animal eats a plant. How is herbivory the same as predation? How is it different from an ecological perspective?

Predators and Competitors

Lecture 65

In today's lecture, we are going to continue our exploration of how species in a biological community may interact with each other. We will begin by looking in some more detail at cases where one species benefits and the other species is harmed—predator-prey or host-parasite interactions.

We begin with an example of a host-parasite interaction and then go on to illustrate how predation or parasitism can influence not only the abundance but also the distribution of a prey or host species. The lecture then shifts to a discussion of competition, another kind of ecological interaction thought to have a major influence on the structure of biological communities. The Lotka-Volterra equations, which model the growth of competing populations, are described and compared to the logistic growth equation, which models population growth of a single species. The lecture concludes by exploring the limitations of the Lotka-Volterra equations for understanding the effects of competition on community structure.

Two broad themes inform our discussion of interactions between species. First, the examination of biological systems—especially at the levels of populations, communities, and ecosystems—often begins by observing a pattern, which suggests a process that could generate the pattern. However, the existence of the pattern does not prove the inferred process; it is necessary to perform experiments to support any hypothesis about process. Second, a fundamental question that concerns ecologists is to explain the abundance and distribution of different species in different places on the planet. Interactions between species can affect abundance, distribution, or both.

An example of a host-parasite interaction illustrates how such an interaction can drive a population cycle, which really is an issue of accounting for the relative abundance of species in a community. Populations of red grouse in Great Britain often show a cyclic fluctuation in population density, typically about four years long. The cycle's magnitude can be extreme, with a local population varying from several thousand individuals to just a handful. Red grouse population cycles have no obvious correspondence to the population size of a predator or the availability of food. Instead, they appear to be driven by a host-parasite interaction, in this case, a roundworm that infects the grouse. The hypothesis is that at high grouse densities, the roundworm is more easily transmitted between individuals. In addition, as population density increases, the total amount of food available per grouse decreases; on average, the grouse are less well fed and more susceptible to roundworm infection. In this case, it is not an increase in the parasite population itself but rather the density-dependent transmission rate and susceptibility to the parasite that are responsible for changes in the population abundance of red grouse. Red grouse population cycles are consistent with this hypothesis; to test the hypothesis, however, researchers treated several grouse populations with a drug that killed roundworms, after which the treated populations stopped exhibiting strong population cycles.

Particularly strong predator-prey or host-parasite interactions can determine not only the abundance of a prey species but also its distribution in local habitats. Predation can be so strong as to completely eliminate a prey population in some habitats. This effect should be more likely in communities in which predators are generalists, as opposed to specialists—that is, they do not rely on one kind of prey.

The discussion of predator-prey interactions has implied a high degree of specialization, but specialist predators are rare because of the potential for a prey species to become rare or locally extinct. Generalist predators are more common and can eliminate prey in some areas. Experiments done on frogs by ecologist Josh van Buskirk illustrate the effect of strong generalist predation on the structure of communities. Frog tadpoles remain in their natal bodies of water for some time after birth while they develop. Van Buskirk found that the tadpoles of Western chorus frogs on islands in Lake Superior were found only in a subset of ponds that otherwise all appeared identically suitable for breeding. Closer examination showed that the ponds without tadpoles included populations of dragonfly nymphs, voracious generalist predators that eat many of the species in their ponds, including tadpoles. Van Buskirk's observations suggested that the presence of dragonfly nymphs restricted tadpoles to a subset of suitable habitats.

This pattern suggested a process in which the predator was responsible for completely eliminating the prey species wherever it existed. Van Buskirk tested this hypothesis in two complementary experiments. The first experiment used two ponds with tadpoles but no dragonfly nymphs. One of these ponds was left alone, and the survival of its tadpoles was monitored over four weeks. The population of tadpoles in this pond remained fairly large. The second pond also began with many tadpoles and no dragonfly nymphs, but van Buskirk introduced a roughly normal density of dragonfly nymphs into it. Within one week, the tadpole population dropped dramatically; within three weeks, the tadpoles were gone. The conclusion then seems fairly straightforward—that the presence of dragonfly nymphs makes it impossible for tadpoles to survive in a pond. However, simply showing that the artificial addition of dragonfly nymphs to a pond causes local tadpole extinction does not mean that the original distribution was due to this effect.

The second experiment was designed to test for this possibility; it used two ponds found to have dragonfly nymphs but no tadpoles. Almost all of the dragonfly nymphs were captured and removed from one pond, after which a normal density of tadpoles was introduced. The tadpoles added to this pond survived at about the same rate as in a normal pond without dragonfly nymphs. Van Buskirk then added more than 200 tadpoles to the other pond, which still had dragonfly nymphs, and all of these tadpoles had been eaten within a week. The second experiment showed that even ponds where tadpoles are not found originally can support a tadpole population as long as the predator is removed. In other words, the predator was the only difference that could be responsible for a pond lacking tadpoles. Van Buskirk's work shows how predator-prey interaction can affect the distribution of a species; it also nicely illustrates how field experiments can be used to support a hypothesis for how a process is responsible for an observed pattern.

Particularly strong predator-prey or host-parasite interactions can determine not only the abundance of a prey species but also its distribution in local habitats.

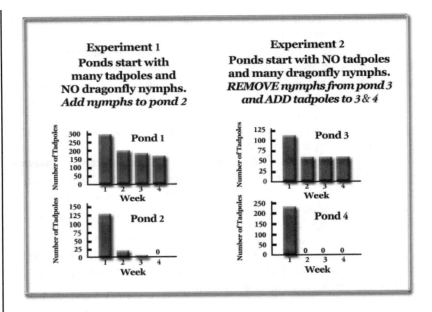

Experiment 1
Ponds start with many tadpoles and NO dragonfly nymphs. Add nymphs to pond 2

Experiment 2
Ponds start with NO tadpoles and many dragonfly nymphs. REMOVE nymphs from pond 3 and ADD tadpoles to 3 & 4

Species in competition use the same set of limiting resources. Competition is thought to be the other interaction with a major effect on abundance and distribution. Instead of one species using the other as a resource, competition involves two species in a community using one set of limiting resources. The effect of competition between two species is conceptually similar to the effects of competition in a single species. As the population density of one or both species increases, resources become less available on average to individuals in either population. As resources become more limiting, mortality increases and/or birth rates decrease, and population growth is curtailed in one or both species.

In the 1920s, mathematicians Alfred J. Lotka and Vittora Volterra independently derived a mathematical model of the effects of interspecies competition on population growth. In the logistic growth equation, as the population (N) approaches the carrying capacity (K), population growth (dN/dt) goes to zero. Lotka and Volterra both realized that, when two species compete for the same resource, each species effectively contributes individuals to the total, and individuals of one species need to be counted against the carrying capacity of the other species.

As a result, the carrying capacity of a species depends on the amount of resources available; many resources will make the carrying capacity larger than if there are few resources. The presence of a competing species essentially uses up resources and would be expected to lower the carrying capacity of both species in competition.

Lotka and Volterra modified the logistic growth model to add the effect of a competing species. The resulting Lotka-Volterra equation for population growth of a species in the presence of a competitor is:

$$\frac{dN_1}{dt} = r_1 N_1 \frac{K_1 - N_1 - \alpha N_2}{K_1}.$$

N_1 refers to the population size of the target species, while N_2 refers to the competitor species; r_1 refers to the growth rate of the target species, K_1 refers to its carrying capacity, and α (alpha) is the competition coefficient.

In words, the growth of the target population approaches zero as a function of both the current population size of the target species and, in part, the size of the competitor species population. The effect of the size of the competitor population is essentially devalued by the competition coefficient, which reflects how much the two species actually overlap in resource use. In effect, the competition coefficient "converts" one individual of the competing species into an equivalent number of individuals of the target species. This coefficient typically is a fraction between 1.0, representing complete overlap in resource use, and 0, representing no overlap in resource use and thus no competition. If there is no competition and $\alpha = 0$, the Lotka-Volterra equation reverts to the logistic growth equation.

In addition, competition between two species requires two equations, one for the population growth of each species. If the competition coefficient of species B on species A is α and the competition coefficient of species A on species B is β, then the population growth of species B is:

$$\frac{dN_2}{dt} = r_2 N_2 \frac{K_2 - N_2 - \beta N_1}{K_2} \,.$$

The Lotka-Volterra equation predicts several outcomes depending on the carrying capacities and competition coefficients of the two species. In most cases, the species with a competitive advantage will win out, and the disadvantaged species will go locally extinct. In a small number of cases, however, neither species can achieve a population density sufficient to overwhelm the other species. The Lotka-Volterra equation suggests that, in most cases, competing species can rarely coexist for very long, but in the real world, species often use the same resources and apparently compete with one another. Clearly, the equation falls short of providing a completely realistic model. ∎

Suggested Reading

Campbell & Reece, *Biology* (6th ed.), chapter 53.

Freeman, *Biological Science*, chapter 49.

Smith & Smith, *Elements of Ecology* (5th ed.), chapter 14.

Questions to Consider

1. Observing a pattern in nature may lead to a hypothesis. Why doesn't the existence of the pattern itself necessarily show that hypothesis to be true?

2. The competition coefficient in the Lotka-Volterra equations that model competition typically is a fraction between 0 and 1. What kind of ecological interaction would be modeled if this coefficient was a *negative* number?

Competition and the Ecological Niche
Lecture 66

In today's lecture, we are going to pick up on our discussion of competition in communities by looking at some empirical studies of how a competitive interaction affects the abundance and distribution of species.

We begin with an overview of early experiments intended to test the Lotka-Volterra equations. These experiments, and real-world observations, ultimately did not fully support predictions made by these equations. Reconciling the difference between theory and observation leads us to consider the concept of a *biological niche*, which represents the pattern of resource use by a species in a community. The fact that niches usually have many dimensions and that species usually do not overlap in all dimensions shows how species in competition may coexist in a community. After establishing the concept of biological niches, we turn to two examples that illustrate competition and niches in nature. The Lotka-Volterra equations modify the logistic growth model to include the population size of a competing species; a theoretical conclusion of these equations is that two competing species can rarely if ever both coexist over the long run.

The work of Lotka and Volterra triggered a number of attempts to study the effects of competition on population growth under controlled laboratory conditions. The first of these attempts was performed by Russian ecologist G. F. Gause in the early 1930s. Gause simulated competition between two species of *Paramecium*: *P. aurelia* and *P. caudatum*. *Paramecium* are single-celled organisms commonly found in fresh water; a population grown in a test tube will follow a logistic growth curve fairly closely, eventually leveling off at some carrying capacity.

When Gause added both *P. aurelia* and *P. caudatum* to the same test tube, the populations of both species increased in the first few days, as expected, but at some intermediate size, the population of *P. caudatum* declined to a few individuals or went completely extinct. Meanwhile, the population of *P. aurelia* continued to grow, eventually leveling off at its carrying capacity.

Based on this observation, Gause developed the *competitive exclusion principle*, which states that if two species are competing for the same limiting resource, the species with most effective resource use will eventually exclude the other species from the local environment. A number of other laboratory studies found the same result, suggesting that competitive exclusion is a general phenomenon. The problem is that many species compete in nature, appearing to use the same resources in the same environment; there are countless examples of natural communities of species sharing resources and maintaining stable populations over the long run.

In a subsequent set of experiments, Gause raised *P. caudatum* with another species called *P. bursaria*. Instead of one species being driven to extinction, however, the populations of both species increased to a maximum and maintained it. When Gause examined his test tube after this stable state was reached, he found the majority of *P. caudatum* in the upper half and the majority of *P. bursaria* in the lower half. All species of *Paramecium* feed on bacteria and yeast, but yeast require less oxygen and were more abundant in the lower half of the test tube; bacteria were more numerous in the upper half.

P. bursaria is more efficient at eating yeast than *P. caudatum*. The uneven distribution of resources in the test tube, coupled with the fact that the two species in the tube used resources in different ways, meant that the two species could coexist. By contrast, the resource use of *P. aurelia* and *P. caudatum* is virtually identical, and these two species cannot coexist in the same test tube.

The conclusion Gause reached from this second set of experiments was that species can coexist in competition if their resource use does not completely overlap. In the real world, species rarely live in homogenous environments where their survival depends on one critical resource; thus, competition in nature does not usually involve highly similar species competing for exactly the same resources. Instead, competition is more likely in cases where species share some but not all critical resources.

Gause's competitive exclusion principle and its apparent exceptions eventually led to the development of the concept of an organism's *ecological niche*. The concept of an ecological niche stems from the idea that each kind of organism in an ecological community may maximize its survival and reproductive success in a different way, which in turn, means that it will use the available resources in a different way. A textbook definition of *ecological niche* is the sum of all the ways an organism uses the resources in its environment. An ecological niche is also often described as an organism's ecological role in an environment and may be defined in terms of the kinds of food an organism eats, its optimal temperature range, and so on.

It is difficult to define a niche rigorously and even more difficult to completely specify an organism's niche in practice. One would have to know absolutely everything about how a particular organism lives and about its environment to completely describe all aspects of its resource use. Nonetheless, the idea of a niche is a useful heuristic concept for understanding competition and its effects in ecological communities.

Without rodents, the largest seeds are not eaten, and the plant with the largest seeds is competitively superior to the plant with smaller seeds.

For example, five species of birds in the genus *Dendroica*—the Cape May warbler, the blackburnian warbler, the black-throated green warbler, the bay-breasted warbler, and the yellow-rumped warbler—all live in mature conifer forests and appear to eat the same kind of food. In large parts of the northeastern United States, all five species can be found breeding in exactly the same area. This observation led to the widely accepted possibility that these warblers represented an exception to the competitive exclusion principle because they appear to play identical ecological roles in their community.

In pioneering work, ecologist Robert MacArthur set out to determine whether or not these birds actually occupied the same niche. He first divided conifer trees into different zones relative to the height of the tree and the distance from the trunk to the center, which allowed him to define precisely where birds were found in the tree. MacArthur then recorded where each species was found to occur, where it performed different behaviors, and any differences in the kinds of behaviors performed. He found that the five species of warblers did not use a tree identically; instead, each species divided its time differently among the different zones of the tree.

MacArthur also found that feeding behavior differed among the five species; for example, the Cape May warbler catches insects on the wing more often than the other species, which tend to glean insects from branches and needles. This detailed study revealed that, though all five species live in an identical, specialized habitat, they divide this habitat and its resources in different ways. These warblers may compete for some resources, but each species has its own specific pattern of resource use.

With this knowledge, the competitive exclusion principle can be restated more accurately as: "Two species cannot occupy identical niches." Because ecological niches typically have many dimensions, species with similar resource needs can coexist in a community when their niches are not completely identical.

A study of barnacles demonstrates how competitive interactions and patterns of niche overlap affect the distribution of species. Barnacles are marine invertebrates whose larvae float in the sea, eventually permanently attaching to rocks and becoming sessile adults. On rocky North Atlantic shores, two species of barnacles often occur in the same place, but with non-overlapping distributions. One species, *Chthamalus stellatus*, is found on higher rocks in a region called the upper intertidal zone; another species, *Balanus balanoides*, is found on lower rocks in the lower intertidal zone. These two species may have non-overlapping ranges because they are specialized to live under different physical conditions. The upper intertidal zone is exposed to air longer, and organisms there may suffer more from desiccation. However, this seems unlikely to account entirely for the distribution of these two species, because the young of both species settle and begin to grow over the entire intertidal zone. The alternative hypothesis is that both species can live along the entire vertical gradient, but that each has a competitive advantage in only one part. To test this, rocks that had begun to be colonized by both species of barnacle were experimentally manipulated by removing one or the other species.

Relative Population Densities

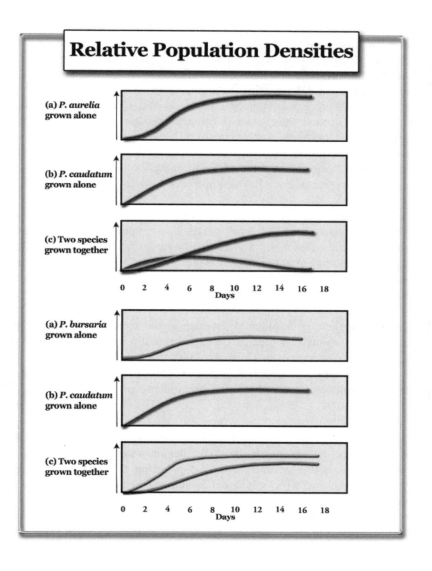

(a) *P. aurelia* grown alone

(b) *P. caudatum* grown alone

(c) Two species grown together

0 2 4 6 8 10 12 14 16 18
Days

(a) *P. bursaria* grown alone

(b) *P. caudatum* grown alone

(c) Two species grown together

0 2 4 6 8 10 12 14 16 18
Days

If *Balanus* were removed, young *Chthamalus* survived well, even in the lower intertidal zone. If *Balanus* were left on rocks, however, they would grow against the *Chthamalus*, crushing them or undercutting them from the rock. In this way, *Balanus* limits *Chthamalus* distribution to a more narrow range of the intertidal zone than it might otherwise occupy. *Balanus* does not eliminate *Chthamalus* entirely, though, because *Chthamalus* can better withstand desiccation; thus, it gains a competitive edge at the upper intertidal zone. The conclusion is that competition between these two species of barnacles is responsible for their non-overlapping pattern along the intertidal zone, with both species capable of living along the entire zone, but each displacing the other where it has a competitive advantage.

An experiment involving ants and rodents demonstrates how competition affects the relative abundance of species in a community. Because ants and rodents in the desert both use seeds as a major food resource, it seems reasonable that they might be in competition with each other. However, ants eat smaller seeds on average than rodents do and would not be expected to competitively exclude rodents, or vice versa.

Nonetheless, there is considerable overlap in the sizes of seeds taken by both kinds of animals. If rodents are experimentally removed from such a community, the number of ants increases markedly. If ants are experimentally removed, the number of rodents increases instead. These results suggest that the population sizes of both ants and rodents are lowered because of competition.

However, to fully support the conclusion that ants and rodents compete for their food supply, seeds must be demonstrated to be a limiting resource. This was experimentally done by using three enclosures, one with only ants, one with only rodents, and one with neither. The same low density of seeds was found in the enclosures with just ants or just rodents, but a higher seed density was found in the enclosures where both ants and rodents were excluded, allowing the conclusion that competition for seeds specifically affects the population size of both rodents and ants.

If rodents are removed from a community for several years, however, the population density of the ants begins to fall again. Without rodents, the largest seeds are not eaten, and the plant with the largest seeds is competitively superior to the plant with smaller seeds. Without rodents, big-seeded plants dominate the enclosures, reducing the number of smaller seeds, which the ants prefer. This long-term effect illustrates how interactions between species are often more complicated than simple competition. Understanding ecological interactions explains only part of the abundance and distribution of species in an environment—a full analysis must include the environment itself, the subject to which we turn next. ■

Suggested Reading

Campbell & Reece, *Biology* (6th ed.), chapter 53.

Freeman, *Biological Science*, chapter 49.

Smith & Smith, *Elements of Ecology* (5th ed.), chapter 14.

Questions to Consider

1. Pick an organism in nature with which you're familiar, such as a common bird or a tree or anything else. What do you think are some of the dimensions that would describe the ecological niche of this organism?

2. What do competition and predation have in common and how do they differ in the way these two kinds of ecological interactions influence the abundance and distribution of species in a community?

Energy in Ecosystems
Lecture 67

A simple reason that ecological interactions alone can't fully predict the structure of a biological community is that the environment itself plays an equally important role in many cases in determining abundance and distribution of species. Ecologists had long recognized this point, but the idea was formalized when the term "ecosystem" was first coined by a plant ecologist named Arthur G. Tansley.

This lecture begins by making the point that the abundance and distribution of species in biological communities may depend as much or more on the physical environment as they do on the ways in which species in a community interact with each other. An *ecosystem* includes both the species found in an area and the physical environment in which they live; the properties of the physical environment determine how critical resources are stored when they are not found in living systems, and how these resources move into and out of living things. The lecture goes on to explore the flow of one resource—energy—through a generalized ecosystem, showing how inefficiencies in energy transfer can determine the abundance of the species at different *trophic levels* in an ecosystem.

Ecological interactions alone cannot fully predict the structure of a biological community. In a 1935 article, Tansley first used the term *ecosystem*:

> The more fundamental conception [of a community] is ... the whole system (in the sense of physics) including not only the organism-complex, but also the whole complex of physical factors forming what we call the environment ... We cannot separate [the organisms] from their special environment with which they form one physical system. It is the [ecosystems] so formed which ... [are] the basic units of nature on the face of the earth.

An *ecosystem* is currently defined as all the organisms living in an area, together with the physical environment with which they interact. The key point of this definition is the inclusion of the physical environment, which is often an important repository of resources used by living systems.

Ecosystems can be studied at many different scales, from small, well-defined units, such as ponds, to systems as large as an entire tropical rainforest. For some purposes, the entire planet—the *biosphere*—might be considered a single global ecosystem. A central focus of ecosystem ecology is to understand how energy and other resources move through living systems, which occurs differently for different kinds of resources. There is a fundamental difference in the way energy and other resources move through ecosystems. Energy enters the biosphere as sunlight and is ultimately lost as heat; thus, the planet is an open system with respect to energy. Other nutrient resources are recycled, so the planet is a closed system with respect to these.

A *food chain* implies a linear transfer of energy and resources from lower trophic levels in an ecosystem to higher trophic levels. No ecosystem is so simple, however, as to be easily characterized by a single, unbranched food chain.

Energy flows through an ecosystem in one direction. Only a small portion of the sunlight that reaches the Earth is actually captured by photosynthetic organisms. For example, a study of the Hubbard Brook Experimental Forest in New Hampshire estimated the total amount of solar energy impinging on the forest over a single year at about 1,250,000 kilocalories per square meter. By measuring the photosynthesis rates of the different plant species, researchers estimated that a little over 10,000 kilocalories per square meter of this energy was captured by photosynthesis—less than 1% of the energy available. The total amount of energy captured by the photosynthetic organisms in an ecosystem is called the *gross primary productivity* of that ecosystem. Photosynthetic organisms in an ecosystem that capture energy are called the *primary producers* (or just *producers*) of that ecosystem.

The gross primary productivity of an ecosystem depends on a number of factors in addition to the amount of sunlight, including the availability of critical mineral nutrients. In terrestrial ecosystems, the availability of water and, not surprisingly, temperature often limit productivity. Only part of the gross primary productivity of an ecosystem becomes available to the rest of the ecosystem. Plants use much of the energy they capture for their own maintenance; only that portion of captured energy that is converted into the organic molecules that make up plant tissues can enter the rest of the ecosystem, which occurs when the plant is eaten. The proportion of energy made available to the rest of the ecosystem varies widely, but is usually very low, often as little as 10%. The portion of the gross primary productivity of an ecosystem incorporated into plant tissue and, thus, that can be harvested by heterotrophic animals, is called the *net primary productivity*. Net productivity can be expressed as either the amount of energy captured per unit area per unit time or as the amount of biomass added to the ecosystem per unit area per unit time.

Understanding productivity illustrates how energy enters an ecosystem, but it is also necessary to understand how this energy is harvested and distributed within an ecosystem. It might seem that any real ecosystem would contain so many different species that it would be impossible to describe how these species compete for or use one another as energy.

Fortunately, the problem can be simplified by grouping together different kinds of organisms according to their sources of energy. Organisms that obtain their energy from a common source in an ecosystem constitute a *trophic level* in that ecosystem. Primary producers are the lowest trophic level; all other organisms in an ecosystem may be generally lumped together as *consumers*. Consumers can be further subdivided by how many steps removed they are from the primary producers. Consumers that gain their energy directly from primary producers are called *primary consumers*. Organisms that gain their energy by eating primary consumers are called *secondary consumers*. Secondary consumers are, by definition, carnivores—they eat something that ate something else. In a terrestrial ecosystem, a mammal that eats herbivorous insects is a secondary consumer, as is the predator that eats the mammal.

Carnivorous secondary consumers may themselves be eaten by and provide the major source of energy for other organisms, which are called *tertiary consumers*. In some ecosystems, *quaternary consumers* eat tertiary consumers. Quaternary consumers are rare because they are so far removed from primary producers. The relationship between organisms at different trophic levels in an ecosystem is sometimes depicted as a food chain with primary producers at the bottom, primary consumers at the next step up, secondary consumers another step up, and so forth.

Another kind of consumer found in all ecosystems is the *decomposer*, or *detritivore*. As the name suggests, these are consumers that derive energy from the organic waste products of other species, which could be feces, fallen leaves, or dead organisms. The most important decomposers are bacteria and fungi, but the decomposers can also include organisms as diverse as earthworms and vultures.

A *food chain* implies a linear transfer of energy and resources from lower trophic levels in an ecosystem to higher trophic levels. No ecosystem is so simple, however, as to be easily characterized by a single, unbranched food chain. A more accurate representation of trophic relationships in an ecosystem is a *food web*, which illustrates complex connections across and within trophic levels.

It is difficult to categorize trophic relationships in a simple chain because many species fit into more than one trophic level. If a hawk catches a mouse, it is a secondary consumer because it is eating a primary consumer; if the same hawk catches a snake, it is acting as a tertiary consumer because the snake is a secondary consumer. Regardless of how it is represented, however, the energy in an ecosystem generally flows from lower trophic levels to higher trophic levels.

The amount of energy eaten by consumers in an ecosystem and converted to new biomass is called the *secondary productivity* of the ecosystem. Not all the high-energy organic compounds eaten by consumers are turned into biomass. Much of this energy is lost from the ecosystem, with more and more energy being lost at each trophic level. In other words, each time one organism eats another, only a fraction of the energy consumed is used to make more organisms.

Energy may be lost at each conversion from one trophic level to another in three ways. First, organisms consuming energy at a particular trophic level use some of that energy for their own maintenance. Organisms with very high maintenance costs may convert only 1–3% of consumed energy into growth and reproduction. Second, some of the biomass consumed by a heterotroph is never digested and is passed as feces or other waste products. Third, some energy is never consumed in the first place. Some of the organisms at one trophic level in an ecosystem will die instead of being eaten, and the energy in their bodies will be lost.

Energy lost as feces and unconsumed dead bodies is not immediately lost from the ecosystem; it is consumed by detritivores, but it is shunted to a lower level and eventually lost through respiration, unless the detritivores are consumed. The percentage of energy transferred to a higher trophic level from a lower one in an ecosystem is called the *ecological efficiency*, or *trophic efficiency*, of that trophic level. Ecological efficiencies in an ecosystem are important because they determine how far the energy captured by primary producers can penetrate to higher trophic levels. The ecological efficiencies of different consumers vary, but in general 80% to 95% of the energy available at any trophic level is lost.

The energy transfer across trophic levels of an ecosystem can be represented as an energy pyramid or productivity pyramid—often depicted as a series of rectangles stacked on top of each other, with the width of each rectangle representing the amount of energy at a particular trophic level in an ecosystem. By one estimate, the productivity pyramid of a typical terrestrial ecosystem would have at its base a very wide rectangle representing 1,000,000 joules of solar energy. The primary producer rectangle above this would be much narrower, with only 10,000 joules of energy captured. Only about 10% of the biomass at each trophic level will be converted into biomass at the next higher trophic level; at the level of tertiary consumers, there are only 10 joules of energy left—1/10th of 1% of the initial energy.

Another way to represent an ecosystem is as a pyramid with the numbers of individual organisms at each trophic level in an ecosystem. In a grassy field in Michigan, for example, researchers estimated about 5,800,000 primary producers and about 700,000 primary consumers. There were only three tertiary consumers, however—the energy brought into the ecosystem by almost 6 million grass plants could support only three top carnivores.

Consumers are far less abundant at and above the tertiary consumer level because there is simply not much energy left at higher trophic levels. As a consequence, there is usually less overall biomass at higher trophic levels. Most of the biomass tied up in the bodies of organisms in an ecosystem occurs at the level of primary producers. ∎

Suggested Reading

Campbell & Reece, *Biology* (6th ed.), chapter 54.

Freeman, *Biological Science*, chapter 51.

Purves et al., *Life* (7th ed.), chapter 55.

Questions to Consider

1. A food web is really a diagram of the predator-prey interactions among species in a community. Explain how other kinds of ecological interactions (e.g., competition, mutualism, and so on) may or may not be modeled by a food web.

2. Why are predators often in more danger of extinction than herbivores?

Nutrients in Ecosystems
Lecture 68

If the carbon that got incorporated into living systems were discarded, we would soon run out of carbon. In fact, we would have run out of carbon long ago on the planet. So life on the planet depends on carbon being recycled into and out of living things, and then back into living things. While the carbon is not in a living thing, it has to reside somewhere else on the planet.

The lecture begins by contrasting the way energy and nutrient resources flow through ecosystems, including the entire biosphere. Whereas energy is continually added to and lost from the biosphere, nutrient resources cannot increase or decrease overall. Instead, critical nutrients cycle into and out of ecosystems, moving between living organisms and non-living reservoirs. After establishing this point in general terms, the lecture compares and contrasts in more detail the cycles of three particularly critical nutrient elements—carbon, nitrogen, and phosphorus.

On the time scale of life on the planet, the Sun provides an essentially inexhaustible supply of energy. The other resources necessary for life, however, exist in finite amounts. The amount of nitrogen on Earth today, for example, is the total amount that is available, ever was available, and ever will be available for living systems. However, organisms use such elements as nitrogen in prodigious amounts. Carbon is also incorporated into virtually every aspect of living things—by one estimate, about 68 billion tons is incorporated into organic matter each year through the Calvin cycle. At the same time, carbon is continually lost from living systems through cellular respiration or decomposition.

If the carbon in living systems was discarded after it passed through an organism, life would have run out of carbon long ago. Life on Earth depends on carbon and other resources being recycled into and out of living systems. When they are not in living systems, carbon and other nutrients must reside elsewhere on the planet.

How nutrient resources are stored in the physical environment and how they are transferred between the physical environment and organisms and back again play an important role in determining the structure and organization of living things on all levels of scale.

Because the movement and utilization of these elements involve both living organisms and physical components of ecosystems, the circulation of a nutrient resource is referred to as a *biogeochemical cycle*. Different elements have distinctive biogeochemical cycles that depend on the nature of the element, how it is used by organisms, and how it is stored in the environment.

Most of the nutrient elements that cycle into and out of living (*biotic*) systems are found in non-living (*abiotic*) reservoirs on the planet, including the atmosphere, bodies of water, and rocks, at any given time. Physical processes, such as evaporation, erosion, and the uplifting of mountains, move these elements between different abiotic parts of the environment.

Most nutrient elements that cycle through biogeochemical cycles are brought into living systems by the action of bacteria or plants. These elements then enter the rest of an ecosystem through the food web. Once nutrient chemicals have entered an ecosystem, they can be recycled in that ecosystem repeatedly. In a typical terrestrial ecosystem, for example, nutrients lost from living plants and animals often accumulate in the soil, only to be taken up by plants again.

Eventually, however, nutrients can be lost from a local ecosystem by being converted into an abiotic form not readily accessible to plants or by physical removal. On a global scale, nutrients are never lost—they are shuttled from one place to another and can be converted from forms that are accessible to living systems to forms that are not easily accessible.

Once nutrients are brought into living systems, they leave through the breakdown of organic compounds, which returns them to an inorganic form. The rate at which this occurs largely depends on the rate at which decomposers in an ecosystem function. The rate of decomposition, in turn, depends on abiotic factors, such as temperature, soil chemistry, or the availability of water and oxygen.

The carbon cycle is intimately associated with photosynthesis and cellular respiration. Most of the CO_2 produced by cellular respiration is released directly into the atmosphere in terrestrial ecosystems. The amount of CO_2 in the atmosphere is fairly low, however; CO_2 is only about 0.03% (300 ppm) of the atmosphere. At the same time, the demand for CO_2 is very high—by one estimate, photosynthetic organisms in terrestrial ecosystems remove $1/7^{th}$ of all CO_2 in the atmosphere each year.

If the carbon in living systems was discarded after it passed through an organism, life would have run out of carbon long ago.

The low amount of CO_2 in the atmosphere raises two important points about the global carbon cycle. First, a lot of carbon is tied up in organisms at any one point in time—most terrestrial carbon is found inside living systems, not outside. Second, the amount of CO_2 removed from the atmosphere is normally approximately counterbalanced by the amount returned through respiration. This equilibrium maintains the normal low level of CO_2 in the atmosphere. The tapping of a major terrestrial reservoir of carbon, however, is starting to disturb this equilibrium. Over geological time, a large amount of carbon has become locked away as fossil fuels, such as oil, natural gas, and coal. Fossil fuels are the undecomposed bodies of plants and animals that became buried before the carbon in them could be oxidized by decomposers. The planet's fossil fuel reservoir represents a substantial amount of carbon—as much as 2.5 to 5 times the amount of carbon in the rest of the global carbon cycle.

The majority of fossil fuels were deposited 360 to 285 million years ago, during the Carboniferous period. When a tree or other organism dies, its body is normally broken down by decomposers. Much of the carbon in trees, in particular, is found in compounds called *lignins*, which are extremely stable and hard to break down. In modern biological communities, *Basidiomycete* mushrooms are the primary lignin decomposers, but they do not appear in the fossil record until 60 million years after the rise of the first great forests on land, allowing the deposition of large amounts of carbon materials before that time.

In the last several hundred years, however, humans have developed ways to use the energy stored in fossil fuels to power industry, produce electricity, run automobiles, and so forth. As a consequence, increasing amounts of CO_2 have been released into the atmosphere, resulting in an increase in the concentration of global atmospheric CO_2.

The oceans are another reservoir of inorganic carbon. The amount of carbon in oceans is much larger than the amount in the atmosphere—as much as 50 times more. Oceanic carbon is linked to the atmosphere by diffusion from the ocean surface. In aquatic food webs, carbon also becomes incorporated in shells and other hard parts, which sink when shelled organisms die, becoming buried in sediments.

Inorganic nitrogen is another key nutrient stored in the atmosphere. Nitrogen is a key element in nucleic acids and proteins, and the amount of nitrogen available in an ecosystem can determine the productivity of that ecosystem. Eighty percent of the atmosphere is nitrogen, but it is in the form of N_2 (nitrogen gas). N_2 cannot be assimilated by plants; it must be converted to nitrate (NO_3^-) or ammonium (NH_4^+) to be incorporated into biological systems. The majority of the nitrogen that enters biological systems does so through the action of certain kinds of bacteria that can fix nitrogen. Most nitrogen-fixing bacteria live in soils or in water, though some live in the roots of plants. Once nitrogen enters an ecosystem, it can cycle in and out of living systems without being returned to the atmosphere as N_2. Organisms excrete nitrogen back into the soil, or when they die, their nitrogen is returned to the soil by decomposers through the process of ammonification. Organic forms of nitrogen in the soil may be reassimilated by plants.

In this way, the majority of nitrogen in most ecosystems comes from local recycling of nitrogenous compounds in the soil, not atmospheric nitrogen. Nitrogenous compounds are gradually lost from ecosystems, however, by denitrifying bacteria that convert nitrates to inorganic N_2 which returns to the atmosphere; thus, exchanges of nitrogen between the soil and atmosphere are important over the long term.

Like nitrogen, phosphorus can determine the productivity of an ecosystem. Phosphorus is another essential element, found in nucleic acids, ATP, and the phospholipids that make up cell membranes. The phosphorus cycle, at first glance, is simpler than the carbon and nitrogen cycles, partly because phosphate (PO_4^{3-}), the inorganic form of phosphorus, can be directly assimilated by the primary producers in an ecosystem. Thus, in contrast with both the carbon cycle and nitrogen cycle, living systems do not require any form of biological fixation to incorporate phosphorus. In addition, phosphorus does not occur in a gaseous form and does not appear to have an atmospheric component.

The majority of the phosphorous cycle is local; plants assimilate phosphate from the soil, which then enters the rest of the ecosystem when these plants are eaten. Phosphorus is lost from the ecosystem largely by leaching, in which water moving through the soil carries away the phosphate in it. This leached phosphate typically ends up in aquatic ecosystems, where it settles out into sedimentary rock over geological time.

Phosphate leaving an ecosystem is replaced by new phosphate that enters from the erosion of rocks, so the phosphorus cycle is really two cycles that differ largely in their time scales. Phosphate is assimilated by plants and returned to the soil over ecological time scales, but it cycles in and out of rocks on a geological time scale.

Recent evidence suggests that there is a short-term global cycle for phosphorus, as well. For example, the productivity of the Amazon rainforest depends critically on adequate levels of phosphorus, but there is relatively little phosphorus available in the Amazon basin. Tropical rainforest soils are notoriously nutrient-poor, and phosphorus regularly leaches through the Amazon River system into the southern Atlantic. Still, the Amazon rainforest is one of the most productive ecosystems in the world—it appears that up to 20 million tons of phosphorus are carried to the Amazon from the Sahara desert each year in the upper atmosphere via the trade winds.

Energy flows through the biosphere, while nutrient resources are recycled; understanding these movements enables a more accurate explanation of the abundance and distribution of different species. Even this information, however, allows only very general predictions about the composition and structure of biological communities in different places on Earth. ∎

Suggested Reading

Campbell & Reece, *Biology* (6th ed.), chapter 54.

Freeman, *Biological Science*, chapter 51.

Purves et al., *Life* (7th ed.), chapter 58.

Questions to Consider

1. Nutrient resources are never lost from the biosphere as a whole but may be lost from a local ecosystem. What is a major difference in the way nutrients are lost from a local ecosystem as compared to the way energy is lost?

2. What features are shared in common by the carbon and nitrogen biogeochemical cycles but not by the phosphorus cycle?

How Predictable Are Ecological Communities?
Lecture 69

We might be able to predict how many species we might find in an area; how many species or individuals of particular species we might find in different trophic levels; or even what kind of ecological interactions we would expect to see given the species that we do find someplace. But, we can rarely, if ever, predict exactly which species we will find.

U p to this point, we have examined how factors affecting population growth, ecological interactions, and the flow of energy and resources in ecosystems help account for the abundance and distribution of species. This lecture begins by pointing out that even complete knowledge of all these factors cannot fully explain abundance and distribution, because of the importance of history and chance. Two distinct views of how ecological communities develop over time—one emphasizing predictability and the other emphasizing chance—competed for several decades until experiments demonstrated the key role of chance events in determining how communities change over time. As a result, ecologists now emphasize the importance of studying patterns of disturbance in communities instead of trying to predict the end-state of ideal communities.

Our discussion of the availability and movement of energy and resources in communities and ecosystems has so far been cast in relatively general terms. For example, we might predict that only a few top predators will occur in an ecosystem because ecological efficiencies allow only a small fraction of energy to reach higher trophic levels. Similarly, we might predict that species in competition will partition the resource over which they are competing so that their niches do not overlap completely. In neither of these cases, however, could we accurately predict the actual species that would be found in a habitat with a particular set of resources, even though we might be able to predict the total number of species, the number of individuals at different trophic levels, or even the kinds of ecological interactions. This simply reflects the reality that factors not directly determined by resource distribution or limitations, such as evolutionary and geological history, and other chance events, may affect abundance and distribution as much as present-day conditions.

In the early days of ecology, in the 1920s and 1930s, there were two competing views about the degree to which communities and ecosystems were predictable. Nebraskan botanist Frederick Clements argued that organisms in a community are highly adapted to coexist with each other and will, therefore, always be found together. Clements saw communities as highly predictable; he drew an analogy between species in a community and the parts of an organism's body, referring to communities and ecosystems as *superorganisms*.

Another feature of Clements's view was that once a community had been established, it would remain stable because the interactions among species would return it to a stable state. This view became known as the *organismic concept* of communities, the *interactive concept*, or the *holistic concept* of community structure.

Henry A. Gleason, a botanist from the University of Chicago, argued that the assemblage of species in a particular community or ecosystem was neither predictable nor stable, but reflected the fact that the species shared the same affinity for the resources, climate, and other physical conditions associated with that ecosystem. Gleason also argued that ecological interactions were secondary consequences of physical overlaps and did not determine the species found in an area. He further said that if a community was disturbed, the return of the same species to the area would essentially be a chance event. Gleason's perspective has become known as the *individualistic concept* of community structure. Clements's holistic concept may seem extreme now, but the debate between Clements's and Gleason's views took a long time to settle, in part because many communities do give the appearance of being predictable and stable over the long run.

The process of ecological succession, the way in which communities develop over time and recover from disturbances, gives an appearance of considerable predictability. A complex community, such as a tropical rainforest or a desert, does not simply spring into existence; instead, it develops over a period of time, in some cases, a long period. The same is true when an existing community is seriously disturbed, such as by a fire. *Primary succession* refers to the development of a new community where no organisms had ever lived before (at least not in recent geological time). *Secondary succession* is the redevelopment of a community in which a disturbance has removed all or most of the organisms in an area.

Fredrick Clements noticed that in a patch of forest cleared by fire or logging, the first plants to re-invade are generally different species than the ones removed, but the original species will reappear at some later point. Furthermore, the community will progress through predictable stages until the reappearance of the original species, when the species mix will remain unchanged unless the community is disturbed again.

Clements and many others documented the predictable successional stages in a number of different communities and argued that these stages always led back to the same climax community, the most stable combination of species, whose stability is maintained by highly evolved interactions among the species.

One well-studied example of predictable secondary succession comes from work on abandoned fields in North Carolina, where many forested areas were logged and cultivated 200 years ago or so but eventually abandoned to return to a wild state. The secondary succession that occurs on these fields is called *old-field succession*. Old-field succession usually begins with the appearance of annual weeds in the first year. Annual weeds have a life span of just one year; individuals do not persist for more than one season. In the next few years, species of perennial weeds and grasses start to invade (perennial individuals survive for more than one season).

Shrubby species of plants grow in these abandoned fields after five years or so, after which pine trees begin to invade. Typically, an abandoned North Carolina field will eventually turn into a pine forest, which may persist for many years. These pine forests, however, are not stable climax communities; they will eventually be replaced by oak and hickory trees within about 100 years. A mature oak forest is considered the climax community, and remains stable unless it is disturbed again. Such a progression appears to always end up in the same place, and the stages along the way are also predictable, both of which seem to support Clements's views.

The mechanisms responsible for successional progression largely depend on the life-history characteristics of the species involved. Two kinds of interactions among species are especially important in succession: *inhibition*, in which one species has a negative effect on another, and *facilitation*, in which one species creates conditions that enable other species to move in. In old-field succession, the first colonizers are usually specialized for long-distance dispersal and rapid reproduction; their seeds arrive first and quickly outcompete other species for water and space. As these weeds decompose, they change the soil by adding nutrients and a structure that holds water better; improved soil then facilitates the entry of new species that could not otherwise survive there. Pine trees require full sun, but the shade of mature pines makes it difficult for younger pines to become established. Young oaks are much more shade-tolerant and can begin to grow under pine trees. These oaks eventually outgrow the pines, creating a moist, shady climate that allows new oaks to grow but inhibits other plants.

Pine trees require full sun, but the shade of mature pines makes it difficult for younger pines to become established.

Studies of succession led many ecologists to subscribe to an equilibrium view of community structure until subsequent experiments generated results that were contrary to this view. Even if communities are not superorganisms, they nonetheless appear to develop predictably and remain in a predictable climax community unless disturbed. However, two realizations in the 1970s and 1980s began to turn opinion toward Gleason's individualistic view.

First, "climax" communities rarely stay intact for long and are often moving through various successional stages. North Carolina oak forests are regularly damaged by hurricanes, ice storms, and violent winds. Each of these events is unpredictable and even relatively uncommon, but in aggregate, they are quite regular. Second, studies looked more thoroughly at whether or not the species composition of a community provided increasing evidence for Gleason's view. Long-term studies of changes in forest communities in North America have shown that species distribution in forest communities has shifted radically over the last 10,000 years, with distributions of different species shifting independently of each other. If Clements's view is true, certain tree species in climax communities should always be found together, even if the communities change location. This is not the case; the geographic distributions of different species in present-day climax communities have changed completely independently of each other over the last several thousand years.

In the 1990s, David Jenkins and Arthur Buikema set up 12 small ponds, all the same size and all located in the same field. After the ponds were established, their water was chlorinated, killing all the organisms in them. Once the chlorine was removed, Jenkins sampled the water from all 12 ponds on a regular basis for a year. If Clements is correct, the 12 different ponds should end up with the same species at the end of succession. If Gleason's view is correct, the 12 ponds would more likely have different combinations of species, because it would be very unlikely for each of the ponds to have the same set of species based on chance alone. By the end of the experiment, the 12 ponds contained more than 60 different species of zooplankton, but any one pond had only 30 to 40 species, supporting Gleason's view that the particular assemblage of species found in any community depends on chance and history.

A newer view of community ecology emphasizes the study of patterns of disturbance. Different ecosystems experience different kinds of disturbances at different frequencies and with differing degrees of predictability. These patterns are called *disturbance regimes*. In some cases, the disturbance regime of a community may play an essential role in determining the number and diversity of species living in an area. The *intermediate disturbance hypothesis* suggests that communities that experience either frequent and severe disturbances or infrequent and mild disturbances tend to have fewer species than communities with some intermediate level of disturbance.

This is because if disturbance rates are too high, only species that are good dispersers and colonizers will survive. Conversely, if disturbance rates are too low, a small number of specialized species can come to dominate the community, excluding other species. An ecosystem with intermediate levels of disturbance may sustain a much more complex community because it will have many different subregions, each in a different successional phase. For example, a forest disturbed occasionally and not severely will have many small or medium-size treefall gaps, in which a variety of plant and animal species may be able to survive. ■

Suggested Reading

Campbell & Reece, *Biology* (6th ed.), chapter 53.

Freeman, *Biological Science*, chapter 50.

Purves et al., *Life* (7th ed.), chapter 55.

Smith & Smith, *Elements of Ecology* (5th ed.), chapter 13.

Questions to Consider

1. If the structure of communities is affected by unpredictable events, then why do some communities exhibit regular patterns of succession?

2. Many organisms appear highly adapted to fit a particular ecological niche in the community in which they live. Does this observation support either Clements's or Gleason's view of ecological communities, and why?

Biogeography
Lecture 70

Today, we are going to pick up on this idea of the role of history and chance in determining the distribution of species. But, we are going to shift our attention to a larger scale, asking how contingencies associated with a longer-term history and chance events can help explain patterns of the distribution of species on a large regional scale, or even on a global scale.

This lecture introduces *biogeography*, the branch of biology that examines factors affecting the distribution of species on a historical time scale and global spatial scale. After defining the two main areas of biogeography, historical and ecological, the lecture discusses each in depth, examining examples and experiments that illustrate how biogeographic analysis helps explain patterns of species distributions. The lecture concludes by exploring the *theory of island biogeography*, which predicts the species richness of an area.

Biogeography is the branch of biology that attempts to account for patterns of distribution of populations, species, and ecological communities on a historical time scale and global spatial scale. Biogeography combines biology and geography to help explain large-scale patterns, such as why certain kinds of organisms are found where they are or why certain regions have more or fewer species than other regions. Biogeography is a broad and integrative discipline but can be separated for the sake of argument into two main subdisciplines.

Historical biogeography takes a long-term, evolutionary perspective on the question of why certain kinds of species are found where they are across broad geographic regions. *Ecological biogeography* focuses on shorter-term ecological processes, such as patterns of dispersal, colonization, and extinction, to explain why different numbers of species are found in different regions.

All biogeographic analysis examines changes in patterns of species distributions over time, but historical biogeography concentrates on effects over long time periods. The weevil species *Lyperobius huttoni* is found on both of New Zealand's islands, in the mountains of the South Island and on mountains on the extreme southwest corner of the North Island. The two islands are separated from each other by Cook Strait, which is about 25 kilometers wide at its narrowest point. Several possibilities could explain this disjunct distribution. One possibility is that the weevil evolved originally on one island and colonized the other island by dispersing to it; however, *Lyperobius* is flightless. Perhaps some weevils floated across Cook Strait on vegetation during a storm. More than 60 other species of plants and animals share the same disjunct distribution, though.

During the Pleiocene era—about 5 million years ago—the present-day southwest corner of what is now the North Island was united with the northern part of the South Island. The water gap separating these islands was far north of the present-day limits of the ranges of these species. The result is that the disjunct distribution of these species was caused not by dispersal but by a change in geography. If a species has a disjunct distribution resulting from a historical change in geography that separates a previously continuous population, it is said to have a *vicariant distribution*. If a species exists in two areas because individuals dispersed across a barrier that was already in place, it is said to have a *dispersal distribution*.

Understanding the historical biogeography of a species or group of species is useful not only for understanding the historical factors that contribute to the present-day distribution of species, but it can also help explain the evolution of new species and the resulting distributions of these species in communities and ecosystems. For example, the black-throated green warbler species complex contains five closely related species that are similar in virtually every regard, including their ecological niche. These five species have mostly non-overlapping ranges; the black-throated green warbler is distributed across the eastern United States, while the other four species each have smaller, mostly non-overlapping ranges in the western part of the country.

One possible reason why only one species appears in the east and several in the west is that the North American continent was repeatedly subdivided during the Pleistocene era (within the last 2 million years or so) by the periodic advance and retreat of glaciers. During times of glacial advance, the populations of many forest songbirds probably were divided into two populations, one in the east and the other in the west. These isolated populations may have become genetically isolated and undergone allopatric speciation.

When the glaciers retreated, the populations had become reproductively isolated and would no longer interbreed. Because glaciers advanced and retreated a number of times, one large population could have "budded off" a number of new species, potentially one with each glaciation event. The result would be the distribution of very similar yet distinct species in the eastern and western United States.

Ecological biogeography attempts to explain the abundance and dispersal of species and the effectiveness of barriers to dispersal, which makes it amenable to experimental tests of particular hypotheses.

A phylogenetic analysis based on an analysis of mitochondrial DNA appears to partially support vicariance caused by glaciation as the cause of occurrence and distribution of these five species. There are some problems with this interpretation, however. First, not all aspects of the species distribution can be accounted for by patterns of glaciation. For example, the hermit and Townsend's warblers diverged after their common ancestor split from the main lineage, and their distributions are non-overlapping in a north-south direction, not an east-west direction. Second, evolutionary divergences do not appear to correspond well to the timing of glaciation events. Whether or not the geographic ranges of these five warblers can be explained by patterns of glaciation, this case illustrates how understanding geological history can potentially help explain some aspects of the distribution of species over continents or the globe.

Ecological biogeography attempts to explain the abundance and dispersal of species and the effectiveness of barriers to dispersal, which makes it amenable to experimental tests of particular hypotheses. In the simplest terms, the number of species living in an area can be affected by two factors:

the number of new species arriving in that area, which are called *immigrant species*, and the number of species that go locally extinct in that area.

In the 1960s, Robert MacArthur and E. O. Wilson modeled the effects of these processes by considering the species richness of oceanic islands. The advantage of looking at islands is that they provide well-defined geographic regions whose species richness can easily be quantified. MacArthur and Wilson were trying to understand a well-established pattern they observed, which was that the species richness of an island varies linearly with the size of the island—larger islands have more species than smaller islands. MacArthur and Wilson also wanted to explain another pattern, which was that the species richness of an island varied with how close the island was to a mainland. All other things being equal, islands closest to a larger mainland had more bird species than islands more distant from the mainland.

To account for these patterns, MacArthur and Wilson developed a model that has become known as the *theory of island biogeography*. A newly formed oceanic island that initially has no species on it may acquire new species through the dispersal of immigrant species from an adjacent mainland. If the time frame is too short for speciation to occur, the species that exist on the mainland represent the total number of species that might ever arrive at the island. This list of available species is called the *species pool*.

As new species colonize the island, its species richness increases. As the number of species on the island continues to increase, however, the rate of colonization will decline, because more of the individuals arriving at the island will be members of a species that has already colonized the island. The rate of colonization would eventually reach zero if all the species available in the species pool colonize the island. As the number of species on the island increases, the extinction rate of these species will also increase, because an increasing number of species must divide the same amount of resources and because there are simply more species that could possibly become extinct. Because the rate of arrival of new species decreases and the extinction rate increases as the number of species increases, the number of species present should reach an equilibrium, which reflects a balance of these two opposing trends.

MacArthur and Wilson reasoned that the size of an island influences both immigration and extinction rates in two ways, both of which would lead to smaller islands having fewer species. Smaller islands would have higher extinction rates for the same number of species, because they have fewer resources to divide. Populations would be proportionately smaller and, thus, more likely to go extinct. Smaller islands may also have lower immigration rates because, being smaller, colonizers are less likely to reach them.

MacArthur and Wilson argued that the distance of an island from a mainland affected the immigration rate, because greater distances made it harder for species to disperse to the island, a negative relationship that has been empirically demonstrated. These equilibria are dynamic; that is, there will be an equilibrium number of species, but the particular species present may be constantly changing.

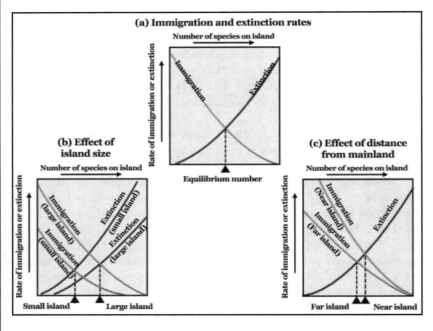

In the late 1960s, Dan Simberloff and E. O. Wilson tested this hypothesis by killing all of the animals on a series of islands and watching patterns of recolonization over a two-year period. Within only 200 days, the number of species on the islands had stabilized; most reached the initial level of species richness, though the species composition was different. Species turnover rates remained quite high, even though the number of species remained constant, just as predicted. Interestingly, a few islands reached a new equilibrium at a lower number of species, which may indicate that the new species competitively interfered with each other more than the original species had or did not exploit resources as thoroughly as the original species did.

The theory of island biogeography provides a theoretical framework for understanding species richness in many circumstances other than islands. Environments are often divided into *habitat islands*, patches of habitat separated from similar patches—a particularly relevant idea as habitats are increasingly fragmented by humans. Island biogeography and historical biogeography also provide another perspective on how, and how much, history and chance events determine the structure of modern communities and ecosystems. ∎

Suggested Reading

Campbell & Reece, *Biology* (6th ed.), chapter 53.

Purves et al., *Life* (7th ed.), chapter 56.

Quammen, *The Song of the Dodo: Island Biogeography in an Age of Extinctions*.

1. Does the fact that the geography of the two islands of New Zealand has changed over geological time prove that the distribution of the weevil *Lyperobius huttoni* is the result of a vicariance event and not a dispersal event? If not, what other kinds of evidence would support this hypothesis?

2. Explain the relevance of MacArthur and Wilson's theory of island biogeography for conservation biology. Do you see any potential difficulties with applying the theory in this way?

Human Population Growth
Lecture 71

The major point that we have come back to time and again in this last third of the course is that life is costly. By "costly" I mean that the structure and function of living systems at all levels in the hierarchy of life depend on energy and other kinds of resources.

This lecture discusses the implications of energy and resource limitations for understanding human population growth. For most of human history, the size of human populations was limited by naturally occurring resources, but humans have continually redefined the ways many resources are obtained and used, leading to a dramatic increase in the size of the global human population. After examining several such important turning points in human history, the lecture begins to explore the consequences of human population growth and human activity on the rest of the biosphere.

The issues surrounding the theme of Energy and Resources have many implications for the global human population. Life is costly—the structure and function of living systems at all levels depend on energy and other resources. Specifically, the structure of living systems at any level can often be understood in light of the fact that there may not be enough energy or resources available to pay those costs entirely. The theme of Energy and Resources is an apt focus for the conclusion of the course because of the astonishing growth of the human population. Anyone older than 40 has seen the human population double in his or her lifetime, and a child born today might easily live to see it double again.

Humans are living longer on average, and more humans are being born; as a result, the human population in recent history has experienced almost exponential growth. This pattern of growth forces us to ask two multifaceted questions:

First, what is the carrying capacity of the human population, and what will happen when humans reach it?

Second, what are the impacts of human population growth on the rest of the planet?

For most of human history, population size was limited by resources immediately available in the environment. Early in human history, humans lived in small, autonomous bands numbering at most a few hundred individuals. As hunter-gatherers, humans depended entirely on the productivity of the plants and animals found in their ecosystems and on their ability to obtain energy and resources from those other species. Thus, the major constraint on human population growth was almost certainly the fact that they depended on the productivity of natural ecosystems for all of their energy and resources.

Estimates vary widely, but the world human population was likely somewhere between 1 million and 10 million people prior to about 10,000 B.C. For the sake of argument, we will take an average figure of about 4 or 5 million. The global human population appears not to have grown much or at all during this early period; the human population was maintained at a natural carrying capacity as long as humans remained tied to natural productivity.

Life changed considerably, however, in the Neolithic period (about 8,000–5,000 B.C.), when humans learned to domesticate some plants and animals. The domestication of crop species and food animals was perhaps the first significant application of an understanding of biology on the part of the humans. Domestication eventually led to the rise of more permanent villages and a greater division of labor in human societies. More important, domestication and agriculture created a larger and more predictable supply of energy and resources, which raised the global carrying capacity of humans.

By the beginning of the Common Era—about 2,000 years ago, or about the time of Christ—the world population of humans is estimated to have been about 300 million people, about 100 times its size before the Neolithic period. The human population continued to increase, although it took more than 1,500 years to double to about 600 million sometime in the 17th century. Although humans continued to increase their carrying capacity, there were measurable declines in world population size during this period, most notably during the 14th century as a result of the bubonic plague, or "Black Death," that ravaged much of Asia and Europe.

Even with improvements in agriculture, human populations were still constrained by their dependence on plants and animals as a sole source of energy. Humans could not obtain more energy than that available at the trophic levels on which they grazed, and the rate of population growth began to decrease as a new carrying capacity was reached.

During the Industrial Revolution of the 1700s, humans learned how to capture the energy stored in fossil fuels and use this energy for a wealth of other activities. The Industrial Revolution involved more than just the development of industrial uses of fossil fuels; it was a period of rapid advances in science and technology in general. Animal labor began to be replaced by machines fueled by coal, allowing food and other goods to be produced, processed, and transported more efficiently.

Other important advances in biology influenced the health of human populations. Edward Jenner developed the technique of vaccination in the late 18th century, and people began to understand basic principles of disease transmission and public health, leading to improved personal hygiene, sanitation, and waste removal.

Just as agriculture did 10,000 years or so earlier, the Industrial Revolution allowed the human species to readjust the way it interacted with its ecosystem and caused the human carrying capacity to increase drastically. Death rates dropped, birth rates soared, and the human population began a steep upward growth trajectory.

Just as agriculture did 10,000 years or so earlier, the Industrial Revolution allowed the human species to readjust the way it interacted with its ecosystem and caused the human carrying capacity to increase drastically.

The annual growth rate of the European population quadrupled between 1750 and 1850; the population of London alone exploded from about 1 million people in 1800 to about 4.5 million people in 1880. Globally, the human population swelled to 1 billion sometime between 1800 and 1850.

Also during this period, Thomas Malthus saw that the human population was experiencing exponential growth and argued—correctly—that exponential growth could not be sustained forever. Malthus saw rising mortality rates as an inevitable consequence of eventual overpopulation. When Malthus wrote his essay in 1798, the world population was approaching 1 billion; 201 years later, the United Nations announced that the world population had reached 6 billion.

As the 20th century approached, the global growth rate of the human population began to slow down, though the human population continued to soar. In the equation for exponential growth, $dN/dt = rN$, the ever-increasing size of N means that a population will grow exponentially as long as r is greater than zero, even if r decreases. This equation holds, however, only if population size is well below the carrying capacity.

In the 20th century, humans once again redefined their ecological relationship to the rest of the planet. At the beginning of the 20th century, scientists began to echo Malthus's concern, warning that the world's population would soon exceed global food production. However, as in the Industrial Revolution, when they essentially "short-circuited" the global carbon cycle, humans took control of the nitrogen cycle in the 20th century.

Nitrogen is a key limiting resource that affects the primary productivity of plants, and adding nitrogen increases primary productivity. Up to the end of the 19th century, humans depended on organic sources of nitrogen to fertilize their crops, but they could extract only so much nitrogen from the natural biogeochemical cycle.

Around 1908, a German chemist named Fritz Haber developed a method to convert inorganic nitrogen gas (N_2) into ammonia (NH_3), an organic form of nitrogen that could be used to make nitrogen fertilizer. His process became known as the Haber-Bosch process, and it won Haber a Nobel Prize in 1918.

The Haber-Bosch process once again decoupled human population growth from an aspect of the natural environment. With the advent of industrial fertilizers, crop yields were no longer tied to organic sources of nitrogen and began to rise. The development of synthetic fertilizers was only the first step in an extraordinary increase in the productivity of food crops and world food production in the 20th century.

Norman Borlaug was a plant physiologist who, in the 1940s, directed a plant-breeding station in northwestern Mexico that was used to breed new strains of high-yield crop plants. Within 20 years, Borlaug's efforts had resulted in strains of wheat that produced more grain, had greater disease resistance, and perhaps most interestingly, were relatively insensitive to day length. Borlaug is considered by many to be the "father of the Green Revolution" and he was awarded the Nobel Peace Prize in 1970 for his efforts. By combining newly developed crop strains with industrial fertilizers and new irrigation technologies, world grain yields soared during the 20th century—by one estimate, increasing productivity by 170% using only 1% more land. An obvious consequence of this "Green Revolution" is another potentially large increase in the human carrying capacity. With the advent of genetic engineering, it is now possible to modify crop plants even more radically at a much faster pace. Though this has disadvantages, crop productivity will likely continue to rise as humans directly manipulate the genomes of organisms.

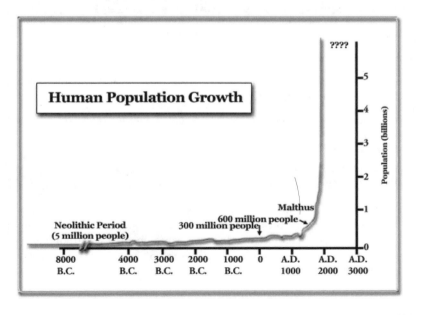

The Green Revolution is not the only application of modern biology that has affected human population size and growth rates in the last century. Modern medicine has had a major impact on decreasing death rates and increasing life expectancy, increasing the potential for population growth. Genomic research and biotechnology promise to accelerate the pace of discovery, potentially leading to faster development of drugs and other means of treating disease.

Some population biologists have argued that the carrying capacity for the planet is only 2 billion and that humans have simply not overshot it long enough for it to catch up with us. Other scientists argue that humans have not reached carrying capacity and are unlikely to do so soon because we continue to develop new ways to increase it. Some point to science-fiction solutions, which may seem outlandish, but it would have been outlandish to suggest to someone at the beginning of the 20th century that we could modify animals and plants by manipulating their genes. In either case, given that Earth has a finite amount of resources, there must be some upper limit. ∎

Suggested Reading

Campbell & Reece, *Biology* (6th ed.), chapter 52.

Freeman, *Biological Science*, chapter 48.2.

Smith & Smith, *Elements of Ecology* (5th ed.), Ecological Application Essay: "Cheating Nature" (chapter 12).

Stoltzenberg, *Fritz Haber: Chemist, Nobel Laureate, German, Jew: A Biography*.

Questions to Consider

1. The ability of humans to "short-circuit" both the global carbon and nitrogen biogeochemical cycles has had a profound effect on the size of the human population. How does the way humans use carbon contrast with the way they use nitrogen, in terms of how increased access to these resources affects human population growth?

2. Does the importance of continued advances in medicine and agriculture to sustain the size of the human population on the planet make you think any differently about the use of biotechnology to create genetically modified organisms?

The Human Asteroid

Lecture 72

The ability of biologists to dissect and manipulate molecules on one end of the scale of biological organization, and to monitor the structure and function of ecosystems on the other end of the scale, and to measure and analyze living systems at all levels in between, has never been greater.

This lecture begins with the point that biologists, at the outset of the 21st century, find themselves on the verge of obtaining a truly integrative and comprehensive understanding of how life works. The optimism of this perspective is tempered, however, by the increasing loss of biodiversity on the planet, which means that fewer and fewer kinds of living things are available to study. After exploring the seriousness of this problem, the lecture discusses the many ways in which biodiversity is important to humans and other species. Human population growth, in particular, has had negative consequences on biodiversity and other aspects of life on Earth, perhaps none so large as global warming. The lecture ends on the optimistic note that it is not too late to preserve much of the natural world around us, using the knowledge we have gained about the "science of life."

Biologists find themselves in a strange position at the beginning of the 21st century. The pace of discovery is astounding, and biologists are now uncovering some of the most fundamental secrets of how life works. At the same time, this excitement is tempered by the realization that much of the life on Earth is in peril. Species, communities, and entire ecosystems are being lost at a frighteningly rapid pace—at no other time in recorded history have species gone extinct so fast or has the face of the planet undergone such a rapid transformation. Just as we come to a deep understanding of the science of life, the biodiversity that makes living systems so interesting is being lost. Humans have had a major impact not only on the organisms with which we interact but also on the biosphere itself.

Biodiversity on the species level is being lost at an alarming rate. One obvious measure of biological diversity (*biodiversity*) is the number of different species that currently exist. However, no one knows how many species exist, and counting them accurately is a Herculean task. About 1.7 million organisms have been documented, but this number must be just a small fraction of the total.

One problem is that many groups of organisms include a very large number of species that are hard to describe. Only about 5,000 species of bacteria have been described, but microbiologists using DNA sequencing typically find evidence for dozens or even hundreds of undescribed species in every sample. Based on this, biologists now suspect that there are millions of bacteria species, virtually all as yet unknown to science.

Another reason we have such an incomplete view of how many species exist today is that biologists have described relatively few species in the tropics, where biodiversity should be highest. E. O. Wilson, for example, found 43 species of ants occurring in the canopy of a single tree in the Amazon— approximately the same number of ant species that have been described for the entire British Isles. All biologists can do at present is estimate the number of species on the planet based on the rate at which new species are found. A conservative estimate suggests that there are at least 10 million species; other estimates suggest that the planet may contain as many as 100 million species. The International Union for the Conservation of Nature lists more than 15% of mammals, 10% of birds, 5% of fish, and 10% of plants as threatened, meaning there is a greater than 10% chance they will go extinct within 100 years. Since 1600, about 2.1% of all known mammals and 1.3% of birds have gone extinct.

An equally important measure of biodiversity is genetic variation, the diversity of different alleles in the gene pool of a population or a species. Genetic variation is essential for long-term survival because it enables adaptation to changing conditions. A third important measure of biodiversity is the diversity of ecosystems. Each different kind of ecosystem contributes in a different way to the amount of resources available to the biosphere as a whole, and some ecosystems are being essentially eliminated.

Biodiversity is important for several reasons. Some people may care about biodiversity from an aesthetic or recreational point of view, but others may not. However, there are important reasons to preserve biodiversity beyond its aesthetic value. The first reason is that biodiversity is a repository of genes that can ultimately benefit humanity. More than 25% of all prescription drugs used in the United States contain compounds originally derived from plants, and new medicines are constantly being isolated from such natural sources. For example, one of the most effective treatments for Hodgkin's disease is a drug derived from the rosy periwinkle, found in Madagascar. Taxol, another common and potent anti-cancer agent, was extracted first from Pacific yew trees in old-growth forests in the northwestern United States. Both the Madagascar rainforest and Pacific Northwest old-growth forests are in serious danger of disappearing because of logging.

Diverse organisms provide an enormous number of benefits other than new drugs. For example, genetic engineering and biotechnology depend on the ability to rapidly replicate DNA in the laboratory through the polymerase chain reaction (PCR). PCR, in turn, relies on a form of DNA polymerase isolated from a species of bacteria adapted to live in hot springs and found originally in Yellowstone National Park. Furthermore, genetic engineering enables us to transfer useful genes from one organism to another. Even those unmoved by biodiversity for aesthetic reasons have a vested interest in preserving what is essentially an untapped warehouse of natural products. As species go extinct, they take their genomes with them. Humans should also preserve ecosystems out of a sense of self-interest. Through their biogeochemical interactions with other ecosystems and the biosphere as a whole, ecosystems maintain the environment. These kinds of functions are called *ecosystem services*, and the loss of an ecosystem often requires expensive alternatives.

Human population growth has had several dire consequences for the biosphere, foremost among them, the phenomenon of global warming. The growth of the human population, especially over the last few hundred years, has contributed greatly to the current loss of biodiversity. Human population growth has had particularly serious consequences, among them, habitat destruction, overharvesting, and the introduction of invasive species to new habitats. In addition to direct ecological impacts, however, the burgeoning human population has also begun to transform the biosphere by disturbing global biogeochemical cycles, such as the carbon and nitrogen cycles.

It is clear that the level of carbon dioxide in the Earth's atmosphere is rising and has been since the onset of the Industrial Revolution. Estimates suggest that the level of atmospheric CO_2 was about 260 to 280 parts per million (ppm) before industrialization began. In 1958, a monitoring station in Hawaii began to monitor atmospheric CO_2 directly. The first measurements recorded a concentration of 315 ppm; the current level is more than 370 ppm. Changes in atmospheric CO_2 are very dynamic, but the overall trend is a steep upward trajectory.

Because CO_2 is transparent to visible light, the amount of CO_2 in the atmosphere has little or no effect on the amount of solar energy the Earth receives. However, CO_2 absorbs and reflects heat, and increased CO_2 may cause more of the heat ordinarily dissipated from Earth to be retained in a process called the *greenhouse effect*. Global temperatures are rising, though there is debate over how much. Climatologists suggest that the mean global temperature has risen on the order of 0.6°C since the turn of the 20th century. Evidence of this trend can be seen in several dimensions; for example, ice thickness at the North Pole has decreased during this same period.

> "[Mankind] will survive only on one condition, and that is that he must take control not only of his own destinies but of the whole of life."
>
> — H. G. Wells

The key question is whether the observed increase in CO_2 level and the observed increase in global temperature are causally related, and most scientists have now concluded that they are. Current projections suggest that in the next 100 years, atmospheric CO_2 levels will rise to somewhere between 500 and 1,200 ppm. A recent study done by a United Nations panel of experts suggested that, if that trend is maintained, global temperatures will rise by 1.4 to 5.8°C in the next 100 years. An increase of only 1.4°C would make the Earth warmer than it has been in the last 100,000 years, which clearly might shift the abundance and distribution of species. There is some evidence, in fact, that species distributions are already shifting.

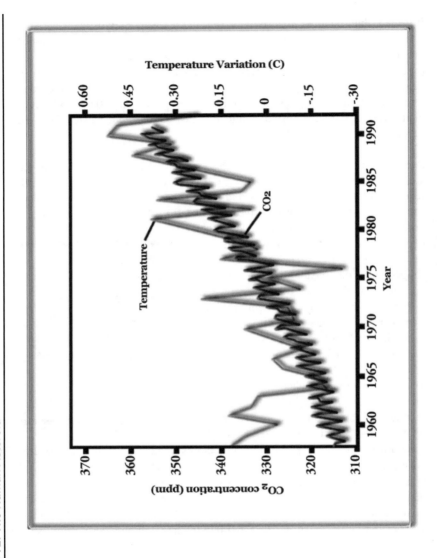

One possible consequence for humans is that sea levels would rise. One estimate suggests that melting of the polar ice cap would result in a rise in sea levels of only 1 meter, but even that is enough to have a negative impact on cities and communities at or near present-day sea levels. A second, perhaps more far-reaching, effect might involve positive and negative effects. Higher temperatures and an increased level of atmospheric CO_2 could increase the agricultural yields of some crops; other crops, however, might have less tolerance for a change in average temperature, reducing yields.

The impact of humans on the biosphere has been called the *human asteroid*, referring to the asteroid that appears to have struck the Earth about 65 million years ago, causing a global disaster that killed more than half of all species on the planet. There is reason to believe that we can avert an ecological disaster and sustain a stable relationship with the biosphere over the long term. Though the global human population continues to grow—growth rates have begun leveling off. The most recent projection made by the United Nations Population Division suggests that the human population will reach only about 7.3 billion by the year 2050 and perhaps even begin to decline. Less optimistic estimates place the world population at as much as 10.7 billion by 2050.

Another source of good news is that biologists, governments, and the public are becoming more aware of the biodiversity crisis and taking concrete steps to minimize further negative impacts. In addition, the biosphere's own response to imbalances, such as increased CO_2, may reduce the impact of such changes.

This course began with a quote from H. G. Wells's *The Science of Life*, in which Wells emphasized the central importance to our everyday lives of understanding biology—a point truer today than it was 75 years ago. At the end of his book, Wells says, "On the whole we believe that our species will survive and triumph over its present perplexities. There is much in life that may make intelligent men impatient, but it is not reasonable to let impatience degenerate into pessimism." Wells concludes, "[Mankind] will survive only on one condition, and that is that he must take control not only of his own destinies but of the whole of life." By understanding biology, we can better take control of our destiny as a part of the global ecosystem in which we live. ■

Suggested Reading

Campbell & Reece, *Biology* (6th ed.), chapter 55.

Dobson, *Conservation and Biodiversity*.

Freeman, *Biological Science*, chapter 52.

McKee, *Sparing Nature: The Conflict between Human Population Growth and Earth's Biodiversity*.

Purves et al., *Life* (7th ed.), chapter 57.

Wilson, *The Future of Life*.

Questions to Consider

1. Should some species be allowed to go extinct? If so, how should those species be chosen?

2. Do you think moral or ethical issues should play a role in the debate over preserving biodiversity, in addition to practical and aesthetic issues? Why or why not?

Timeline

c. 4.6 bya[1] .... Formation of Earth from accretion of planetary material is completed.

c. 3.5 bya .... Life clearly established on Earth, as evidenced by oldest confirmed fossil cells.

c. 2.7 bya .... Evolution of oxygen-producing photosynthetic biochemical pathways, leading to eventual transformation of Earth's atmosphere from "reducing" to "oxidizing."

c. 2.0 bya .... Oldest eukaryotic cells.

c. 1.8 bya .... Amount of oxygen in atmosphere approaches current levels.

c. 600 mya[2] .... Earliest confirmed fossil of a multicellular organism (although most biologists agree that multicellularity arose as early as 1.5 bya).

c. 8000 B.C. .... Beginning of Neolithic Period, during which humans begin to domesticate plants and animals; size of world human population is somewhere in the range of 4 or 5 million people.

---

[1] Billion years ago

[2] Million years ago

430 B.C. .... Thucydides describes the acquired immune response in his account of the Athens plague.

384–322 B.C. .... Life of Aristotle, who contributed many fundamental ideas to early and even contemporary views of biology.

1700s A.D. .... Industrial Revolution begins in England.

1735.. Linnaeus publishes the first edition of *Systema naturae*, in which he establishes his hierarchical system of classification.

1796.. Edward Jenner uses pus from cowpox sores to "vaccinate" patients against smallpox infection.

1798.. Thomas Malthus publishes *Essay on the Principle of Population.*

1809.. Jean-Baptiste Lamarck proposes the *theory of acquired characteristics* as a mechanism for biological evolution in his book *Philosophie Zoologique.*

1831–1836...................................... Charles Darwin travels around the world collecting specimens as a naturalist aboard H.M.S. *Beagle.*

1858.. Alfred Russel Wallace sends a manuscript to Darwin describing essentially the same idea for how natural selection works as Darwin had conceived; both Wallace's manuscript and a paper by Darwin are read at the Royal Society of London.

1859.. Darwin publishes *On the Origin of Species by Means of Natural Selection.*

1865.. Claude Bernard publishes *Introduction à l'Étude de la Médecine Expérimentale*, in which he develops the concept of physiological homeostasis.

1866.. Gregor Mendel publishes his work on trait transmission in garden peas, outlining Mendel's Laws of Inheritance.

1883.. August Weismann proposes the *germ plasm theory of development.*

1902–1903.. Walter Sutton and Theodor Boveri independently propose the *chromosomal theory of inheritance.*

1908.. Fritz Haber develops method for converting nitrogen gas into ammonia, leading to industrial production of nitrogen fertilizer.

1910... Thomas Hunt Morgan describes the white-eyed mutant in fruit flies, leading to the discovery of sex-linked traits and definitive proof that "genes" are on chromosomes.

1924... Hilde Mangold and Hans Spemann demonstrate the importance of "organizer" tissues in development through their transplant experiments with newt embryos.

1928... Frederick Griffith discovers the *transforming principle* in his experiments with *Streptococcus pneumoniae.*

1929... H. G. Wells publishes *The Science of Life*, along with his son G. P. Wells and biologist Julian Huxley.

1930s–1940s .... The *modern synthesis* in evolutionary biology leads to a reconciliation between Darwinian views on natural selection and evolution and Mendelian genetics.

1932... G. F. Gause introduces the *competitive exclusion principle* based on his work on competition among different species of *Paramecium.*

1935... Arthur Tansley coins the term *ecosystem* in a paper published in the journal *Ecology.*

1937.. Sir Hans Krebs proposes key elements of the pathways of cellular respiration that would eventually become known as the *Krebs cycle.*

1942.. Ernst Mayr promulgates the *biological species concept* in his book *Systematics and the Origin of Species.*

1944.. Oswald Avery, Maclyn McCarty, and Colin MacLeod's biochemical experiments suggest that Griffith's transforming principle is DNA; Norman Borlaug appointed to lead experimental agricultural station in Mexico funded by the Rockefeller Foundation, marking the start of the Green Revolution in agriculture.

1949.. Donald O. Hebb publishes *Organization of Behavior*, in which he proposes that memory involves permanent changes in synapse strength.

1952.. Alfred Hershey and Martha Chase use bacteriophage viruses with radio-labeled protein or DNA to demonstrate conclusively that Griffith's transforming principle is DNA; Robert Briggs and Thomas King successfully transplant the nucleus of a mature cell into the enucleated ovum of a frog, leading to the development of a normal embryo, thus paving the way for subsequent work on "cloning" of animals.

1953.................................... Stanley Miller, working with Harold
Urey at the University of Chicago,
successfully synthesizes organic
compounds abiotically in an atmosphere
resembling that of early Earth; James
Watson and Francis Crick publish
the double-helix model for the three-
dimensional structure of DNA.

1955.................................... Frederick Sanger is the first to
determine the complete amino acid
sequence of a protein, insulin.

1957.................................... Matthew Meselson and Frank Stahl
verify the "semi-conservative" model
of DNA replication using DNA that
had been "labeled" with a heavy
isotope of nitrogen and density-gradient
centrifugation to separate DNA based
on subtle weight differences.

1958.................................... Arthur Kornberg uses the enzyme
DNA polymerase to synthesize DNA
in the laboratory.

1959.................................... Sidney Fox demonstrates abiotic
synthesis of organic polymers in the
laboratory under early Earth conditions.

1961.................................... Francois Jacob and Jacques Monod
publish a summary model of control
of gene expression for the *lac* operon;
Marshall Nirenberg and J. Heinrich
Matthaei synthesize artificial RNAs
in the laboratory, paving the way for

the "genetic code" to be cracked over the next several years; Peter Mitchell proposes the chemiosmotic theory of ATP production associated with electron transport chains.

1967.. Robert MacArthur and Edward O. Wilson publish *The Theory of Island Biogeography*.

1970.. David Baltimore and co-workers discover retroviruses and describe the enzyme reverse transcriptase that can synthesize DNA from an RNA template.

1972.. First recombinant DNA made *in vitro*.

1979.. First production of human insulin through genetic engineering.

1981.. Lynn Margulis proposes the *endosymbiotic theory* for the evolution of eukaryotic cells.

1982.. Thomas Cech demonstrates that "ribozymes" can catalyze reactions, suggesting that RNA could have functioned both as an information-storing molecule and a catalytic molecule in an early "RNA world."

1997.. Ian Wilmut and colleagues successfully clone the sheep Dolly using nuclear transplantation.

1999.. United Nations announces on October 12th that the world human population has reached 6 billion.

2050.. United Nations Population Division estimates that the size of the world's human population will reach as few as 7.3 billion or as many as 10.7 billion people.

Glossary

action potential: stereotypic ("all-or-none") change in the electrical potential across a neuron's cell membrane resulting from the rapid opening and closing of voltage-gated ion channels selective for sodium and potassium ions.

activation energy: energy that must be added to a chemical reaction in order for that reaction to proceed.

aerobic: in the presence of oxygen, used especially with reference to catabolic pathways that require oxygen for the breakdown of glucose or other organic compounds.

alleles: alternate forms of a gene at a particular genetic locus.

allopatric: occurring in different geographic locales, used with reference to the distribution of different species or populations of the same species (as in *allopatric speciation*).

amensalism: ecological interaction in which one species is harmed by the presence of another, while the second species remains unaffected by the first.

amino acid: the molecular sub-unit from which proteins are built; 20 different kinds of amino acids are found in naturally occurring proteins.

anabolic reaction: a biochemical reaction that creates a more complex product from chemically simpler reactants and that usually requires energy to run.

anaerobic: in the absence of oxygen; used especially with reference to catabolic pathways that do not require oxygen for the breakdown of glucose or other organic compounds.

antibody: a kind of protein produced by B cells of the immune system that recognizes and binds to a foreign substance (antigen) in a highly specific fashion, facilitating the destruction and removal of that foreign substance by other elements of the immune system.

anticodon: the sequence of three nucleotides found on one end of a transfer RNA molecule that recognizes and binds to a corresponding codon on a molecule of messenger RNA during protein synthesis.

antigen: a foreign substance that stimulates the production of antibodies and other elements of the immune response by the immune system (shortened from *antibody generator*).

ATP (adenosine triphosphate): a molecule that stores energy in chemical bonds joining phosphate groups (phosphate/oxygen compounds), used by cells as a fundamental energy currency; ATP gives up energy that can be used for other processes when it loses a phosphate group, forming ADP (adenosine diphosphate).

autotroph: an organism that can produce its own food from inorganic energy sources; most autotrophs are photoautotrophs, using sunlight as an energy source.

base: with reference to nucleic acids, the nitrogen compound that characterizes different kinds of nucleotides; the term *base* or *base-pair* is often used in the context of describing the length or particular order of a sequence of nucleotides in a nucleic acid.

biogeochemical cycles: physical and biological processes involved in the movement of elements between organisms and storage reservoirs in the environment.

biomass: the total mass of some set of organisms, delineated, for example, by type of organism, physical locale, or trophic level; often used as a measure of productivity.

biosphere: the entire planet Earth considered as a single, interconnected ecosystem.

Calvin cycle: the metabolic pathways in photosynthesis in which inorganic carbon obtained from carbon dioxide is reduced and incorporated into high-energy sugars; also called the *dark reactions*.

carbohydrates: one of the four major classes of organic compounds; carbohydrates include such compounds as sugars and polymers of sugars, including starch, glycogen, and cellulose, among others.

carrying capacity: the theoretical maximum number of individuals of a species that can be supported by the energy and resources available in some habitat.

catabolic reaction: a biochemical reaction that creates simpler products from a chemically more complex reactant and that usually yields energy when run.

catalyst: any agent that accelerates the rate at which a chemical reaction proceeds by lowering the activation energy of that reaction without itself being consumed by the reaction; enzymes serve as catalysts for most biochemical reactions in the cell.

cellular respiration: the metabolic processes through which energy is obtained by cells through the oxidation of organic molecules involving the Krebs cycle and oxidative phosphorylation associated with the electron transport chain and chemiosmosis; *cellular respiration* is sometimes more loosely used to refer to all energy-obtaining metabolic pathways, including glycolysis.

chemiosmosis: the mechanism by which energy released by the redox reactions of an electron transport chain is stored in the form of a concentration gradient across a membrane and used to power the synthesis of ATP in mitochondria and chloroplasts (see also **oxidative phosphorylation**).

chloroplast: cellular organelle that serves as the site of photosynthesis.

chromatid: one of the two copies of a chromosome that result from DNA replication, found joined together with its "sister chromatid" at a central point (the *centromere*) until the chromatids separate during mitosis or the second cell division of meiosis.

chromatin: the combination of DNA and proteins that form chromosomes in eukaryotic cells.

chromosome: in prokaryotic cells, the circular molecule of double-stranded DNA that contains the genetic information of the cell; in eukaryotic cells, one of several linear molecules of double-stranded DNA, combined with various proteins in the form of chromatin, containing the genetic information of the cell.

cleavage: the cell divisions that occur rapidly during the earliest phase of development in animals, in which DNA replicates and is divided among daughter cells, but no cell growth occurs.

clones: genetically identical cells or organisms.

codon: a sequence of three nucleotides in a molecule of DNA or messenger RNA that corresponds to a particular amino acid, representing the basic unit of the genetic code.

commensalism: ecological interaction in which one species benefits from the presence of another while the second species remains unaffected by the first.

competition: ecological interaction in which two species use one or more of the same limiting resources and, thus, the presence of either species has a negative impact on the other; individuals of the same species also may compete for some limiting resource.

crossing over: the exchange of corresponding segments of non-sister chromatids leading to genetic recombination between homologous chromosomes during meiosis.

cytoplasmic determinants: proteins or messenger RNAs found in female gametes (eggs) that influence many aspects of the earliest stages of development in animals.

determination: the progressive narrowing during development of the phenotypic fate of a cell.

detritivore: an organism that acquires energy and resources by consuming dead bodies or waste products of other organisms; also referred to as a *decomposer.*

differentiation: the expression during development of the phenotypic characteristics associated with a cell's specialized form and function.

diploid: having two copies (a homologous pair) of each chromosome type, one inherited from each parent.

DNA (deoxyribonucleic acid): the molecule responsible for storing and transmitting genetic information in all organisms; a kind of nucleic acid.

DNA polymerase: an enzyme that catalyzes the replication of DNA, by adding nucleotides to the growing polymer that are complementary to the single-stranded DNA being used as a template.

ecological niche: the functional role of an organism in its environment, in terms of the way it uses resources found in that environment.

ecological succession: the consistent sequence of kinds of organisms that occupy an area following a disturbance that removes most or all of the organisms in a community.

ecosystem: the organisms found in an area (which can be defined at widely different scales), together with the physical characteristics of the environment in which those organisms live.

electron transport: the transfer of electrons through a series of oxidation-reduction reactions along a series of electron-accepting molecules, resulting in the release of energy stored in those electrons as they transition to a lower energy state; *electron transport chains* provide the energy to drive chemiosmosis in both mitochondria and chloroplasts.

electronegativity: the tendency of an atom to attract electrons, with strongly electronegative elements, such as oxygen, having a greater draw on electrons than weakly electronegative elements, such as carbon.

endomembrane system: the internal membrane system of eukaryotic cells that includes the endoplasmic reticulum and Golgi apparatus, along with related structures, such as lysosomes and transport vesicles.

enzyme: a protein that serves as a catalyst for a biochemical reaction in the cell.

eukaryote: an organism having cells that include internal membrane-enclosed structures, most notably a nucleus; all multicellular organisms are eukaryotes, as are many single-celled organisms (compare **prokaryote**).

exon: a portion of a gene that includes information coding for part of a protein (contrast with **intron**).

fitness: the contribution of an individual to the genetic composition (gene pool) of a population in a subsequent generation, usually measured as number of offspring produced relative to other individuals in the population in a given environment; more formally known as *Darwinian fitness.*

fixed action pattern: a behavior performed in a stereotypic fashion and carried to completion once it is begun.

food web: a summary of the trophic relationships among species in a community; also referred to as a *food chain* if those relationships are simplified to a simple linear set of trophic levels.

free energy: the energy in a system available for doing work.

gamete: a haploid reproductive cell, often called a *sperm* when produced by males or called an *egg* or *ovum* when produced by females; two gametes fuse to form a diploid zygote during sexual reproduction.

gastrulation: critical stage in the early development of animals, when a single-layered hollow ball of cells (the *blastula*) transforms into a more complex structure (the *gastrula*) that has a primitive gut and three cell layers fated to become the three major tissue types of the developing organism.

gene: the basic unit of heredity; on the molecular level, a *gene* refers to the portion of a molecule of DNA (or RNA in some viruses) that codes for a protein or other functional entity, such as a transfer RNA molecule.

gene pool: all of the alleles of all the genes in a population of organisms; often used in a more limited sense to refer to all the alleles of a single gene or the genes responsible for a single trait in a population.

genetic drift: evolutionary change in allele frequencies in a gene pool that results from random processes associated with small population size.

genetic recombination: the production of novel genotypes (and, thus, potentially novel phenotypes) in offspring due to independent assortment of homologous chromosomes and crossing over during sexual reproduction.

genome: the entire DNA sequence of all the chromosomes of an organism.

genotype: the genetic make-up of an individual, represented by the alleles possessed by that individual for a particular trait or set of traits.

glycolysis: the catabolic pathway associated with the breakdown of glucose to pyruvate, capturing a small amount of stored energy in the form of ATP produced through substrate-level phosphorylation.

haploid: having one copy of each chromosome type.

heterotroph: an organism that must obtain food by consuming other organisms, using the organic compounds obtained this way as a source of energy.

heterozygous: referring to a diploid organism having two different alleles at a particular genetic locus.

homeostasis: the maintenance of a constant physiological state or internal environment.

homolog: one of a pair of chromosomes in a diploid organism carrying the same set of genes (although not necessarily the same alleles for those genes); two chromosomes carrying the same set of genes are referred to as a *homologous pair.*

homologous: in evolutionary biology, referring to a similarity between two structures that is due to common ancestry.

homozygous: referring to a diploid organism having two copies of the same alleles at a particular genetic locus.

inclusive fitness: the total contribution of an individual to the genetic composition (gene pool) of a population in a subsequent generation due to its own reproductive success and the reproductive success of family members (who carry some proportion of the same alleles, depending on how closely related they are to the individual).

induction: the process in which one cell or tissue influences the developmental fate of another cell or tissue.

intron: a non-coding region of a gene that is excised after transcription but before translation of that gene (contrast with **exon**).

ion channel: a transmembrane protein or protein complex that allows charged ions, often just one kind of ion, to cross a cell membrane; ion channels may be passive, in which case ions move through them down a concentration gradient, or active, in which case energy is expended to pump ions up their concentration gradient; ion channels also may be gated, in which case they open or close in response to some stimulus, such as the binding of a ligand or a change in the electrical potential across the membrane.

Krebs cycle: the catabolic pathway associated with the complete oxidation of the carbons in pyruvate, capturing stored energy in the form of some ATP produced through substrate-level phosphorylation and in the form of reduced electron carrier molecules that subsequently donate electrons and the energy they store to the electron transport chain in mitochondria; also called the *citric acid cycle.*

ligand: a molecule acting as a signal that binds to a receptor site of another molecule acting as a receptor in the process of chemical signaling among cells.

linkage: an association between genes that do not show random assortment because they occur on the same chromosome; *sex-linkage* refers more specifically to a pattern of inheritance of a gene located on a sex chromosome.

lipids: one of the four major classes of organic compounds, commonly referred to as *fats* and including, for example, phospholipids that form the primary component of cell membranes and steroids that act as hormones in animals.

locus: a specific location on a chromosome where a particular gene is located, often used synonymously with the word *gene.*

lymphocyte: a class of white blood cells associated with the acquired immune response and including B cells and T cells.

meiosis: a kind of eukaryotic cell division specialized for sexual reproduction that produces four haploid cells called *gametes* from a single diploid cell.

metabolism: the total set of biochemical reactions that occur in a cell.

mitochondrion (pl: mitochondria): cellular organelle that serves as the site of cellular respiration.

mitosis: a kind of cell division in eukaryotes that provides a complete complement of the parent cell's chromosomes into each of two daughter cells.

mutation: a permanent change in the DNA of a cell that is not due to genetic recombination.

mutualism: ecological interaction in which both of a pair of species benefits from the presence of the other species.

natural selection: evolutionary mechanism by which differential reproduction by individuals in a population in a given environment leads to a change in allele frequencies of the gene pool of that population.

neuromuscular junction: the chemical synapse between a neuron and a muscle fiber.

neuron: a type of cell specialized for electrical signal transmission in the nervous system, often characterized by having one long process called an *axon* extending for some distance from the cell body and several shorter processes called *dendrites.*

neurotransmitter: a chemical signal released by one neuron on the *presynaptic* side of a synapse that causes gated ion channels on the *postsynaptic* side of the synapse to open or close, changing the membrane potential of the postsynaptic cell.

nucleic acids: one of the four major classes of organic compounds; nucleic acids are polymers of nucleotides and include most notably DNA, which occurs in a double-stranded form, and RNA, which is single-stranded.

nucleotide: the basic chemical unit that is polymerized to form nucleic acids; DNA is a polymer of the nucleotides cytosine (C), guanine (G), adenine (A), and thymine (T), while RNA is composed of cytosine, guanine, adenine, and uracil (U).

nucleus: the organelle in eukaryotic cells in which chromosomal DNA is stored and replicated.

operon: a unit of transcription in prokaryotic cells, including several genes for functionally related proteins.

organic compound: a chemical compound based on carbon, characteristic of living systems.

organizer: an area of tissue in a developing embryo that influences the developmental fate of other cells or tissues through induction.

oxidation-reduction reaction: a chemical reaction in which one compound loses electrons ("is oxidized") and another compound gains those electrons ("is reduced"); also referred to as a *redox* reaction.

oxidative phosphorylation: process in which ATP is synthesized using energy obtained from electron transport and chemiosmosis in mitochondria.

parasitism: ecological interaction in which individuals of one species consume parts of individuals of a second species, benefiting the first species and causing harm to the second species but not necessarily killing it.

pathogen: a disease-causing organism.

phagocyte: a cell that engulfs and ingests pathogens or other foreign material as part of an immune response.

phenotype: the physical, physiological, or other functional traits expressed by an organism.

phosphorylation: the addition of a phosphate group to a molecule; often used in cells to store energy or to change the functional configuration of a protein.

photosynthesis: the biochemical processes in which energy in sunlight is captured and used to synthesize high-energy organic compounds; involves the *light reactions*, in which light energy is trapped and stored in the form of ATP and reduced electron carrier molecules, and the Calvin cycle (or *dark reactions*), in which this captured energy is used to reduce inorganic carbon (from carbon dioxide) and incorporate it into sugars.

photosystem: a group of chlorophyll molecules occurring on internal membranes (*thylakoid membranes*) in chloroplasts that, because of their organization and proximity to each other, are capable of capturing light energy and transferring this energy in the form of electrons to an electron-acceptor molecule.

phylogeny: the evolutionary history of a group of organisms, often illustrated in the form of a tree-like branching diagram.

pleiotropy: condition in which a single gene affects more than one phenotypic characteristic.

polymer: a large molecule composed of a chain of smaller, chemically related subunits (called *monomers*); for example, proteins are polymers of amino acids and nucleic acids are polymers of nucleotides.

polypeptide: a polymer of amino acids (named for the chemical *peptide* bond that joins the amino acids); large polypeptides are usually called *proteins*, and the two terms are sometimes used interchangeably.

predation: ecological interaction in which one species uses another species as a food source, with the interaction obviously benefiting the first species (the *predator*) and harming the second species (the *prey*).

prion: an infectious protein that affects the configuration of other proteins it contacts, rendering them dysfunctional.

prokaryote: a single-celled organism that lacks a nucleus and other internal membrane-enclosed structures; prokaryotic cells arose earlier in evolutionary history than eukaryotic cells.

promoter: a sequence of nucleotides on a DNA molecule to which RNA polymerase attaches as the first step in transcription.

proteins: one of the four major classes of organic compounds; proteins are polymers of amino acids; they serve as enzymes, structural elements, molecular motors, chemical signals, signal receptors, and in many other functional capacities in cells.

quantitative character: a physical, physiological, or other phenotypic character of an organism that varies continuously and depends on the contribution of several or many genes for its expression.

recombinant DNA: DNA created from the cutting and splicing of DNA from different species.

releaser: a simple stimulus that triggers a relatively stereotypic and complex behavioral response, such as a fixed action pattern.

replication: the copying of DNA by a cell; essentially, DNA synthesis based on an existing DNA template.

restriction endonuclease: an enzyme produced by bacteria as a defense against viral infection that cuts DNA molecules at specific sites determined by short sequences of bases; often referred to as a *restriction enzyme* and used extensively in genetic engineering technology.

retrovirus: a virus that uses RNA as its information-storage molecule and that uses reverse transcriptase to synthesize DNA from an RNA template.

reverse transcriptase: an enzyme that synthesizes DNA from an RNA template, used by retroviruses for their reproduction and as an important tool in genetic engineering technology.

ribosome: a cellular organelle made of both ribosomal RNA and protein that acts as the site of protein synthesis.

ribozyme: an RNA molecule that can catalyze a biochemical reaction, similar to an enzyme.

RNA (ribonucleic acid): a kind of nucleic acid, most often occurring as a single strand, that serves various roles in the process of translating DNA into protein, including as an intermediate *messenger*, as a *transfer molecule*, or as one component of ribosomes.

RNA polymerase: an enzyme that catalyzes the transcription of DNA to produce messenger RNA, using single-stranded DNA as a template.

second messenger: an ion or small molecule that is produced in a cell in response to the binding of an external chemical signal (a *first messenger*) to an extracellular receptor and that acts as a corresponding signal on the inside of the cell.

sexual selection: selection for characteristics that specifically enhance an individual's ability to obtain mates.

species richness: the number of species living in an area.

stem cell: a relatively undifferentiated cell in an animal that retains the ability to divide and differentiate into a variety of different types of tissues.

substrate-level phosphorylation: process in which an enzyme synthesizes ATP by directly transferring a phosphate group to ADP using energy obtained from a catabolic reaction.

sympatric: occurring in the same geographic locale, used with reference to the distribution of different species or populations of the same species (as in *sympatric speciation*).

synapse: a functional connection between two neurons or between a neuron and a muscle fiber that allows the depolarization of one cell to affect the membrane potential of the other cell.

template strand: the strand of DNA that is transcribed in a double-stranded molecule of DNA; that is, the strand of a DNA double helix that actually carries the information of a gene.

totipotency: in reference to a cell, the ability to produce an entire organism.

transcription: the synthesis of RNA based on a DNA template; the first step in converting a sequence of nucleotides in a DNA molecule into a sequence of amino acids in a protein.

transcription factor: a protein that interacts with a regulatory region on a DNA molecule and with RNA polymerase and, in so doing, contributes to determining if a particular gene is transcribed or not.

transgenic organism: an organism that has had recombinant DNA incorporated into its genome.

translation: the synthesis of protein based on an RNA template.

trophic level: a group of organisms in the food web (or food chain) of a community defined by the number of steps they are removed from the primary producers in that community; primary producers represent the lowest trophic level in a community, with primary consumers being the next trophic level, and so forth.

vicariant event: the splitting of a population of organisms into two distinct populations because of the formation of an insurmountable geographic barrier, such as a mountain range or body of water.

virus: a non-cellular infectious entity composed almost exclusively of proteins and nucleic acids and incapable of reproducing without taking control of the replication, transcription, and translation machinery of a cell it infects.

zygote: the diploid cell formed by the fusion of two haploid gametes during sexual reproduction.

Biographical Notes

Aristotle (384–322 B.C.): Greek philosopher who promulgated many fundamental ideas about the nature of living things, including views of evolution, classification, and development, some of which remain current to this day.

Claude Bernard (1813–1878): French physiologist and physician who established the concept of *homeostasis* as central to the functioning of living organisms, in addition to arguing that scientific studies of physiology should provide the basis for modern medical training and treatment.

Norman Borlaug (1914–): American plant biologist who was appointed director of the Rockefeller Foundation's Cooperative Wheat Research and Production Program in Mexico in 1944, a program that went on to develop many improved breeds of crop plants. Commonly known as the "Father of the Green Revolution," Borlaug won the Nobel Peace Prize in 1970 for his contributions to alleviating famine in developing nations.

Theodor Boveri (1862–1915): German cell biologist whose early analyses of chromosomes and their movements (along with independent work by Walter Sutton) led to the *chromosomal theory of inheritance*, an important first step in establishing that genes are found on chromosomes.

Melvin Calvin (1911–1997): Russian-American biochemist whose work established the major metabolic pathways associated with the dark reactions of photosynthesis, also commonly known as the *Calvin cycle*. Calvin was awarded the Nobel Prize in Chemistry in 1961 for this work.

Erwin Chargaff (1905–2002): Austrian-born biochemist whose work at Columbia University showed that any sample of DNA always contained equal amounts of adenine and thymine and of guanine and cytosine, a relationship known as *Chargaff's Rule* that led to the discovery of the importance of complementary base pairing in the structure and function of DNA.

Frederick Clements (1874–1945): Plant ecologist from the University of Nebraska who developed the *holistic concept* of community structure, which argues that communities were highly integrated entities that functioned like a super-organism and thus were highly predictable and stable. Clements' views contrasted with the "individualistic concept" of communities supported by Henry Gleason.

Francis Crick (1916–): British biophysicist who collaborated with James Watson in the discovery of the three-dimensional structure of the DNA double helix and who continued to be a leading theoretician in molecular biology. Crick was awarded the Nobel Prize in Physiology or Medicine in 1962, along with Watson and Maurice Wilkins, for his discovery of the double helix.

Charles Darwin (1809–1882): British naturalist who proposed the theory of natural selection in his 1859 book *On the Origin of Species*.

Rosalind Franklin (1920–1958): British chemist whose x-ray crystallographs of DNA provided essential evidence needed to deduce the three-dimensional structure of the DNA double helix. Franklin also made fundamentally important contributions to understanding the structure of inorganic carbon materials, such as graphite, but she died before a Nobel Prize was given for the structure of DNA and, thus, was deprived of sharing this award.

G. F. Gause (1910–1986): Russian microbiologist whose work on population growth of *Paramecium* cultures in the laboratory led him to formulate the *competitive exclusion principle* and, in so doing, stimulated subsequent theoretical and empirical work on ecological niches and competition in biological communities.

Henry Gleason (1882–1975): American botanist from the University of Chicago whose extensive studies of North American plant communities led him to propose the *individualistic concept* of communities, which argues that community structure is unpredictable and unstable, in contrast to the *holistic concept* championed by Frederick Clements.

Frederick Griffith (1881–1941): British physician and bacteriologist who showed that live *Streptococcus pneumoniae* bacteria of a non-virulent strain become pathogenic when injected into a mouse with heat-killed bacteria of a virulent strain, thus leading to the discovery of the *transforming principle* and providing the foundation for subsequent work demonstrating that DNA is the genetic material.

Fritz Haber (1868–1934): German chemist who developed a technique for synthesizing ammonia from nitrogen gas, eventually leading to the widespread production and use of nitrogen fertilizer in human agriculture. Haber, who was awarded the Nobel Prize in Chemistry in 1918 for his work on what is now known as the *Haber-Bosch process*, also was a key figure in the deployment of chemical weapons in World War I.

Francois Jacob (1920–): French geneticist who, in collaboration with Jacques Monod, discovered how proteins regulate gene expression in their work on the *lac* operon of *E. coli* bacteria and who was awarded the Nobel Prize in Physiology or Medicine for this work in 1965, along with Monod and André Lwoff.

Edward Jenner (1749–1823): English physician who pioneered the technique of "vaccination," in which exposure to a mild form of a disease, such as cowpox, confers lasting immunity to a more virulent form of disease, such as smallpox. Although Jenner was not the first person to use this approach, his work eventually led to improved methods and the widespread use of vaccination.

Arthur Kornberg (1918–): American biochemist whose discovery of DNA polymerase served as a foundation for uncovering the fundamental mechanisms of DNA replication, as well as an essential cornerstone in the development of molecular biology as a discipline and the application of molecular biology tools in biotechnology and genetic engineering. Kornberg shared the Nobel Prize for Physiology or Medicine in 1959 with Severo Ochoa for this work.

Hans Krebs (1900–1981): German-born biochemist who outlined the fundamental metabolic pathways associated with cellular respiration, now called the *Krebs cycle* in his honor. Krebs moved to Great Britain in 1933 when the National Socialist government terminated his German academic appointment; he was awarded the Nobel Prize in Physiology or Medicine in 1953, along with Fritz Lipmann, who had discovered the role of co-enzyme A in cellular respiration.

Jean-Baptiste Lamarck (1744–1829): French naturalist who proposed the *theory of acquired characteristics* as a mechanism of evolutionary change. Although the evolutionary mechanism Lamarck proposed proved to be incorrect, his work represents the beginning of a growing acceptance in the 19th century that life evolves.

Linnaeus (1707–1778): Swedish naturalist, also known as Carl von Linné or Carolus Linnaeus, who introduced the system for naming and classifying organisms that is still used by biologists today.

Konrad Lorenz (1903–1989): Austrian-born physician who helped to establish the modern study of animal behavior, through his work on releasers and fixed action patterns in the behavior of greylag geese and other animals. Lorenz was awarded the Nobel Prize in Physiology or Medicine in 1973 with Niko Tinbergen and Karl von Frisch for their work on the "organization and elicitation of individual and social behaviour patterns."

Thomas Malthus (1766–1834): English political economist who argued in his 1798 *Essay on the Principle of Population* that humans, like plants and other animals, generally produce more offspring than can survive, an idea that proved essential to the formulation of Darwin's theory of natural selection.

Ernst Mayr (1904–): German-born Harvard biologist who advanced the *biological species concept* in his 1942 book *Systematics and the Origin of Species*, a landmark contribution to the "modern synthesis" of evolutionary biology

Gregor Mendel (1822–1884): Augustinian monk, born in Heizendorf, Austria, and trained at the University of Vienna, who discovered fundamental principles of inheritance through his work on trait transmission in garden peas. Although he published only a single paper and his work was largely forgotten for almost four decades, Mendel is credited with having established most of the key foundations of modern genetics.

Elie Metchnikoff (1845-1916): Russian embryologist and physiologist, also known as Ilya Metchnikoff, who identified the importance of phagocytic cells in the immune response of animals through his work on marine invertebrates. Metchnikoff shared the 1908 Nobel Prize in Physiology or Medicine for his work on immune function with the German biologist Paul Ehrlich.

Stanley Miller (1930–): American chemist who, as a graduate student working with Harold Urey at the University of Chicago, demonstrated that organic compounds could be created abiotically under the conditions thought to prevail on the early Earth. Miller's work set the stage for many subsequent experiments designed to ask if and how life could have arisen spontaneously from non-living matter at the beginning of Earth's history.

Peter Mitchell (1920–1992): British biochemist who proposed the *chemiosmotic theory* as an alternative hypothesis for the mechanism by which the redox reactions of an electron transport chain power the production of ATP. Although Mitchell's theory was initially rejected, subsequent empirical studies proved him right, and he was awarded the Nobel Prize in Chemistry in 1978.

Jacques Monod (1910–1976): French biochemist and geneticist who elucidated the mechanism by which proteins regulate gene expression in the *lac* operon system of *E. coli* bacteria in collaboration with Francois Jacob and who was awarded the Nobel Prize in Physiology or Medicine for this discovery in 1965, along with Jacob and André Lwoff.

Thomas Hunt Morgan (1866–1945): American embryologist and geneticist who introduced the fruit fly as a model system for modern genetics studies. Morgan's work and that of his many important students unambiguously demonstrated that genes occur on chromosomes, giving rise to the reemergence of Mendel's ideas, establishing the modern study of genetics, and earning him the Nobel Prize in Physiology or Medicine in 1933.

Johannes Müller (1801–1858): German physiologist and anatomist who articulated the *Law of Specific Sensory Energies* as an explanation for how sensory neurons encoded different qualities of sensory information.

Hans Spemann (1869–1941): German embryologist whose work with doctoral student Hilde Mangold uncovered the importance of induction by "organizer" tissues in development. Spemann was awarded the Nobel Prize for Physiology or Medicine in 1935 for his contributions to the understanding of developmental mechanisms.

Walter Sutton (1877–1916): American cell biologist whose work on the behavior of chromosomes during cell division (along with independent work by Theodor Boveri) led to the *chromosomal theory of inheritance*, a key step in establishing that genes are found on chromosomes and in rediscovering the importance of Mendel's work.

Leo Szilard (1898–1964): Hungarian-born physicist who contributed critical insights into the work of Jacob and Monod on gene regulation, as well as many other issues in molecular biology. Szilard is also known for his earlier work in nuclear physics, having played a key role in the development of the atomic bomb but later expressing opposition to the use of the atomic bomb and the development of the hydrogen bomb.

Alfred Russel Wallace (1823–1913): English naturalist who independently proposed natural selection as a mechanism underlying biological evolution. Wallace sent Darwin a manuscript describing his idea in 1858, prompting Darwin to publish *On the Origin of Species* the following year, but after Darwin had Wallace's paper and a brief communication of his own read at the Royal Society of London.

James Watson (1928–): American biochemist who collaborated with Francis Crick in the discovery of the three-dimensional structure of the DNA double helix, sharing the Nobel Prize in Physiology or Medicine in 1962 for his discovery.

August Weismann (1834–1914): German experimental biologist who proposed the germ plasm theory, arguing that the body is divided into germ cells, which can transmit genetic information to subsequent generations, and somatic cells, which cannot because they progressively lose genetic material as development proceeds. Weismann was correct in his assertion that some cells are sequestered for reproduction but incorrect in his view that genetic material is lost as somatic cells divide.

Maurice Wilkins (1916–): British biophysicist who, in collaboration with Rosalind Franklin, obtained x-ray crytallographs of DNA that proved essential for deducing the three-dimensional structure of the DNA double helix. Wilkins shared the 1962 Nobel Prize in Physiology or Medicine with James Watson and Francis Crick for the discovery of the double helix.

Bibliography

Essential Reading:

There are a number of outstanding university-level introductory biology textbooks on the market. Different texts often take different perspectives and emphasize different material, but most of them provide broad coverage of the discipline. I've chosen three textbooks that I've found particularly useful in teaching, and I provide essential readings from two or three of these texts as background for each lecture. In most cases, the readings in different texts overlap in the material they cover. Note that new editions of science textbooks appear every two years or so, and chapter numbers may change as material is added or deleted; however, these texts have detailed tables of contents and extensive indexes, making it easy for the reader to find information on a particular subject.

Campbell, Neil A., and Jane B. Reece. *Biology*, 6th ed. San Francisco: Benjamin Cummings, 2002. Neil Campbell's book stands as one of the most successful and most clearly written introductory biology textbooks to have appeared over the last decade or more. Most lectures have been referenced to one or more chapters in this text; thus, it is probably the single most useful reference for this course.

Freeman, Scott. *Biological Science*. Upper Saddle River, NJ: Prentice Hall, 2002. Freeman's text is a new addition to the list of outstanding university-level biology textbooks available, one that especially emphasizes the process of science. Although this text is only in its first edition, it already has been adopted by a large number of colleges and universities for their introductory biology courses.

Purves, William K., David Sadava, Gordon H. Orians, and H. Craig Heller. *Life: The Science of Biology*, 7th ed. Sunderland, MA: Sinauer Associates, 2004. This is another of the bestselling university-level biology textbooks available. Written by a team of scientists, each a distinguished researcher in his or her field, this book provides a detailed account of many of the subjects addressed in this course.

Watson, James D., and Berry, A. *DNA: The Secret of Life*. New York: Knopf, 2003. An accessible account of DNA and molecular genetics, authored by one of the co-discoverers of the double helix. This book provides an updated version of the story of the discovery of DNA and is a good source of background in molecular genetics in general; more important, it delivers on the promise of its title, providing an interesting modern perspective on our understanding of what it means to say that something is "living."

Supplemental Reading:

Alberts, Bruce, Alexander Johnson, Julian Lewis, Martin Raff, Dennis Bray, Karen Hopkins, Keith Roberts, and Peter Walter. *Essential Cell Biology*, 2nd ed. New York, Garland Publishing, 2003. This intermediate-level textbook provides background on many of the topics in cell and molecular biology discussed in this course. A distillation of one of the most widely circulated texts in this area, the writing is lucid and accessible to the non-specialist interested in delving deeper into the details.

Alcock, John. *The Triumph of Sociobiology*. New York: Oxford University Press, 2001. In this volume, Alcock assesses the current status of "sociobiology," the sometimes-maligned branch of behavioral ecology that attempts to explain human social behavior in evolutionary terms. The title is misleading; Alcock presents a balanced view of the successes and failures of this endeavor, and along the way, he provides particularly lucid explanations of many of the fundamental concepts of behavioral ecology.

Bazin, Hervé. *The Eradication of Smallpox: Edward Jenner and the First and Only Eradication of a Human Infectious Disease*. London: Academic Press, 2000. A biography of Jenner, cast in the broader picture of the story of smallpox and how modern medicine has eliminated this deadly disease.

Bernard, Claude. *An Introduction to the Study of Experimental Medicine*. New York: Dover Publications, 1957 (reprint of the 1927 translation by Henry C. Greene of the 1865 original). This classic still remains a useful treatise on the nature and importance of homeostasis in living systems. It also provides unique historical insight into the rise of modern medical practice, which took surprisingly long to incorporate the findings and methods of experimental physiology.

Blunt, Wilfrid. *Linnaeus: The Compleat Naturalist*. Princeton, NJ: Princeton University Press, 2002. This reprint of a well-regarded 1971 biography of the great taxonomist is an outstanding account of the role of 18th-century natural history in the rise of modern biology. The book is beautifully illustrated and includes updated explanations of Linnaeus's taxonomic system and more modern approaches to biological systematics.

Calvin, Melvin. *Following the Trail of Light: A Scientific Odyssey*. Washington, DC: American Chemical Society, 1992. Part of a series of autobiographies of great chemists published by the American Chemical Society, this book recounts the life and work of Melvin Calvin, for whom the light reactions of photosynthesis are named. Although the writing can be a little dry at times and sometimes ventures into technical accounts, the book reads as though Calvin is simply conversing with you, telling you about the normal life of a biochemist who went on to become a Nobel laureate.

Darwin, Charles. *On the Origin of Species by Means of Natural Selection—A Facsimile of the First Edition*. Cambridge, MA: Harvard University Press, 1975. This wonderful facsimile of the 1859 first edition of Darwin's book is well worth reading, along with the historical introduction written by Ernst Mayr, one of the leaders of the modern synthesis of evolutionary biology in the 20th century. Not only does this book reveal the extraordinary thoughtfulness and detail of Darwin's argument, but the prose in which it is written provides charming insight into the nature of scientific discourse in the middle of the 19th century.

Dawkins, Richard. *The Selfish Gene*, 2nd ed. Oxford: Oxford University Press, 1989. Originally published in 1976, this book has remained an international bestseller for decades. In it, Dawkins builds on the idea of inclusive fitness to argue that natural selection selects for genes that are good at making more of themselves, even if the result leads to behaviors that may be detrimental to the individuals carrying those genes.

Dobson, Andrew P. *Conservation and Biodiversity*. New York: W. H. Freeman, 1996. Dobson does a superb job in this book of reviewing in lay terms the science behind conservation biology and efforts to preserve biodiversity, and he does so without oversimplifying the complexity of the issues. This volume is equally suitable for browsing at the coffee table or reading cover to cover as an introduction to this area.

Editors of Scientific American. *Understanding Cloning*. New York: Warner Books, 2002. A collection of *Scientific American* articles on cloning and related topics. A good starting point for readers looking to increase their knowledge in this area.

Enriquez, Juan. *As the Future Catches You: How Genomics and Other Forces Are Changing Your Life, Work, Health and Wealth*. New York: Crown Publishing, 2001. An exploration of the likely economic and social consequences of the genomics revolution, presented in a quirky but engaging fashion. The book is more of a montage of ideas than anything else, but it is thought provoking and worth perusing.

Freeman, Scott, and Jon C. Herron. *Evolutionary Analysis*, 2nd ed. Upper Saddle River, NJ: Prentice Hall, 2001. This is a particularly readable textbook written for upper-level evolutionary biology courses. There are many details found here that the non-specialist may wish to skip over, but the basic concepts underlying evolutionary mechanisms are explained clearly and illustrated with a wealth of real-world examples.

Gehring, Walter J. *Master Control Genes in Development and Evolution: The Homeobox Story*. New Haven: Yale University Press, 1998. The story of the discovery of the fundamental "toolbox" of developmental genetics, told in down-to-earth terms by one of the leading researchers in the field. Not only does this book provide an excellent introduction to developmental genetics, but it also paints a lucid picture of how science proceeds in this cutting-edge area of research.

Gerhart, John, and Marc Kirshner. *Cells, Embryos and Evolution: Toward a Cellular and Developmental Understanding of Phenotypic Variation and Evolutionary Adaptability*. Malden, MA: Blackwell Scientific, 1997. An examination of what modern developmental genetics tells us about how evolution works. This book gets technical at times but should be readily accessible to readers with an introductory biology background.

Gilbert, Scott. *Developmental Biology*, 7th ed. Sunderland, MA: Sinauer Associates, 2003. One of the best textbooks written in any field, Gilbert's *Developmental Biology* is a treasure trove of insight into classic and modern research in this field.

Gould, Stephen J., ed. *The Book of Life: An Illustrated History of the Evolution of Life on Earth*. New York: W. W. Norton, 2001. A collection of essays written by leading researchers about the history of life on Earth. Edited by Stephen J. Gould, well known for his popular essays on evolution in *Natural History* magazine and an important evolutionary theorist, this lavishly illustrated book picks up the story of the history of early life where the course leaves off and is a rewarding read.

Harold, Franklin M. *The Way of the Cell: Molecules, Organisms and the Order of Life*. Oxford and New York: Oxford University Press, 2001. A detailed account of the life of a cell, immersed in the larger discussion of what it means to be a living organism. This book has no shortage of technical terms, but the writing is both clear and eloquent, and it brings the concept of what it means to be an "organism" into sharp focus.

Henig, Robin Marantz. *The Monk in the Garden: The Lost and Found Genius of Gregor Mendel, the Father of Genetics*. Boston: Houghton Mifflin, 2000. Although there are few details known of Mendel's life, this book takes what is available and weaves it into a fascinating biography. Specialists might quibble with the way the author has filled in details, but the book does a fine job explaining Mendel's life and work.

Holmes, Frederic Lawrence. *Meselson, Stahl, and the Replication of DNA: A History of "The Most Beautiful Experiment in Biology."* New Haven: Yale University Press, 2001. An exciting account of the key experiment that showed how the DNA double helix is replicated. This book not only explains the ideas that led up to Meselson and Stahl's seminal experiment, but it also provides a rich description of the working lives of molecular biologists at the dawn of the molecular genetic revolution.

Hooper, Judith. *Of Moths and Men. An Evolutionary Tale: The Untold Story of Science and the Peppered Moth*. New York: W. W. Norton & Company, 2002. A history of H. B. D. Kettlewell's famous research on the English peppered moth. This book takes a critical view of the significance of Kettlewell's work, arguing that his experiments were poorly conducted but widely accepted nonetheless because of the scientific community's urge to find direct evidence for natural selection in the wild. The book provides an interesting perspective on how the process of science can be influenced by the personalities of the people involved.

Jacob, Francois. *The Statue Within: An Autobiography* (translated by Franklin Philip). New York, Basic Books, 1988. The autobiography of one the central figures in 20th-century molecular biology. This colorful story emphasizes Jacob's life and the remarkable times during which he lived more than it does the details of his scientific work, but in so doing, it shows how science contributes to personal and philosophical insight as much as it does to an understanding of nature.

Johnson, Steven. *Mind Wide Open: Your Brain and the Neuroscience of Everyday Life*. New York: Scribner, 2004. A popular account of cutting-edge research in the neurosciences. This book takes a broad view of higher brain function, providing a wide-ranging and highly accessible follow-up to our discussion of how neurons and synapses work.

Judson, Horace Freeland. *The Eighth Day of Creation: Makers of the Revolution in Biology*, expanded edition. Plainview: Cold Spring Harbor Press, 1996. A detailed account of the people and ideas that shaped modern molecular biology in the middle of the 20th century. This book requires some concentration, but it is acclaimed by scientists—including those who participated in the genetics revolution—as being a thorough and accurate account of this momentous time in the history of biology.

Kingsland, Sharon E. *Modeling Nature: Episodes in the History of Population Ecology*, 2nd ed. Chicago: University of Chicago Press, 1995. As the name suggests, this is a history of the field of population ecology, told in the framework of short biographies of the scientists who established the field. The book offers rich reading about the intellectual development of ecology over the course of the 20th century, and it provides a useful and satisfying backdrop to much of the third section of this course.

Krebs, John, and Nicholas B. Davies. *An Introduction to Behavioural Ecology*, 3rd ed. Oxford and Boston: Blackwell Scientific, 1993. One of the standard textbooks in the field of behavioral ecology, intended as an undergraduate text but highly accessible to the general reader. Although now a bit out of date, this book remains influential and has the added benefit of clearly explaining how experiments are done and how conclusions are reached in this area of research.

Kruuk, Hans. *Niko's Nature: The Life of Niko Tinbergen and His Science of Animal Behaviour*. Oxford: Oxford University Press, 2003. Tinbergen was one of the founders of the modern study of animal behavior, winning the Nobel Prize in Physiology or Medicine in 1973 with Konrad Lorenz and Karl von Frisch for this work. This biography, written by a well-known researcher and former student, weaves the story of Tinbergen's remarkable life with a history of ideas in the field of animal behavior.

LeDoux, Joseph E. *Synaptic Self: How Our Brains Become Who We Are*. New York: Viking, 2002. Written by a leading researcher in the field, this book develops the argument that most if not all aspects of how our brains work can be explained by how synapses—the connections between nerve cells—work. Although intended for the non-specialist, the book does not water down details and demands some attention, but the effort is well worth it for anyone interested in exploring the workings of nervous systems and brains in more detail.

Liebes, Sidney, Elisabet Sahtouris, and Brian Swimme. *A Walk through Time: From Stardust to Us: The Evolution of Life on Earth*. New York: John Wiley & Sons, 1998. A beautifully illustrated book that takes the reader from the Big Bang to the present day, outlining the story of the evolution of life on Earth in a clear and compelling manner.

Lorenz, Konrad. *King Solomon's Ring* (reprint of the 1952 original translation by Marjorie Kerr Wilson). New York: Meridian, 1997. One of the most widely read books ever written about animal behavior, by the Nobel laureate who helped establish modern studies of instinct and learning in animals. Many of the conclusions reached here are dated, but the book provides a charming and highly readable view of the early days of animal behavior research and outlines many of the central questions still discussed in this field today.

Maddox, Brenda. *Rosalind Franklin: The Dark Lady of DNA*. New York: HarperCollins, 2002. A recent retelling of the story of the discovery of the DNA double helix from the perspective of the researcher whose data were central to this discovery, but who was initially denied much of the credit because of politics and her untimely early death. Franklin's story is a complex one, and this book does justice to that complexity.

McKee, Jeffrey K. *Sparing Nature: The Conflict between Human Population Growth and Earth's Biodiversity*. New Brunswick, NJ: Rutgers University Press, 2003. The title of this book says it all; the author persuasively articulates the view that the most important thing humans can do to slow the loss of biodiversity is to limit their own population growth. While the book may be pessimistic at times, it presents issues in a clear fashion, and it is compelling to read.

Peterson, Rolf O. *The Wolves of Isle Royale: A Broken Balance*. Minoqua, WI: Willow Creek Press, 1995. A charming and well-illustrated book by a wildlife ecologist who has been studying the wolf population on Isle Royale for more than a quarter century. It blends a biologist's account of the ecological interaction between wolves and their moose prey with a narrative of the natural history of the island. This book is out of print but is still widely available.

Pines, Maya, ed. *Exploring the Biomedical Revolution*. Chevy Chase, MD: Howard Hughes Biomedical Institute, 1999. A collection of short essays about cutting-edge advances in biomedicine. Written by leading researchers and presented for the lay reader in an engaging format that includes beautiful photographs and illustrations, pull-out charts and diagrams, and even a stereo viewer for use with three-dimensional images. This is a good resource for understanding complex issues in molecular biology and physiology, such as how the immune system works.

Pinker, Steven. *How the Mind Works*. New York: W. W. Norton & Company, 1999. This bestselling book about the mind is written by a leading researcher who has a knack for combining wit and excitement with great clarity and interesting insights. Pinker doesn't delve much into the details of neurophysiology, but he develops an argument for how the human mind has evolved from selection acting on the physiological underpinnings of brain function.

Prebble, John, and Bruce Weber. *Wandering in the Gardens of the Mind: Peter Mitchell and the Making of Glynn*. Oxford and New York: Oxford University Press, 2003. A scientific biography of Peter Mitchell, the brilliant biochemist who struggled for many years to have his radical chemiosmotic theory accepted. As part of this odyssey, Mitchell established a private research institute at Glynn to carry on his studies, with his ideas eventually earning him a Nobel Prize.

Quammen, David. *The Song of the Dodo: Island Biogeography in an Age of Extinctions*. New York: Touchstone, 1997. An acclaimed book that puts MacArthur and Wilson's theory of island biogeography at center stage as it explores questions about the distribution of species in nature and how the activity of humans is affecting this distribution. Some biologists will take umbrage with the treatment of Darwin in the history presented here, and the book raises as many questions as it answers, but it is both informative and a good read.

Raven, Peter H., Ray F. Evert, and Susan E. Eichhorn. *Biology of Plants*, 6th ed. New York: W. H. Freeman & Company, 1998. A particularly well-written and useful introductory botany textbook that provides a wealth of additional background on plant form and function.

Schilthuizen, Menno. *Frogs, Flies, and Dandelions: Speciation—The Evolution of New Species.* Oxford and New York: Oxford University Press, 2001. This is an engaging popular account of current theory and research on speciation. Although aimed at readers with little or no technical background, this book provides an excellent overview of questions and controversies in one of the most active areas of research in evolutionary biology today.

Schmidt-Nielsen, Knut. *Animal Physiology: Adaptation and Environment*, 5th ed. Cambridge: Cambridge University Press, 1997. First published in 1975, this classic textbook on comparative animal physiology remains one of the most influential treatises on the subject to this day. Schmidt-Nielsen is known for the clarity of thought he brought to his science, and this clarity is equally obvious in his writing.

————. *How Animals Work.* Cambridge: Cambridge University Press, 1972. An older but still widely available book by Schmidt-Nielsen, the world-renowned physiologist known for figuring out such things as how birds breathe and how camels survive in the desert for long periods without drinking. If Darwin lived today and wanted to find compelling physiological examples of the consequences of natural selection, he would consult this book.

Shine, Ian B., and Sylvia Wrobel. *Thomas Hunt Morgan: Pioneer of Genetics.* Lexington: University Press of Kentucky, 1976. An academic biography of Morgan and his famous "fly lab." Although Morgan has been much celebrated and written about in academic circles, I know of no popular biography of Morgan written. However, Shine and Wrobel's biography provides a wealth of information for those interested in this man and his work.

Smith, Robert L., and Thomas M. Smith. *Elements of Ecology*, 5th ed. San Francisco: Benjamin Cummings, 2003. A widely used intermediate-level textbook for university ecology courses. Even if the reader chooses to skip over some of the details presented here, the book provides a thorough and highly readable introduction to the many facets of this discipline.

Sterns, Stephen C. *The Evolution of Life Histories*. Oxford: Oxford University Press, 1992. A book that revolutionized evolutionary thinking about resources and life histories. This is an advanced textbook and certainly not bedtime reading, but those who are interested in pursuing this area in more detail could find no better introduction.

Stock, Gregory. *Redesigning Humans: Our Inevitable Genetic Future*. Boston: Houghton Mifflin, 2002. Some readers will find this book startling and perhaps frightening. Whether or not you agree with its premise—that humans will someday be routinely genetically engineered—the book provides much food for thought.

Stoltzenberg, Dietrich. *Fritz Haber: Chemist, Nobel Laureate, German, Jew: A Biography*. Philadelphia: Chemical Heritage Foundation, 2004. Haber's work on the industrial production of nitrogen fertilizers led to the start of "green revolution"; the same man directed the first use of chemical weapons in warfare. Any biography would be interesting given these and many other contrasts in Haber's life; this biography does the subject justice.

Tanford, Charles, and Jacqueline Reynolds. *Nature's Robots: A History of Proteins*. Oxford: Oxford University Press, 2001. The story of proteins told as a history of scientific discoveries. Although this book is written for a general audience, some background is useful for understanding the details. Even so, it's hard not to get excited about proteins and the people who have studied them when reading this excellent book.

Vogel, Steven. *Prime Mover: A Natural History of Muscle*. New York: W. W. Norton & Company, 2002. An exceptionally fun and accessible account of how muscles work, from the molecular mechanisms responsible for contraction to the biomechanics of animal locomotion. Vogel helped establish the field of comparative biomechanics, and he is an award-winning science writer as well. This book is among his best.

Watson, James D. *The Double Helix: A Personal Account of the Discovery of the Structure of DNA*. New York: Touchstone, 2001 (reprint of original hardcover edition first published by Atheneum Publishers, New York, in 1968). One of the most widely read scientific autobiographies of all time, this book tells the story of the discovery of the DNA double helix in the words of one of its discoverers. *The Double Helix* has been criticized as presenting a biased view of events, especially with respect to the contributions of Rosalind Franklin, but it nonetheless conveys the excitement of the moment and lays out, in an engaging and understandable fashion, the major findings and ideas that led to Watson and Crick's initial description of the double helix.

Weinberg, Robert A. *One Renegade Cell: How Cancer Begins*. New York: Basic Books, 2000. An introduction to the biological underpinnings of cancer by a leading biomedical researcher who has a flare for clearly explaining complex processes. This book provides a broader overview of cancer biology than is covered in this course and does so in a historical context that reads as much like a detective story as a scientific treatise.

Weiner, Jonathan. *The Beak of the Finch: A Story of Evolution in Our Time*. New York: Alfred A. Knopf, 1994. The Pulitzer Prize–winning account of Peter and Rosemary Grant's decades-long studies of Darwin's finches on the Galapagos Islands. This book is both a charming biography of the two Princeton University professors whose life's work has provided some of the most important evidence for how natural selection works in wild populations and an unusually lucid primer of evolutionary biology theory for the lay person.

Wells, H. G., Julian S. Huxley, and G. P. Wells. *The Science of Life*. New York: The Literary Guild, 1934. An extraordinary early attempt—probably the first—to synthesize all knowledge about biology in a format that is accessible to the educated lay person. Although much of the information in this book is dated, the argument it makes at the outset for why biology matters and why it should be understood by the non-specialist remains compelling to this day. This book is not in print and may be hard to locate, although it probably can be found in libraries or through used-book sellers.

Wilson, Edward O. *The Future of Life*. New York: Alfred A. Knopf, 2002. An engaging, informative, and optimistic assessment of the future of the natural world, written by the Pulitzer Prize–winning Harvard professor who has become one of the world's most articulate advocates for conservation.

Web Sites:

The Biology Project. A great interactive learning resource set up by the Department of Biochemistry and Molecular Biophysics at the University of Arizona. This site is still developing and focuses on topics in cell and molecular biology at present. Originally intended as a learning resource for college students, the site now includes material for high school students and teachers, science writers, and medical students. http://www.biology.arizona.edu.

DevBio. A companion to the *Developmental Biology* textbook by Scott Gilbert. Unlike most textbook support sites, this site is useful as a stand-alone learning tool and also completely free. This is an excellent resource for learning about developmental biology. http://www.devbio.com.

DNA From the Beginning. A very well-produced primer on the basics of DNA, genes, and heredity, developed by the Dolan DNA Learning Center of Cold Spring Harbor Laboratory and funded by the Howard Hughes Medical Institute. Many of the activities and features found here are aimed at high-school students, but the site is equally useful to college-level and older students. http://www.dnaftb.org/dnaftb.

DNA Interactive. Another site developed by the Dolan DNA Learning Center of the Cold Spring Harbor Laboratory. The material covered at this site overlaps with the "DNA From the Beginning" site, but there is more emphasis on genetic engineering and genomics, and the presentation is aimed more at the college level. http://www.dnai.org/index.htm.

The Virtual Cell Website. This is an award-winning virtual tour of the cell, providing 3-D images of cells and organelles coupled with background information. http://www.ibiblio.org/virtualcell/index.htm.

Biology Web Site References for Students and Teachers. There are countless sites on the web having to do with biology; this site attempts to keep track of the best ones, sorting them by general area. This is just a list of links, but the links are checked regularly by the webmaster, who is a retired biology teacher. This is a great place to start looking for information on just about any topic in biology. http://www.kensbiorefs.com.

The Tree of Life. This website represents the collaborative effort of hundreds of biologists around the world to make available information about the diversity, history, and characteristics of all organisms on Earth. This ambitious project was begun by David Maddison of the University of Arizona and it has taken on a life of its own. Of course, the site isn't complete—we don't even know how many species there are on the planet, so it probably never will be complete!—but it is a terrific resource for learning about diversity and evolutionary biology. http://tolweb.org/tree/phylogeny.html.

Kimball's Biology Pages. This is a remarkable web site set up as an on-line textbook by John Kimball, a retired biology professor. Kimball has published six editions of a general biology textbook, as well as books on cell biology and immunology, so the information presented here is sure to be accurate and it is updated regularly. Unlike many other on-line textbook resources, this site also is entirely free. The graphics aren't flashy but the site is very usable, and very useful as a source of additional details or explanations of most topics in biology. http://users.rcn.com/jkimball.ma.ultranet/BiologyPages.

Credits

Biological Science by Scott Freeman, 1st Edition, © 2002. Reprinted by permission of Pearson Education, Inc., Upper Saddle River, NJ.

Used with permission, Sinauer Associates. *Life: The Science of Biology* by Purves et al., 7th edition, © 2004.

Notes

Notes

Notes

Notes